GRAVITATIONAL WAVES IN EINSTEIN'S THEORY

V. D. Zakharov

GRAVITATIONAL WAVES IN EINSTEIN'S THEORY

Translated from Russian
by R.N. SEN
Department of Physics
Technion — Israel Institute of Technology

ISRAEL PROGRAM FOR SCIENTIFIC TRANSLATIONS
JERUSALEM · LONDON

HALSTED PRESS
A DIVISION OF JOHN WILEY & SONS, INC.
NEW YORK

Sole distributors for the Western Hemisphere

HALSTED PRESS, a division of
JOHN WILEY & SONS, INC., NEW YORK

Distributors for the U.K., Europe, Africa and
the Middle East

JOHN WILEY & SONS, LTD., CHICHESTER

Distributed in the rest of the world by

KETER PUBLISHING HOUSE, JERUSALEM

Library of Congress Catalog Card Number 72 14247
ISBN 0 7065 1287 1 IPST, Jerusalem
ISBN 0 470 98113 X Halsted/Wiley, N.Y.
IPST cat. no. 22046

This book is a translation from Russian of
GRAVITATSIONNYE VOLNY V TEORII TYAGOTENIYA EINSHTEINA
Izdatel'stvo "Nauka"
Glavnaya redaktsiya fiziko-matematicheskoi literatury
Moskva 1972

Printed and bound by Keter Press, Jerusalem

Contents

This book is an up-to-date review of work on gravitational waves in general relativity. Its central theme is the exposition of rigorous approaches to the problem, principally the definitions and criteria for distinguishing wavelike gravitational fields from other solutions of Einstein's equations. The introductory chapter (Chapter 1) contains a review of approximation methods. The mathematical apparatus required for setting up the problem of rigorous (generally covariant) wave criteria — Cauchy's problem for gravitational equations and the Petrov classification of gravitational fields — is given in Chapters 2 and 3. Chapters 4—8 describe the well-known generally covariant criteria for gravitational waves of Pirani, Bell, Lichnerowicz, Zel'manov et al. Related to these is Chapter 12, which is devoted to the chronometrically invariant analysis of gravitational-inertial waves. Chapter 9 deals with the theory of propagation of gravitational waves and their classification according to the nature of the wave front (plane and spherical waves). Chapter 10 discusses the special case of spaces with plane gravitational waves, more specifically spaces that admit of an absolutely parallel vector field. Chapter 11 reviews work on the asymptotic behavior of wavelike gravitational fields generated by insular distributions of sources, while the last chapter gives a brief review of the problem of experimental detection of gravitational waves and of the basic results arrived at experimentally to date.

Bibliography comprising 465 entries.

FOREWORD

The modern theory of gravitation — Einstein's general theory of relativity — has received practically no experimental confirmation outside of the amazingly accurate predictions about the advance of the perihelion of Mercury and the deflection of light rays in the Sun's gravitational field. Moreover, in the course of its development the theory itself has generated a whole series of fundamental problems. The latter include the problem of gravitational energy, related problems of gravitational waves and quantization of gravitation, and a number of other unsolved ones.

This situation is due first and foremost to the absence of the basis required for the construction of a theory representing reality, i. e., absence of experiments which can be duplicated and which admit of variation of the parameters. Experiments have been inhibited chiefly by the state of the experimental technology. Recently, however, a concrete program of experiments on the detection of gravitational waves has emerged in the works of Weber, Schiff, Braginskii and others. These investigations are certain to be followed by further experimental work, and the theory of gravitation is sure to acquire a more secure experimental base.

Whenever a branch of science, although definitely relevant today, lacks a sufficiently solid experimental foundation, elements of formal theorizing begin to creep into its development. To some extent at least, the modern theory of gravitation is no exception: suffice it to mention the many variants of a "unified theory," by no means all of which will withstand the test of time.

Of all the unsolved problems relating to gravitation, that of gravitational waves has attracted the most attention among physicists, theoretical and experimental. This is because it is closely related to other unsolved problems in this field (the energy problem, the problem of the construction of a quantum gravidynamics, and so on), and its solution on the theoretical and experimental planes would be a stimulus to the study of many other problems of gravitation.

A vast corpus of work has been devoted to gravitational waves, including both large monographs and isolated articles dealing with theoretical approaches to the problem. Authors differ in their approaches: one can find the approximate approach, based on analogy with Einstein's method; definitions based on geometric or physical considerations; or lastly theories based on the analogy with electromagnetic theory.

To construct a theory of gravitational waves it is necessary, of course, to start from some definition. Yet in Einstein's theory of gravitation, two fundamental difficulties arise at precisely this point. The first is that the geometrical object which determines the energy and momentum of the field is not tensorial in character, and the second is that the field of gravitation itself becomes identical with the space-time continuum, complicating the problem very considerably. One might mention that there exists at present no physical theory (discounting "unified theories") in which such a situation prevails.

As we saw, the number of approaches to gravitational waves is very large, and the first concern of the present author, V. D. Zakharov, has been to arrange them according to some basic principle. Having chosen the definition of the concept of gravitational waves as guiding principle, the author arrives at seven groups of theories. Of course, these groups are not very clearly demarcated, but at any rate the author has succeeded in putting some sort of order in the truly enormous material and making it more susceptible of review.

The significance of the various theories considered in this book is worth discussing at some little length. It is evident that until experiments have yielded decisive results, no criterion can be given by which to estimate the adequacy of any given theory; many of the approaches described by the author will eventually seem to be of historical interest alone if one considers them on the whole as closed theories of gravitational radiation. Still, each one of them contains something of objective value — be it a constructive invention, a fine point of physics, a true physical idea, a mathematical device or something else. And although some of the approaches analyzed by the author are likely to fail the test of time, many elements which enter into their makeup will remain in the final theory, proving useful and necessary.

Thus at present writing gravitation research is still at a stage where one must speak of a theory in the making, rather than of a completed theory. Partly for this reason the book has the following structure: analysis, interpretation, arrangement of the vast theoretical material now available; the author's own results; and, to a lesser extent, comparison with new experimental studies. This particular structure is easily explained in the light of the present situation in gravitation. In addition, of course, the book's contents depend on the personal views of its author. As the author points out in his introduction, the stress here is on works which give a rigorous invariant definition of the concept of gravitational waves, in the sense of necessary and sufficient conditions imposed upon the quantities characterizing the space-time manifold, in order that it describe a wavelike gravitational field. Other possible approaches to the problem are described in less detail. This appears to be a feature of all authors.

And yet surely there is one very important rule which authors writing on any physical problem must obey: relate theory to experiment (and observation). Zakharov seeks to adhere to this rule, and a special chapter has been devoted to the experimental aspects of the problem. The trouble is that for the present there exist very few such comparisons with experiment (disregarding classical astronomical observations and first attempts at detection of gravitational waves by Weber, Braginskii and a few others).

Five to seven years from now, many of the theories considered in this book will have been sifted out by the experimental sieve, to lie upon the shelves of history. But nothing of value in them will go to waste; rather, it will become incorporated organically in the fabric of the future theory of gravitation. Here Zakharov's monograph will play a useful part. On the other hand, for this very reason, as well as because of the large number of works involved, the author was physically unable to devote space to detailed analysis of any given author. Basically his plan is as follows: set forth clearly the principal premises of the theory; indicate the basic conclusions which follow from these premises; sketch in the contours of the theory on the basis of the foregoing. Occasionally the theory is linked to other theories, equivalences between theories, if any, are established. A more detailed exposition would have meant enlarging the book by a factor of four or more, a size hardly conducive to legibility and possibly defeating the author's principal objective — to give the fullest possible review of the present state of the problem of gravitational waves. As to the author's own studies, they have been described objectively, and inserted in their proper place, on equal terms with other approaches, and connections with the work of other authors (mainly Zel'manov's theory) have been indicated.

A theory of gravitational waves within the framework of Einstein's theory of gravitation — speaking now of the fundamental difficulties encountered in constructing the theory — involves answering at least three questions (which entrain, incidentally, other questions as well): a) if one attempts to introduce integral invariants based on the ordinary theorem of Ostrogradskii [Gauss], the gravitational field energy is expressed not in terms of tensors (which would have been expected) but in terms of geometric objects which can be made to vanish in a chosen coordinate system; b) when one defines the field energy in terms of tensor quantities and equates the field and the space-time continuum according to Einstein, it becomes necessary to disentangle the concept of "energy of space and time"; if one discards the concept of energy and momentum of the gravitational field (a standpoint also to be found), any analogy with other fields must be deleted in advance; c) since the concept of a privileged coordinate system does not occur in the general theory of relativity, difficult problems of coordinate interpretation arise in concrete cases. These and other problems Zakharov presents acutely enough to his readers, affording them a purely constructive grasp of the principal difficulties in present-day theory of gravitation. Certain authors of popular publications either skirt the problem or simply fail to understand it, painting an optimistic picture in which the general theory of relativity is made to appear complete and capable of answering all questions put before it.

Today one of the oldest branches of physics — the science of gravity — is undergoing a period of reevaluation based on contemporary experimental research, and one may assume that the theory of gravitation will be presented very soon with more substantial data. In particular the latter would be of use in studying the very interesting phenomenon of gravitational waves — if these exist. It would then be possible to reevaluate the hypotheses discussed in Zakharov's monograph, picking out such elements as have been confirmed experimentally.

Is it possible, from the material given by the author and, in general, from the present situation, to arrive at a preference for a particular theory of gravitational radiation? The author of this foreword believes, from data known to him, that this cannot be done at present. Experimental proof is lacking; a more fundamental base is needed, and the theories under consideration are heuristic in nature. Strictly speaking — so the author of the foreword believes — none of the structures considered in the book will merit the name of theory, in the strict sense of the word, until it has been verified experimentally and has led to experimentally detectable consequences, that is until it has "begun to function" within this plan.

Furthermore, new theoretical constructions introduced as the monograph was being sent to press (e. g., based on the principle of modelling of gravitational fields) have not been included. This unavoidable occurrence does not detract from the overall value of the book and the overall good marks which it deserves.

Mention should be made of the truly tremendous bibliographical task accomplished by the author, which required considerable knowledge of modern physics and of the mathematical apparatus. The bibliography (about 450 items) is of exceptional value thanks to the thematically well thought out selection and it is a great time-saver for the reader who would otherwise drown in the sea of information. With the possible exception of the last two years, it reflects practically all major work on gravitational waves.

In evaluating Zakharov's monograph it should also be recalled that it is of immediate relevance today. Of this the author is well aware, and he unfolds a sweeping and varied view of the researches of many different theoreticians (Soviet scientists being well represented) while deriving his book from the rigid frameworks of textbooks now largely outdated as regards presentation of problems and especially as regards physical data. Today, with the flow of information threatening to engulf the reader, the need for such books, for review works on particular problems, is especially acute. Although not entirely free from flaws (somewhat schematic exposition, subjectivity in the evaluation of certain hypotheses, and so on), Zakharov's monograph has the unquestionable merit of being the first attempt in the literature to sketch a sweeping picture of the various theoretical constructions related to the problem of gravitational waves. There is at present no work of this type dealing with gravitational waves, despite the obvious need for one. For this reason there is no doubt whatsoever that Zakharov's monograph will be swift to find readers.

A. Z. Petrov

AUTHOR'S PREFACE

In the present state of the problem of gravitational waves it is impossible to present a mathematical exposition of the theory (in practice, as yet unconstructed) of gravitational waves, or of laboratory methods for their detection. The material at the author's disposal consists of disconnected ideas and approaches, rigorous or approximate in varying degrees. Any review of these must of necessity be fragmentary to some extent, the more so as many have not been developed fully enough, despite the extensive literature in the journals.

This being the situation, with subjective under- or over-evaluation of a given result not being ruled out, the author has decided to concentrate on concepts admitting of mathematically rigorous exposition. This has led to a definite selection of themes and a definite emphasis. More specifically, the central theme of the book is the problem of the generally covariant formulation of a criterion for gravitational waves, resting upon mathematically rigorous methods for solving Cauchy's problem for Einstein's equations of gravitation. Cauchy's problem and the principal results of the theory of characteristics for Einstein's equations are given in Chapter 2.

In Chapter 3 the statement of the problem of gravitational waves is formulated and two main methods of describing them — the one algebraic and the other differential — are presented. Necessary information from the basic mathematical apparatus used in the theory of gravitational waves — Petrov's algebraic classification of gravitational fields — is also given here. Both these chapters are introductory with reference to Chapters 4 — 8, which are devoted to algebraic methods of invariant description of gravitational waves. Chapter 12 and parts of Chapters 7 and 8 are devoted to differential methods.

The second most important theme of the book consists of problems of propagation of gravitational wave fronts, as well as of an investigation into the asymptotic properties of fields of gravitational emission whose sources are isolated material systems (Chapters 9 and 11).

Finally, exact and approximate solutions of Einstein's equations describing gravitational waves are analyzed throughout the book (except for Chapters 2 and 3), solutions describing plane gravitational waves being specially examined in Chapter 10.

These three themes constitute the main outline of the book and have determined its overall aim: to serve as a "working review," singling out the most complete and, in the author's estimate, most promising approaches to the study of gravitational waves. In this context mention should be made of two other themes discussed in the book: approximate methods of investigation of wavelike gravitational fields (their review is the subject of the introductory chapter), and analysis of methods and prospects in the experimental detection of gravitational waves; the latter plays the part of physical conclusion to the book as a whole (final chapter — Ch. 13).

This particular orientation of the book also determined the treatment of the problem of the energy transmitted by gravitational waves. Since at this point the problem of the theory of gravitational waves intersects another no less complex problem — that of the energy of the gravitational field — it is also the focus about which are grouped the fundamental difficulties encountered in the modern theory of gravitation.

The author's personal opinions have obviously played some role in the selection or in the elucidation of material. The reader may discern a tendency on the author's part to reduce a rapidly evolving branch of science to a dead mathematical skeleton, the result of the vivisection of a living, evolving organism. Here the author may be exposing himself to sneering remarks, in the spirit of Goethe's Mephistopheles:

> Wer will was Lebendigs erkennen und beschreiben,
> Sucht erst den Geist herauszutreiben,
> Dann hat er die Teile in seiner Hand,
> Fehlt leider! nur das geistige Band.

However, the author did not set himself the lofty aim of adequately depicting "the splendid colors of living nature," mindful as he is of the fact that the "tree of knowledge" is not the "tree of life." Without a "mathematical skeleton" there can be no theory; this is why the question of the interaction of gravitational waves and the atomic structure of matter, in particular, have been regorously excluded from the book. A satisfactory solution of this problem will only be achieved, it seems, providing there is substantial generalization or extension of Einstein's theory to the phenomena of the microuniverse. The creation of such a "quantum theory of gravitation" will be the concern of the future; in our book the problem of gravitational waves is considered exclusively on the basis of the classical Einsteinian theory of gravitation.

It is the author's hope that the publication of this book will to some extent make up for a severe deficiency in the systematic reviews on gravitational waves, a deficiency which is acutely felt today inspite of the fact that the reader has at his disposal many outstanding monographs dealing more or less with the same material as the present book. Thus in Weber's "General Relativity and Gravitational Waves" the problem of gravitational waves is examined only insofar as needed by the author for possible laboratory methods of detection; moreover, the book's publication (1961) dates back to a period when most modern lines of investigation had not yet been defined. Braginskii's recently published thorough monograph, "Fizicheskie eksperimenty s probnymi telami" (Physical Experiments with Test Bodies) deals with the problem at an up-to-date level but is limited to the experimental approach to gravitational fields. Other reviews (lectures by Pirani and Sachs, Petrov's review and so on) are either of necessity very brief, or devoted exclusively to the research of the authors themselves.

The book assumes previous acquaintance with the foundations of the general theory of relativity and is intended mainly for students at higher levels and candidates for a degree, as well as for all specialists in gravitation to whom it may be of use as a reference manual. For this reason the author has sought to provide as complete a bibliography as possible, without claiming, of course, to list all works on gravitational waves. Well aware of the risks he assumed when he took upon himself to write a broad monographic review of so vigorously evolving a problem as that of gravitational waves, the author apologizes in advance to those colleagues whose works might have significantly enriched the book but escaped the author's attention.

The author is grateful to reviewers A. Z. Petrov, I. D. Novikov and N. V. Mitskevich and editor V. N. Zakharov for reading the manuscript, as well as to Ya. B. Zel'dovich, K. P. Stanyukovich, K. S. Thorne, V. B. Braginskii and A. L. Zel'manov all of whom contributed in some form to the book's publication.

INTRODUCTION

The problem of describing gravitational waves theoretically, which is intimately related to problems arising in their experimental study, has become one of the most pressing and interesting problems not just of gravitation but of modern physics in general. Emerging almost simultaneously with Einstein's theory of gravitation (the first analysis of the problem was carried out by Einstein himself in 1916 — 1918), it has so far defied fully satisfactory solution.

In the last ten to fifteen years (roughly since 1957), interest in this problem has increased considerably owing to the creation of a powerful new mathematical apparatus. This is the Petrov classification of gravitational fields, which has initiated many new theoretical approaches. On the other hand, recent advances in the experimental field and in particular Weber's experiments hold out prospects of laboratory detection of gravitational waves.

Heightened interest in the question of gravitational waves has led to numerous publications in the journals; these now number in the hundreds. Such works may be divided into several groups reflecting different lines of research.

The first group of works seeks to give a rigorous definition of the the concept of gravitational waves, i.e., to formulate, in generally covariant form, the necessary and sufficient conditions which the space-time metric must satisfy in order to describe a wavelike gravitational field. To this group belong the works of Pirani /69, 262, 263/, Lichnerowicz /62, 87—90, 264/, Bel /56, 68, 75—80/, Debever /66, 81, 109, 265—268/, Trautman /55, 269, 270/, Petrov /271/, Ehlers and Sachs /185, 272—274/, Hely /111—117/, Roy and Radhakrishna /96/, Zakharov /94, 100, 101, 275, 276/, Staruszkiewicz /277/, Parizet /278/, Zund and Levine /118—120/, Misra and Singh /127, 128/, Maldybaeva /121, 123, 279/, Sokolik and Konopleva /92, 93, 124/, Aichelburg /280/, Lukačević /281/, Coburn /282/, Yadav /283/ and Nikolaenko /126/.

The above workers treat the definition of gravitational waves in its purely geometric aspect, on the basis of the albegraic properties of gravitational fields as defined in Petrov's classification /57, 64, 65/.

In the second group of works the authors start from a chosen definition of the energy of the gravitational field and proceed to define gravitational waves. These works, in contrast with the geometrical works of the first group, are physical in approach, and include the researches of Infeld /8, 284—287/, Synge /83/, Peres and Rosen /288—290/, Arnowitt, Deser and Misner /291—293/, Geissler, Treder and Papapetrou /294/, Araki /295/, Brill /296/, Möller /297—299/, Gutman /300—302/, Shirokov and Bud'ko /303—305/, Petrov /306/, Wu T'han Khiet /307/, Denisov /308/, Signore /309—311/, Isaakson /38/, Rodichev and Dozmorov /312—314/, Zakharov /315—316/. It should be mentioned that certain authors (e. g., Synge, Wu T'han Khiet, Møller (1961), Rodichev and Dozmorov, Denison, Gutman, Isaacson) employ a generally covariant (or tetrad) definition of the gravitational field energy. In this respect (covariance of the criterion) their approach may equally well be classed with the first. A traditional "pseudotensorial" approach was used by Peres, Rosen, Møller (1958) et al. Lastly, Araki, Brill, Geissler, Treder and Papapetrou determine the energy of the gravitational field in a specially chosen coordinate system.

The third group comprises works which study either waves of a specific form (plane, spherical), or the gravitational emission of isolated systems of sources. These include: plane waves — Rosen /155/, Boardman and Bergmann /156/, Bondi, Pirani and Robinson /143/, Kundt and Ehlers /137, 145—147/, Weber and Zipoy /95, 317/, Kerr and Goldberg /318/, Avez /157/, Newman /150/, Penrose /144/, Chevreton /149/, Johari /154/; spherical waves — Robinson and Trautman /129, 131/, Cahen and Leroy /319, 320/, Foster and Newman /138/, Marder /321/; emission of isolated systems — Bondi /20, 171, 322—325/, Stachel /188, 203/, Janis, Newman, Torrence and Couch /182, 326/, Hawking /202/, Bičak /327, 328/, Van der Burg /329/, Isaacson, Winicour and Derry /330/, Le Denmat /331/, Madore /45, 46/, Persides /197/, Halliday and Janis /332/, as well as works of Sachs /110/, Newman and Tamburino /333/, Szekeres /134/, Unti and Torrence /334/, and Collinson and French /335—336/,

The fourth group is composed of works on exact or approximate solutions of Einstein's equations describing gravitational waves in the sense of a certain criterion. Exact wave solutions known today and analyses of these may be found in the works of Einstein and Rosen /187, 337, 338/, Takeno /102, 153, 163, 168, 339—347/, Petrov /57, 97, 348/, Weber and Wheeler /193/, Marder /190—192, 349/, Lichnerowicz /89/, Geissler and Treder /350—352/, Kompaneets /189, 353, 354/, Peres /108, 160/, Robinson and Trautman /129, 130/, Pandya and Vaidya /164, 355—357/, Sciama /358/, Bonnor /359, 360/, Friedlander /361—363/, Nordtvedt and

Pagels /104/, Krishna Rao and Pandey /194–196, 364, 365/, Harrison /366/, Leroy /367/, Wyman and Trollope /72, 73/, Zakharov /91, 101, 103, 105, 107, 170, 368/, Johari /154, 369/, Misra /370, 371/, Bartrum /135/, Foster and Newman /138/, Lal and Prasad /372/, Dăngvu /159, 373/, Hoffman /374/, Dozmorov /375–377/, Szekeres /378/ and Aichelburg /379/.

Approximate wave solutions are investigated in the works of Rosen and Shamir /19/, Bonnor /11, 12, 17, 380–382/, Pirani /383/, Peres /384/, Lias /385/, Mehra, Vaidya and Kushwaha /386/, and Murenbeeld and Trollope /387/. A general method for constructing approximate wave solutions is given in the works of Choquet-Bruhat /388, 389/.

In the fifth group of works gravitational waves are treated by approximation methods: either using linearized equations of gravitation (Einstein /1, 2/, Eddington /23/, Matte /82/, Dirac /390/, Vavilov /391/, Gertsenshtein and Pustovoit /392, 393/, Bonnor /6/, Carmeli /394/, Cooperstock /24, 243, 395/, Rotenberg /21, 25, 29/, Campbell /22/), or by representation of the equations in an approximate form of specified order of smallness (Bonnor /11, 12, 17, 396/, Fock /9, 397/, Infeld /8, 398/, Papapetrou /399–401/, Tonnelat /402, 403/, Isaacson and Winicour /37, 38, 44/, Treder /404/, Cooperstock /405/, Unt /406, 407/, Zerilli /408/, Vishveshwara /179/, Couch, Kinnersley and Torrence /180, 181/), or, finally, by deriving the wave equation from modified ("Maxwellized") equations of gravitation (Rumer /409/, Kroki /410/, Mavrides /411, 412/, Synge /413/, Berger/414/).

Investigations in the sixth category deal with the gravitational emission of elementary particles. First and foremost is a monograph by Stanyukovich /415/ which reviews previous works in this field by the author (/416–419/), followed by works by De Witt /420/, Kundt and Thompson /186/, Halpern, Laurent and Desbrandes /254, 421/. In view of the fact that Einstein's theory of gravitation is inapplicable to the description of microscopic systems, Stanyukovich replaces Einstein's equations with others involving a variable "constant" of gravitation. As mentioned earlier, works belonging to this trend are not touched upon in this book.

The seventh group consists of works devoted to problems of experimental investigation of gravitational waves, primarily detection. Workers in this field include Weber /31, 95, 212, 227–229, 422– 429/, Braginskii, Rudenko, Rukman /213, 237, 430–434/, Gertsenshtein and Pustovoit /435, 436/, Kopvillem and Nagibarov /247–251, 255, 256/, Bashkov /437, 438/, Mironovskii /241, 439/, Petrov /306/, Forward and Berman /215/, Heintzman /242/, Winterberg /244/, Zipoy and Bertotti /245/, Dyson /258, 259/,

Slabkii /440/, Vodyanitskii and Dimanshtein /465/, Lavrent'ev /252, 253/, Dautcourt /441/, Melosh /225/, Wick /442/, Papini /443/, Boccaletti, de Sabbata, Gualdi and Fortini /444/.

A number of works in this category deal with estimates of the power of gravitational radiation from cosmic sources, and prospects for laboratory study of the latter; these include work by Wheeler /36/, Fowler /445/, Zel'dovich and Novikov /34/, Thorne /30, 218−222, 446/, Cooperstock /32, 33/, Carmeli /35/, Weber /31/, Boccaletti, de Sabbata, Gualdi and Fortini /239, 240/, Weinberg /447/, Shklovskii /216/, Greenstein /230/, Kafka /232, 233, 448/, Sciama, Field and Rees /231, 234, 235, 449/, Kaufman /450/, Peters /451/, Alladin and Sastry /452/, Chandrasekhar /453−455/, Ezawa /456/, and Chau and Henriksen /457, 458/.

The purely astrophysical aspect of the problem and in particular the role of gravitational emission in the energy balance of cosmic objects has been allotted limited space. A detailed exposition of this specialized astrophysical question would have stood out against the general outline of the book, which is devoted primarily to theoretical aspects — questions of principle — of the problem of gravitational waves. A rapid summary of experimental results and problematics in this category is given in Chapter 13.

Works discussing the velocity of propagation of gravitational waves — by Finzi /59/, Arifov /459/, Krzywoblocki /460/, Mitskevich /461/ — constitute a group apart. Various aspects of the problem of gravitational waves are the subject of reviews by Pirani /70, 71, 262/, Sachs /148/, Trautman /131/, Petrov /462/, Bondi /463, 464/, et al. (e.g., the review section in /165/).

In conclusion we note that the bibliography consists chiefly of works published prior to 1971.

Chapter 1

APPROXIMATION METHODS FOR THE
INVESTIGATION OF GRAVITATIONAL WAVES

1. Linear approximation

The fact that radiative and wave processes are a natural element
of the modern theory of gravitation — that is, of Einstein's general
theory of relativity — becomes apparent when one considers the
case of weak gravitational fields. Here the overall picture becomes
so strikingly simplified that many complex concepts and relations
of this theory become analogous to known ones in classical field
theory. Although the main subject of this treatise is the problem of
the invariant formulation of the concept of gravitational waves, it
would not be complete enough or motivated well enough unless we
were to carry out a preliminary analysis of the methods of approximate description of wavelike gravitational fields.

Einstein's equations

$$R_{\alpha\beta} = -\lambda \left(T_{\alpha\beta} - \frac{1}{2} T g_{\alpha\beta} \right) \qquad (1.1)$$

were first treated in the weak-field approximation by their author
/1, 2/. Here $R_{\alpha\beta}$ is the Ricci tensor, $T_{\alpha\beta}$ is the energy-momentum tensor of "matter," i.e., of matter and of all fields other than
the gravitational one, $T = g^{\alpha\beta} T_{\alpha\beta}$ and λ is Einstein's gravitational
constant. The summation convention is employed throughout the
book; the Greek indices run from 0 to 3, and small Latin indices
from 1 to 3.

If the metric tensor $g_{\alpha\beta}$ is only slightly different from the

Minkowski metric $\overset{(00)}{g_{\alpha\beta}}$,

$$g_{\alpha\beta} = \overset{(00)}{g_{\alpha\beta}} + h_{\alpha\beta}, \qquad (1.2)$$

1

then the quantities $h_{\alpha\beta}$ are small compared with unity. We assume that their partial derivatives are of the same order of smallness:*

$$h_{\alpha\beta,\mu} \sim h_{\alpha\beta,\mu\nu} \sim h_{\alpha\beta}. \tag{1.3}$$

Then in the linear approximation in $h_{\alpha\beta}$ the Riemann-Christoffel tensor is given by

$$R_{\alpha\beta\gamma\delta} \approx \frac{1}{2}(h_{\alpha\gamma,\beta\delta} + h_{\beta\delta,\gamma\alpha} - h_{\alpha\delta,\gamma\beta} - h_{\beta\gamma,\alpha\delta}). \tag{1.4}$$

We find the expression for the Ricci tensor from the above and write equation (1.1) in the linear approximation:

$$\frac{1}{2}(\overset{(00)}{g}{}^{\beta\delta}h_{\alpha\gamma,\beta\delta} + h_{,\alpha\gamma} - h^{\delta}_{\alpha,\gamma\delta} - h^{\delta}_{\gamma,\alpha\delta}) = -\lambda\left(T_{\alpha\gamma} - \frac{1}{2}T\overset{(00)}{g}_{\alpha\gamma}\right). \tag{1.5}$$

Here we exploited the obvious fact that in the linear approximation

$$g^{\alpha\beta} = \overset{(00)}{g}{}^{\alpha\beta} - h^{\alpha\beta}, \quad h^{\alpha\beta} = h_{\sigma\tau}\overset{(00)}{g}{}^{\sigma\alpha}\overset{(00)}{g}{}^{\tau\beta}, \quad h = \overset{(00)}{g}{}^{\alpha\beta}h_{\alpha\beta}.$$

Multiplying (1.5) by $\overset{(00)}{g}{}^{\alpha\gamma}$, we arrive at the scalar equation

$$\Box h + h^{\mu\nu}_{,\mu\nu} = -\lambda T, \tag{1.6}$$

where**

$$\Box = -\overset{(00)}{g}{}^{\alpha\beta}\partial_{\alpha}\partial_{\beta} = \Delta - \partial_0\partial_0 \tag{1.7}$$

is the d'Alembertian of the special theory of relativity and Δ the Laplacian:

---

* Strictly speaking, derivatives of $h_{\alpha\beta}$ of different orders have different dimensionalities; their orders of smallness should therefore be evaluated with reference to the characteristic linear dimensions (such as the radius of curvature) of the space-time background. But as, in this case, the latter is flat (infinite radius of curvature), the orders of smallness of the first and second derivatives can be regarded as the same in the approximations under consideration. Estimates for a nonflat background metric may be found, for instance, in the works of Isaacson, discussed later in the present chapter.

** In most sections of the book, partial derivatives with respect to the coordinates are denoted by indices following a comma (for example, $Q_{\alpha\beta,\gamma} \equiv \dfrac{\partial}{\partial x^{\gamma}}Q_{\alpha\beta}$), while covariant derivatives are denoted by indices following a semicolon (for example, $Q_{\mu\nu;\lambda} \equiv \dfrac{\partial}{\partial x^{\lambda}}Q_{\mu\nu} - \Gamma^{\alpha}_{\lambda\mu}Q_{\alpha\nu} - \Gamma^{\alpha}_{\lambda\nu}Q_{\mu\alpha}$); however, wherever it is necessary to bring out the operator nature of these indices, the more explicit notation $Q_{\alpha\beta,\gamma} \equiv \partial_{\gamma}Q_{\alpha\beta}$ and $Q_{\alpha\beta;\gamma} \equiv \nabla_{\gamma}Q_{\alpha\beta}$ is used. Other instances in which a special notation is used for differentiation are indicated in the text.

$$\Delta = \sum_{i}^{3} \partial_i \partial_i. \tag{1.8}$$

Multiplying equation (1.6) by $\overset{(00)}{g_{\alpha\gamma}}$ and introducing the expression obtained for $\lambda T \overset{(00)}{g_{\alpha\gamma}}$ in (1.5), we arrive at a system of equations which is conveniently written as follows:

$$\Box\psi_{\alpha\beta} + \psi^{\mu}_{\alpha,\beta\mu} + \psi^{\mu}_{\beta,\alpha\mu} - \overset{(00)}{g_{\alpha\beta}}\psi^{\mu\nu}_{,\mu\nu} = 2\lambda T_{\alpha\beta}, \tag{1.9}$$

where we introduced the quantities

$$\psi_{\alpha\beta} = h_{\alpha\beta} - \frac{1}{2} h \overset{(00)}{g_{\alpha\beta}}. \tag{1.10}$$

The system (1.9) can be simplified further if we recall that Hilbert's conditions can always be satisfied in the weak-field approximation /3, 4/:

$$\psi^{\beta}_{\alpha,\beta} = 0. \tag{1.11}$$

The field equations then assume the standard form

$$\Box\psi_{\alpha\beta} = 2\lambda T_{\alpha\beta}, \quad \psi^{\beta}_{\alpha,\beta} = 0. \tag{1.12}$$

Thus in the linear approximation Einstein's equations are wave equations for the potentials $\psi_{\alpha\beta}$, their right-hand sides describing the sources of the gravitational field. Consequently, in the linear approximation the equations of gravitation describe the propagation of gravitational waves with the fundamental velocity* c ($x^0 = ct$); conditions (1.11) are the analogues of the condition of gauge invariance in classical field theory.

Let us choose the origin of the Cartesian system of coordinates within the volume V occupied by the sources. Let x be the radius vector of an arbitrary point P lying outside V and ξ, the radius vector of an arbitrary point 0 within V. The general solution of the system of equations (1.12) for zero initial values ($\psi_{\alpha\beta} = 0$ and $\psi_{\alpha\beta,0} = 0$ for $x^0 = 0$) is given by**

$$\psi_{\alpha\beta} = -\frac{\lambda}{2\pi} \int_{V} \frac{T_{\alpha\beta}\left(\xi^i, t - |r|\right)}{|r|} \, d^3\xi^i, \tag{1.13}$$

---

* The system of units with $c = 1$ will be used throughout; the only exception will be the beginning of Section 2 of the present chapter.

** The mathematical theory of the inhomogeneous d'Alembert equation is given (for example) in Sobolev's book /5/.

where $r = x - \xi$. Thus the solution of Einstein's equations in the linear approximation is given by the retarded potentials (1.13).

By expanding the integrand in (1.13) in powers of $|\xi|/|x|$, one can study the multipole emission of the material system to all orders. The corresponding components of the radiation are characterized by the multipole moment tensors. The rank s of the tensor of the 2^s-pole moment characterizing the mass distribution of the sources is determined by the number s of the corresponding term in the multipole expansion. Thus, introducing the following three-dimensional tensors (Bonnor /6/):

$$M = \int_V T_{00}\, dV, \quad A_i = \int_V T_{0i}\, dV, \quad S_{ij} = \int_V T_{ij}\, dV,$$

$$M_{kl\ldots m} = \int_V T_{00}\, \xi_k \xi_l \ldots \xi_m\, dV,$$

$$A_{i|kl\ldots m} = \int_V T_{0i}\xi_k \xi_l \ldots \xi_m\, dV,$$

$$S_{ij|kl\ldots m} = \int_V T_{ij}\xi_k \xi_l \ldots \xi_m\, dV,$$

(1.14)

and defining the corresponding traceless multipole moment tensors in terms of these,

$$\hat{M}_{kl} = 3M_{kl} - \delta_{kl}M_{pp},$$

$$\hat{M}_{klm} = 5M_{klm} - \delta_{kl}M_{ppm} - \delta_{lm}M_{kpp} - \delta_{mk}M_{plp},$$

$$\hat{A}_{i|k} = 3A_{i|k} - \delta_{ik}A_{p|p},$$

$$\hat{S}_{ij|k} = 5S_{ij|k} + \delta_{ij}(S_{kp|p} - 2S_{pp|k}) + \frac{1}{2}\delta_{ki}(S_{pp|j} - 3S_{jp|p}) +$$

$$+ \frac{1}{2}\delta_{jk}(S_{pp|i} - 3S_{ip|p}),$$

(1.15)

. . . .

one obtains the multipole expansion of the components of the retarded potentials ψ_α^β:

$$\psi_{ij} = -\frac{4\hat{S}_{ij}}{3|x|} - \frac{4x_k}{5|x|^2}\left(\hat{S}_{ij|k} + \frac{\dot{\hat{S}}_{ij|k}}{|x|} + \cdots\right),$$

$$\psi_{0i} = -\frac{4x_k}{3|x|^2}\left(\hat{A}_{i|k} + \frac{\dot{\hat{A}}_{i|k}}{|x|}\right) - \frac{2x_k x_l}{5|x|^3}\left(\hat{A}_{i|kl} + \frac{3\dot{\hat{A}}_{i|kl}}{|x|} + \frac{3\hat{A}_{i|kl}}{|x|^2}\right) + \cdots, \quad (1.16)$$

$$\psi_{00} = -\frac{4M}{|x|} - \frac{2x_k x_l}{3|x|^3}\left(\ddot{\hat{M}}_{kl} + \frac{3\dot{\hat{M}}_{kl}}{|x|} + \frac{3\hat{M}_{kl}}{|x|^2}\right) -$$

$$- \frac{2x_k x_l x_m}{15|x|^4}\left(\dddot{\hat{M}}_{klm} + \frac{6\ddot{\hat{M}}_{klm}}{|x|} + \frac{15\dot{\hat{M}}_{klm}}{|x|^2} + \frac{15\hat{M}_{klm}}{|x|^3}\right) + \cdots,$$

where the dots above a symbol designate differentiation with respect to the retarded time $t - r$. The first term of the expansion for ψ_{00} is obviously the Newtonian potential, while the succeeding terms correspond to the quadrupole and octupole moments of the mass distribution. The absence of the dipole term shows that, in particular, a spherically symmetric system of sources cannot emit gravitational waves. Thus the solution (1.16) of the wave equation (1.12) describes gravitational waves in the linear approximation, the first "radiative" term in the expansion of the potentials $\psi_{\alpha\beta}$ being the quadrupole term.

2. Higher-order approximations

To obtain nonlinear approximations of the equations of gravitation, we can use the classical Einstein-Infeld-Hoffman method of approximations /7/, which was first used to study the equations of motion and is based on expansion of the potentials of the gravitational field in the small parameter $1/c$ (c being the fundamental velocity)*. This method has been applied to the problem of gravitational radiation by Infeld (see /8/), Fock /9/ and Bonnor /6, 11/. Expansion in the parameter $1/c$ makes it possible to obtain the equations of Newton's theory in the zeroeth order, which in turn makes it possible to substantially simplify the treatment of higher-order approximations. Thus by choosing a suitable coordinate system one can ensure that in the expansion of the components $h_{\mu\nu}$

$$h_{\mu\nu} = \sum_{n=0}^{\infty} c^{-n} \underset{(n)}{h_{\mu\nu}} (x^\alpha)$$

the first nonzero terms will be of second order for h_{00} and h_{ij}, and of third order for h_{0i}.

Correspondingly, the first nonzero term of the expansion of ψ_{00} will be $\underset{(2)}{\psi_{00}}$; for ψ_{0i} it will be $\underset{(3)}{\psi_{0i}}$, and for ψ_{ij}, the terms $\underset{(4)}{\psi_{ij}}$ of the fourth order of smallness. The field equations in these approximations become

$$\underset{(2)}{\Delta\psi_{00}} = 2\lambda \underset{(0)}{T_{00}}, \qquad \underset{(3)}{\Delta\psi_{0i}} = 2\lambda \underset{(2)}{T_{0i}}, \qquad \underset{(4)}{\Delta\psi_{ij}} = 2\lambda \underset{(4)}{T_{ij}} + \underset{(4)}{N_{ij}}, \qquad (1.17)$$

---

* To the formal expansion in the parameter $1/c$ corresponds an actual expansion in a dimensionless parameter of the type U/c^2, where U is the Newtonian gravitational potential, or in v^2/c^2, where v is the velocity of one of the bodies forming the system of sources.

where N_{ij} are the nonlinear terms, first appearing as corrections
(4)
to terms of the fourth order.

As Gupta shows /10/ (see also Bonnor /11/), analogous
equations can be obtained in the n-th order approximation by
another method based on expansion of the metric $g_{\alpha\beta}$ and the energy-
momentum tensor $T_{\alpha\beta}$ in the parameter λ (gravitational constant):

$$g_{\alpha\beta}(x^\sigma, \lambda) = \overset{(00)}{g_{\alpha\beta}} + \sum_{n=1}^{\infty} \lambda^n \underset{(n)}{h_{\alpha\beta}}, \quad T_{\alpha\beta}(x^\sigma, \lambda) = \sum_{n=0}^{\infty} \lambda^n \underset{(n)}{T_{\alpha\beta}}(x^\sigma),$$

where $\underset{(n)}{h_{\alpha\beta}}$ and $\underset{(n)}{T_{\alpha\beta}}$ are independent of λ. By inserting these expansions in the field equations one can express the latter as equa-
tions (with zero on the right side) for analytic functions expanded in
series in λ. Equating the coefficients of λ^n to zero, we obtain the
equations of gravitation in the n-th order approximation. Making
use once more of the definition (1.10) for $\psi_{\alpha\beta}$, we can write (for
$n \geqslant 2$)

$$\underset{(n)}{\Delta\psi_{\alpha\beta}} = 2\,[\underset{(n-1)}{T_{\alpha\beta}} - \underset{(n)}{N_{\alpha\beta}}], \tag{1.18}$$

where $\underset{(n)}{N_{\alpha\beta}}$ denotes nonlinear terms dependent only on combinations
of $\psi_{\alpha\beta}$ of order lower than n, and independent of $\underset{(n)}{\psi_{\alpha\beta}}$ and λ.
Equations (1.18) are taken, by definition, to be Einstein's equations
of gravitation in the n-th order approximation (Havas and Goldberg
/13, 14/).

In approximations of arbitrarily high order, equations of the
type of (1.17)—(1.18) may no longer be interpreted — generally
speaking — as wave equations. However, in the case of isolated
distribution of matter it is natural to assume that the classical
concept of mass-energy of the system of sources used in the linear
approximation is also applicable for higher-order approximations.
Using this assumption and starting from the solution of the
equations of gravitation of arbitrarily high order, one can calculate
the variation of the energy of the system over a characteristic time
interval (e. g., over a complete period of 2^s-pole oscillations) with
the aid of the energy-momentum pseudotensor which determines the
energy transfer by gravitational waves in the linear approximation
(Eddington /15/, Landau and Lifshits /16/).

Another method which can be used to calculate the energy loss
$\Delta m = m_2 - m_1$ consists of comparison with the Schwarzschild field,
provided the stationary states of the system at the instants t_1 and t_2,
corresponding to the mass values m_1 and m_2, can be described by

Schwarzschild's solution. Obviously, this method is applicable only to those source distributions (and to such systems of reference) which go over to Schwarzschild's metric at sufficiently large distances from the system of sources. Then the change Δm in the mass of the system over the oscillation period $\Delta t = t_2 - t_1$ can be interpreted as a consequence of the transfer of energy by the gravitational waves.

With this aim in view, the so-called method of double parameter approximations, which extends the foregoing method of expansion of the metric in powers of the gravitational constant, was put forward by Bonnor and Rotenberg /17, 18/ in application to sources of the insular type (in vacuum $T_{\alpha\beta} = 0$). If the quantity m characterizing the total mass of the system is used as a parameter to replace the gravitational constant λ, and the characteristic parameter a of the system, with the dimension of length, is chosen as the other parameter which arises naturally on definition of the multipole oscillations of the system, then the solution of the equations of gravitation which can be expanded in converging Taylor series in m and a in the neighborhood of $m = 0$ and $a = 0$ may be written as

$$g_{\alpha\beta} = \sum_{p=0}^{\infty} \sum_{s=0}^{\infty} m^p a^s \overset{(ps)}{g_{\alpha\beta}}, \tag{1.19}$$

where the coefficients $\overset{(ps)}{g_{\alpha\beta}}$ are independent of m and a. Ordinary expansion in powers of the gravitational constant is equivalent to expansion in the single parameter m ($s = 0$).

Inserting this expansion in the equation for the field in vacuum

$$R_{\alpha\beta} = 0$$

and setting the expansion coefficients before $m^p a^s$ equal to zero, we obtain a system of ten second-order differential equations known as the "field equations in the ps-approximation":

$$\overset{(ps)}{\Phi_{\alpha\beta}}(g_{\mu\nu}) = \overset{(ps)}{\Psi_{\alpha\beta}}(\overset{(qr)}{g_{\mu\nu}}) \qquad (q \leqslant p-1,\ r \leqslant s). \tag{1.20}$$

The left-hand sides of the above are linear in $\overset{(ps)}{g_{\mu\nu}}$ (and their derivatives) while the right-hand sides are nonlinear in $\overset{(qr)}{g_{\mu\nu}}$ (and their derivatives), the latter being already known from the approximation of preceding order.

The 00 approximation obviously corresponds to the flat space-time metric: $g_{\alpha\beta} = \overset{(00)}{g_{\alpha\beta}}..$ All approximations of order $1s$ are linear and homogeneous in $\overset{(1s)}{g_{\alpha\beta}}$ and their derivatives,

$$\overset{(1s)}{\Psi_{\alpha\beta}} = 0,$$

and are therefore equivalent to the Einstein-Infeld-Hoffman approximations discussed earlier. Approximations of ps-orders with $p \geqslant 2$ are nonlinear; $2s$-approximations correspond to the second order of smallness ($s = 0, 1, 2, \ldots$), $3s$-approximations to the third order ($s = 0, 1, 2, \ldots$), and so forth.

The solution of the equations of gravitation in the linear approximation in the form of a multipole expansion is given by formulas (1.16). In our notation (1.19), it can be written as

$$g_{\alpha\beta} = \overset{(00)}{g_{\alpha\beta}} + \sum_{s=0}^{\infty} ma^s \overset{(1s)}{g_{\alpha\beta}},$$

where dipole terms are absent ($\overset{(11)}{g_{\alpha\beta}} = 0$), monopole terms $\overset{(10)}{g_{\alpha\beta}}$ (i. e., the static part, $\overset{(00)}{g_{\alpha\beta}} + m \overset{(10)}{g_{\alpha\beta}}$) correspond to the linear approximation to Schwarzschild's metric, while the terms $\overset{(12)}{g_{\alpha\beta}}, \overset{(13)}{g_{\alpha\beta}}, \ldots, \overset{(1s)}{g_{\alpha\beta}}, \ldots$ are known respectively as quadrupole, octupole, $\ldots$, 2^s-pole wave solutions in approximations of $1s$-orders. This corresponds to the definition of the 2^s-pole moment of an axially symmetric system of sources distributed linearly along the axis of symmetry

$$Q^{(s)}(u) = ma^s h^{(s)}(u), \qquad (1.21)$$

where $u = t - r$, and the coefficients $h^{(s)}(u)$ are independent of m and a.

To determine the order of the approximation in which an isolated system of sources will exhibit secular variation of mass due to emission of gravitational waves, consider a nonstationary system which (for $a \to 0$) admits of passage to the limit of the stationary field of a point source (Schwarzschild field). The simplest system of this kind is an axially symmetric distribution of finite length, * described (in the spherical coordinates r, θ, φ, t) by the metric

$$ds^2 = -A\, dr^2 - r^2\, (B\, d\theta^2 + C \sin^2 \theta\, d\varphi^2) + D\, dt^2, \qquad (1.22)$$

where A, B, C, D are functions of r, θ, t. Writing down the field equations (1.20) in the ps-approximation for this metric and

---

* An example of such a system would be two equal point masses, connected by a spring and describing symmetric oscillations.

integrating them (Rosen and Shamir /19/, Bonnor /17/), we obtain:

$$\Box A = P - \int (M_1 + r^{-1}M)\, dt -$$

$$- \int \Big\{ (L_1 + r^{-1}L) - \int (N_{11} + r^{-1}N_1)\, dt \Big\} d\theta - (\eta_1 + r^{-1}\eta) +$$

$$+ \int (\sigma_{11} + r^{-1}\sigma_1)\, d\theta - (\chi_1 + r^{-1}\chi),$$

$$C = - A \cosec^2 \theta \int \Big[2A + r^{-1}\int \Big\{ 2A + r \Big(\int M\, dt + \eta \Big) \Big\} dr + \qquad (1.23)$$

$$+ r^{-1}\tau \Big] \sin\theta \cos\theta\, d\theta + \cosec^2 \theta \int \Big(\int N\, dt + \sigma \Big) \sin^2\theta\, d\theta + \mu \cosec^2 \theta,$$

$$B = - C + r^{-1}\int \Big\{ 2A + r \Big(\int M\, dt + \eta \Big) \Big\} dr + r^{-1}\tau,$$

$$D = A + r \int \Big[2r^{-2}A + r^{-1}\Big\{ \int \Big(L - \int N_1 dt - \sigma_1 \Big) d\theta + \chi \Big\} \Big] dr + r\nu,$$

where $\Box$ is the d'Alembertian in the coordinates r, θ, φ, t; P, M, L and N are the right-hand (nonlinear) sides of equations (1.20), assumed to be known from the qr-approximation ($q \leqslant p - 1$, $r \leqslant s$):

$$P = \Psi_{11}, \quad M = \Psi_{10}, \quad L = \Psi_{12}, \quad N = \Psi_{20};$$

for the remaining values of the indices α and β equations (1.20) become identical; lastly, $\eta\,(r,\ \theta)$, $\sigma\,(r,\ \theta)$, $\chi\,(r,\ t)$, $\tau\,(\theta,\ t)$, $\nu\,(\theta,\ t)$, $\mu\,(r,\ t)$ are six integration constants, by choosing which one can satisfy the requirement of flatness at infinity and ensure the absence of singularity of the metric along the axis of symmetry. The subscript 1 in equations (1.23) designates differentiation with respect to r.

Thus the solution of the equations of the ps-approximation for the metric (1.22) reduces to integration of an inhomogeneous wave equation for the functions $\overset{(ps)}{A}$, after which the expressions for $\overset{(ps)}{C}$, $\overset{(ps)}{B}$ and $\overset{(ps)}{D}$ follow automatically from the remaining relations in the system (1.23). In particular, for a linear approximation of $1s$-order the functions P, M, N and L are equal to zero in view of (1.20) and we obtain the homogeneous wave equation examined earlier for the functions $\psi_{\alpha\beta}$.

The change in energy of the system of sources in the ps-approximation is evaluated by Bondi's method /20/, which is based on expansion of the $\overset{(ps)}{g}_{\alpha\beta}$ in inverse powers of r:

$$\sum_{n=1}^{l} r^{-n} \overset{(n)}{\delta}(\theta, u) \qquad (u = t - r). \qquad (1.24)$$

The gravitational mass of a system can be evaluated by establishing a correspondence between a given stationary solution and the equivalent field which would be set up by a certain Schwarzschild mass; in the terms $\overset{(ps)}{\Psi}_{\alpha\beta}$ it is sufficient to retain coefficients of order $1/r$, while in the terms $\overset{(ps)}{\Phi}_{\alpha\beta}$ of equations (1.20) it is sufficient to retain coefficients of order no higher than $1/r^3$. One should take into account only such terms as describe the secular variation of the state of the system over the period Δt, ignoring the terms $\overset{(ps)}{g}_{\alpha\beta}$, which do not change form as a result of oscillation. Thus all terms $\overset{(p0)}{g}_{\alpha\beta}$ describe only the constant (unvarying throughout the oscillation period) component of the field, i.e., the approximation of $p0$-order to the (strictly) Schwarzschild metric (to the field of the central mass m for which the linear dimension $a=0$). From this it is easy to see, in particular, why expansions in the parameter m or λ only do not describe gravitational waves.

Nonlinear terms of the order $\overset{(21)}{\Psi}_{\alpha\beta}$ may contain only combinations of the form

$$\overset{(11)}{g}_{\alpha\beta} \cdot \overset{(10)}{g}_{\alpha\beta}$$

and thus vanish owing to the absence of the dipole terms ($\overset{(11)}{g}_{\alpha\beta} = 0$). It is therefore sufficient to apply expansion (1.24) to terms of the order of $\overset{(ps)}{g}_{\alpha\beta}$ with $s \geqslant 2$, exclusively. But Rotenberg has shown that, for isolated axially symmetric systems of sources, energy and momentum, determined by the pseudotensor $t^{\alpha\beta}$, are conserved /21/* in the $1s$-order. The absence of secular mass variation in 22- and 23-orders is easy to show by expanding the corresponding $\overset{(22)}{g}_{\alpha\beta}$ and $\overset{(23)}{g}_{\alpha\beta}$ in series such as (1.24) and evaluating $\overset{(22)}{\Psi}_{\alpha\beta}$ and $\overset{(23)}{\Psi}_{\alpha\beta}$ in the $1/r$ approximation.

Thus the 24-order approximation is the lowest one which can contribute to the secular variation of mass of a system. A rigorous solution of the equations for the 24-approximation has been given

---

* On the other hand already in the $(1s)$ approximation it can be shown that an isolated system of sources loses angular momentum due to the emission of gravitational waves (Campbell /22/). For comparison we might note that, in the $1s$-order, a rod rotating about an axis of symmetry orthogonal to itself — unlike the system under consideration — loses not only energy due to gravitational emission (Eddington /23/) but also momentum (Cooperstock /24/, Rotenberg /25/), in addition to losing angular momentum due to octupole gravitational waves (Cooperstock and Booth /26/).

by Hunter and Rotenberg /27/. The nonlinear terms $\overset{(24)}{\Psi}_{\alpha\beta}$ should contain combinations of the form

$$\overset{(10)}{g}_{\alpha\beta} \cdot \overset{(14)}{g}_{\alpha\beta}, \quad \overset{(11)}{g}_{\alpha\beta} \cdot \overset{(13)}{g}_{\alpha\beta}, \quad \overset{(12)}{g}_{\alpha\beta} \cdot \overset{(12)}{g}_{\alpha\beta},$$

of which only the last (quadrupole-quadrupole emission) can make a secular contribution to the mass variation. Indeed, the second combination vanishes identically ($\overset{(11)}{g}_{\alpha\beta} = 0$), while for the first (monopole-2^4-pole emission) the right-hand sides $\overset{(24)}{\Psi}_{\alpha\beta}$ of equations (1.20) will not contain secular terms of order $1/r$. For quadrupole-quadrupole emission, on the other hand, the functions $\overset{(24)}{\Psi}_{\alpha\beta}$ already contain secular terms of order $1/r$, causing the change Δm in the Schwarzschild mass over the oscillation period:

$$\Delta m = -\frac{2}{15}(\alpha - \beta)\int_{T} [\overset{(2)}{Q}'''(u)]^2 \, du; \tag{1.25}$$

here $\overset{(2)}{Q}(u)$ is the quadrupole moment (1.21) of the system, the primes denote differentiation with respect to the parameter $u = t - r$, and α and β are parameters characterizing the nonstationary character of the system ($\alpha + \beta = 1$). From (1.25) it follows that the system fails to emit energy only in the strictly stationary case $\alpha = \beta = \frac{1}{2}$, or for oscillations of a very special type characterized by the condition $\overset{(2)}{Q}'''(u) = 0$. As it happens, the mass-energy losses calculated from this formula correspond exactly to those obtained with the help of the energy-momentum pseudotensor in the linear approximation (Rotenberg /28/)*.

3. Critique of the approximation methods

A significant drawback of the foregoing methods of approximate analysis of wavelike gravitational fields (Bonnor-Rotenberg,

---

* Bonnor's method of double-parameter approximations can be extended as well to the case of a nonempty space-time. Thus Rotenberg has obtained a solution of the *ps*-approximation equations for spaces filled with electromagnetic radiation /29/. The corresponding inhomogeneous wave equation in the *ps*-approximation for the metric (1.22) describes the gravitational and electromagnetic radiation. Bonnor's method has also been extended to isolated axially symmetric fields of gravitation of a more general form than the distribution with the metric (1.22) (Rotenberg /21/). However, it is more convenient to deal with gravitational emission of arbitrarily isolated axially symmetric systems using the general method suggested by Bondi, Metzner and Van der Burg (see Ch.11).

Einstein-Infeld-Hoffman, Fock, Bondi) is that in the zeroeth
approximation they deal with the flat space-time metric $\overset{(00)}{g_{\alpha\beta}}$, which
corresponds to absence of a gravitational field. The correction to
the metric plays the part of an infinitesimal of specified order and
therefore can describe only weak gravitational fields. Thus these
methods make it possible to determine the state of weak gravitational emission only, and only against the background of a flat
space-time.

Recent astronomical observations, however, point to the
possible existence in the universe of sources of very strong gravitational waves. Thus according to computations by Thorne /30/, a
neutron star undergoing nonspherical oscillatory perturbations
(pulsations) may lose, by emission of gravitational waves, an energy
of the order of 10^{51} ergs (0.1% of the rest mass of the star itself)
within a single period of pulsation ($10^{-4} - 10^{-3}$ sec). Similar power
estimates have been obtained by Weber /31/ for pulsars, Cooperstock /32, 33/ for quasars and binary stars, Zel'dovich and
Novikov /34/ for collapsed stars, Carmeli /35/ for gravitational
bremsstrahlung of the sun and Wheeler /36/ for the metagalaxy.
Moreover, in actual fields of gravitation one should expect that, in
addition to the gravitational waves causing strong perturbation of
the space-time metric, the background metric itself may respond
to the strong gravitational field.

An important step towards the resolution of this difficulty was
taken by Isaacson /37, 38/ when he applied the Brill-Hartle method
of approximations /39/ to the description of so-called "high-
frequency" gravitational waves propagating against the background
of a highly curved space-time. The idea of the method is based on
expansion of the quantities $h_{\mu\nu}$, i.e., the correction to the background
metric $\gamma_{\mu\nu}$, in series in powers of the ratio $\varepsilon = l/L$, where l is the
characteristic dimension of the wave perturbation (which can be
interpreted as its "wavelength") and L the characteristic dimension
of the gravitational field of the background, comparable condition-
ally to the "radius of curvature" of the space-time background. *
This method is an extension of Bonnor's method. Since ε is of the
order of $(l^2 m/r^3)^{1/2}$, the gravitational emission of an isolated system
at large distances r from this system can always be regarded as
"high-frequency emission," corresponding to the case where $L \to \infty$.

According to the rigorous definition, a space-time V_4 with the
metric $g_{\mu\nu}$ describes high-frequency gravitational waves if it admits
of a one-parameter family of coordinate systems (in the sense of a

---

* Indeed, the smallness of the ratio $\varepsilon = l/L$ is interpreted as the relative shortwave character
  (high frequency) of the traveling perturbation $h_{\mu\nu}$, i.e., waves on the background of the curved
  space-time.

one-parameter Lie group G with the parameter ε) in which $g_{\mu\nu}$ assumes the form

$$g_{\mu\nu}(x) = \gamma_{\mu\nu}(x) + \varepsilon h_{\mu\nu}(x, \varepsilon) \qquad (\varepsilon \ll 1), \tag{1.26}$$

where

$$\gamma_{\mu\nu} = O(1), \qquad \partial_\alpha \gamma_{\mu\nu} = O(1), \qquad \partial_{\alpha\beta} \gamma_{\mu\nu} = O(1), \tag{1.27}$$

$$h_{\mu\nu} = O(1), \qquad \partial_\alpha h_{\mu\nu} = O(\varepsilon^{-1}), \qquad \partial_{\alpha\beta} h_{\mu\nu} = O(\varepsilon^{-2}). \tag{1.28}$$

The conditions (1.27) mean that the curvature of the background metric $\gamma_{\mu\nu}$ is of the order of unity, i.e., the background space-time is curved and its Riemann tensor

$$R^{(0)}_{\alpha\beta\gamma\delta} \equiv R_{\alpha\beta\gamma\delta}(\gamma_{\mu\nu}) = 0.$$

However, it follows from conditions (1.28) that the order of magnitude of the total curvature of V_4 may even exceed the curvature of the background:

$$R_{\alpha\beta\gamma\delta}(\gamma_{\mu\nu} + \varepsilon h_{\mu\nu}) = R^{(0)}_{\alpha\beta\gamma\delta} + \varepsilon R^{(1)}_{\alpha\beta\gamma\delta} + \varepsilon^2 R^{(2)}_{\alpha\beta\gamma\delta} + \ldots; \tag{1.29}$$

here

$$R^{(1)}_{\alpha\beta\gamma\delta} = \frac{1}{2}(h_{\alpha\gamma;\beta\delta} + h_{\beta\delta;\alpha\gamma} - h_{\beta\gamma;\alpha\delta} - h_{\alpha\delta;\beta\gamma} + R^{(0)}_{\alpha\sigma\gamma\delta}h^\sigma_\beta - R^{(0)}_{\beta\sigma\gamma\delta}h^\sigma_\alpha).$$

In the above the covariant differentiation is with respect to the background metric $\gamma_{\mu\nu}$, which is also used to raise and lower the indices. The second term in expansion (1.29),

$$\varepsilon R^{(1)}_{\alpha\beta\gamma\delta} \approx O(\varepsilon^{-1}),$$

dominates over the other terms in order of magnitude, since, for example,

$$\varepsilon^2 R^{(2)}_{\alpha\beta\gamma\delta} \approx O(1), \qquad \varepsilon^3 R^{(3)}_{\alpha\beta\gamma\delta} \approx O(\varepsilon),$$

and so forth. Similarly, for the Ricci tensor $R_{\alpha\beta}$ of the total metric we obtain the expansion

$$R_{\alpha\beta}(\gamma_{\mu\nu} + \varepsilon h_{\mu\nu}) = R^{(0)}_{\alpha\beta} + \varepsilon R^{(1)}_{\alpha\beta} + \varepsilon^2 R^{(2)}_{\alpha\beta} + \cdots,$$

where

$$R^{(0)}_{\alpha\beta} = R_{\alpha\beta}(\gamma_{\mu\nu}), \qquad R^{(1)}_{\alpha\beta} = \frac{1}{2}\gamma^{\rho\tau}(h_{\rho\tau;\alpha\beta} + h_{\alpha\beta;\rho\tau} - h_{\tau\alpha;\beta\rho} - h_{\tau\beta;\alpha\rho}),$$

the dominant term being again the second term

$$\varepsilon R^{(1)}_{\alpha\beta} \approx O(\varepsilon^{-1}),$$

whereas

$$\varepsilon^2 R^{(2)}_{\alpha\beta} \approx O(1).$$

Hence the vacuum field equations for the first-order approximation will be given by

$$R^{(1)}_{\alpha\beta} = 0, \tag{1.30}$$

those for the second-order approximation will be given by

$$R^{(0)}_{\alpha\beta} = -\varepsilon^2 R^{(2)}_{\alpha\beta}, \tag{1.31}$$

and so forth.   Introducing the quantities

$$\hat{\psi}_{\mu\nu} = h_{\mu\nu} - \frac{1}{2}\gamma_{\mu\nu}h, \qquad \hat{\psi} = \gamma^{\alpha\beta}\hat{\psi}_{\alpha\beta},$$

where $h \equiv \gamma^{\alpha\beta}h_{\alpha\beta}$, we can express equations (1.30) for the first approximation in the form

$$\gamma^{\alpha\beta}\hat{\psi}_{\mu\nu;\beta} - \frac{1}{2}\gamma_{\mu\nu}\gamma^{\alpha\beta}\hat{\psi}_{;\alpha\beta} - \hat{\psi}^{\beta}_{\mu;\nu\beta} - \hat{\psi}^{\beta}_{\nu;\mu\beta} + 2R^{(0)}_{\sigma\nu\mu\beta}\hat{\psi}^{\beta\sigma} + $$
$$+ R^{(0)}_{\mu\sigma}\hat{\psi}^{\sigma}_{\nu} + R^{(0)}_{\nu\sigma}\hat{\psi}^{\sigma}_{\mu} = 0, \tag{1.32}$$

where the covariant differentiation is again with respect to $\gamma_{\mu\nu}$. For the case of a weak gravitational field, given by the metric (1.2), the functions $\hat{\psi}_{\mu\nu}$ transform into the $\psi_{\mu\nu}$ obtained earlier.

In order to reduce equation (1.32) to the standard form of a wave equation for the potentials $\hat{\psi}_{\mu\nu}$, it is necessary to show that the second, third and fourth terms in this equation can be removed by "gauge" transformations, i.e., by choosing a suitable generator ξ^{μ} of the Lie group G which will induce admissible transformations

$$\bar{h}_{\mu\nu} = h_{\mu\nu} - \xi_{\mu;\nu} - \xi_{\nu;\mu}$$

and will not alter the first term in (1.32).

To prove this we shall make use of formulas expressing the relation between the tensors $R_{\alpha\beta}$ and $R_{\alpha\beta\gamma\delta}$ and the barred tensors /40/ $\bar{R}_{\alpha\beta}$ and $\bar{R}_{\alpha\beta\gamma\delta}$:

$$\bar{R}^{(1)}_{\alpha\beta} = R^{(1)}_{\alpha\beta} - \mathcal{L}_{\xi}R^{(0)}_{\alpha\beta}, \qquad \bar{R}^{(1)}_{\alpha\beta\gamma\delta} = R^{(1)}_{\alpha\beta\gamma\delta} - \mathcal{L}_{\xi}R^{(0)}_{\alpha\beta\gamma\delta},$$

where $\mathscr{L}_\xi$ represents the Lie derivative in the direction of the generator ξ^α of the group G. Using the formulas for the Lie derivatives of the tensors $R_{\alpha\beta}$ and $R_{\alpha\beta\gamma\delta}$ (see, for instance, /41/), we can show that the quantities $\mathscr{L}_\xi R^{(0)}_{\alpha\beta}$ and $\mathscr{L}_\xi R^{(0)}_{\alpha\beta\gamma\delta}$ are of the second order in ε, i.e., in the high-frequency approximation $(\varepsilon \to 0)$ the tensors $R^{(1)}_{\alpha\beta}$ and $R^{(1)}_{\alpha\beta\gamma\delta}$ remain invariant under transformations of the group G (are "gauge-invariant" /37/). Using the law of transformation of the quantities $\hat{\psi}^\alpha_{\mu;\alpha}$ and $\hat{\psi}^\alpha_\alpha$ under infinitesimal transformations of the group G $(x^\alpha \to x^\alpha + \varepsilon\xi^\alpha)$,

$$\hat{\psi}^\alpha_{\mu;\alpha} \to \hat{\psi}^\alpha_{\mu;\alpha} - \gamma^{\alpha\beta}\xi_{\mu;\beta} + R^{(0)}_{\mu\alpha}\xi^\alpha,$$

$$\hat{\psi} \to \hat{\psi} + 2\xi^\alpha_{;\alpha},$$

we choose ξ^μ so as to satisfy the system of equations

$$\gamma^{\alpha\beta}\xi_{\mu;\alpha\beta} - R^{(0)}_{\mu\alpha}\xi^\alpha = \hat{\psi}^\alpha_{;\alpha}, \quad \xi^\alpha_{;\alpha} = -\frac{1}{2}\hat{\psi}^\alpha_\alpha.$$

Then, obviously, the following conditions will be fulfilled in the new coordinate system:

$$\hat{\psi}^\alpha_{\mu;\alpha} = 0, \quad \hat{\psi} = 0,$$

bringing equations (1.32) to the desired form

$$-\Delta\hat{\psi}_{\mu\nu} \equiv \gamma^{\alpha\beta}\hat{\psi}_{\mu\nu;\alpha\beta} + 2R^{(0)}_{\sigma\mu\nu\beta}\hat{\psi}^{\sigma\beta} + R^{(0)}_{\mu\sigma}\hat{\psi}^\sigma_\nu + R^{(0)}_{\nu\sigma}\hat{\psi}^\sigma_\mu = 0. \qquad (1.33)$$

In the case of a flat background metric, $\gamma_{\mu\nu} = \overset{(00)}{g}_{\mu\nu}$; due to the equality $R^{(0)}_{\delta\mu\nu\beta} = 0$ all terms apart from $\gamma^{\alpha\beta}\hat{\psi}_{\mu\nu;\alpha\beta}$ vanish and we recover the wave equation considered earlier, (1.12). For the non-flat metric $\gamma_{\mu\nu}$ the left-hand side of equation (1.33) is de Rahm's generalized topological d'Alembertian /42/, which lies at the base of the definition of wavelike gravitational fields* proposed by Lichnerowicz /43/.

Thus gravitational emission on the curved space-time background finds an elegant definition at the high-frequency limit.

Isaacson's approach resolves two significant difficulties that arise when searching for a definition of gravitational waves valid in an approximation of specified order. The first difficulty, as we saw earlier, arises from the assumption that the gravitational field set up by the wave perturbation is weak. The second arises from the assumption of flatness of the background metric. This restricts

---

* The rigorous approach to the definition of gravitational waves on the basis of de Rahm's operator is considered in Ch.8.

the validity of the approximation methods to asymptotically flat gravitational fields only (in particular, to fields of isolated sources).

However, the Isaacson-Brill-Hartle method, together with the other methods described above, fail to resolve a third difficulty common to all attempts of defining gravitational waves on the basis of approximation methods: there exists no proof that the series of successive approximations converges. Thus Bonnor's method is based on the assumption of convergence of the series (1.19) in the neighborhood of $m = 0$ and $a = 0$, which, however, does not guarantee its convergence at sufficiently large distances from the source system. As Fock has shown /9/, upon expansion of the integrand in (1.13) for the wave function $\psi^{\alpha\beta}$, sufficient convergence of the series is guaranteed only for "moderately large" distances r, namely for distances large compared with the dimensions of the source system but small compared with the length of the emitted waves. Inside the "wave zone" (i.e., the region situated at at a large distance from the sources compared with the length of the emitted waves) convergence of the series cannot, in general, be guaranteed unequivocally. Yet this very case constitutes the region of applicability of the Isaacson-Brill-Hartle method. This critical situation is further aggravated by the absence of reliable experimental data concerning the properties of gravitational waves, whence the particular urgency of a rigorous proof that the series of successive approximations does indeed converge inside the wave zone.

Lastly, every one of the methods of approximation considered above presupposes the selection of a definite system of coordinates (or a class of admissible coordinate systems) the existence of which cannot be guaranteed a priori in the specified gravitational field. For example, when the gravitational emission of an isolated axially symmetric system of bodies is treated by Bondi's method, the harmonic coordinate system becomes inapplicable, although it was applied successfully by V. A. Fock to the description of gravitational waves by the method of expansion of the potentials in the parameter $1/c$. The reason for this is the appearance of the logarithmic term $r^{-1} \log r$ in place of $1/r$ in the expansion of the gravitational potentials, precluding passage to the limit of the Schwarzschild metric (Bonnor /11/), Isaacson and Winicour /44/). Consequently, for fairly large distances from the isolated source of gravitational emission the wave solution of the linearized theory of gravitation in harmonic coordinates cannot serve as a first approximation to the exact wave solution, although at distances significantly smaller than the length of the propagating wave this description proves satisfactory /45, 46/.

At the same time, the equations for the gravitational field are generally covariant. Therefore every physical consequence of the theory must admit of a generally covariant formulation. Hence our next task will be to consider rigorous generally covariant methods of describing gravitational waves. Our starting point will be the Cauchy problem for Einstein's equations of gravitation.

Henceforth it will be convenient to distinguish between the term g r a v i t a t i o n a l w a v e s and the term g r a v i t a t i o n a l e m i s s i o n. With the former we will associate the field in the true wave zone, where it does not interact with the sources. The latter will mean the overall gravitational field of the source which is inducing the waves. In the case of an empty space-time, we will refer to the gravitational waves as f r e e.

Chapter 2

THE CAUCHY PROBLEM FOR EINSTEIN'S EQUATIONS

1. Einstein's equations as a system of the hyperbolic type

Rigorous formulation of the problem of gravitational waves in the general theory of relativity became possible only after De Donder /47/ and Lanczos /48/ had proved that Einstein's system of equations was of the hyperbolic type, i.e., that its characteristics were identical with those of a wave equation of the form*

$$\Box\psi = \frac{1}{\sqrt{-g}}\, \partial_\beta\,(\sqrt{-g}\,g^{\alpha\beta}\partial_\alpha\psi) = 0. \tag{2.1}$$

Indeed, Einstein's equations in empty space

$$R_{\mu\nu} = 0 \tag{2.2}$$

can be reduced by identity transformation (see, for instance, /9/) to the form

$$\frac{1}{2}g^{\alpha\beta}g_{\mu\nu;\alpha\beta} + \Gamma_{\mu\nu} - L_{\mu\nu} = 0, \tag{2.3}$$

where we set

$$\Gamma_{\mu\nu} = \frac{1}{2}(\Gamma_{\mu,\nu} + \Gamma_{\nu,\mu}) - \Gamma^\rho_{\mu\nu}\Gamma_\rho, \tag{2.4}$$

$$\Gamma_\rho = g_{\rho\sigma}\Gamma^\sigma, \quad \Gamma^\sigma = -g^{\alpha\beta}\Gamma^\sigma_{\alpha\beta}, \tag{2.5}$$

so that the $L_{\mu\nu}$ are expressed only in terms of components of the metric tensor and their first derivatives:

---

* Henceforth the d'Alembertian symbol will be interpreted in the sense of (2.1).

18

$$L_{\mu\nu} = g^{\alpha\beta}g^{\rho\sigma}g_{\mu\sigma,\beta}g_{\rho\nu,\sigma} - g^{\alpha\rho}g^{\beta\sigma}\Gamma_{\mu\rho\sigma}\Gamma_{\nu\alpha\beta}. \tag{2.6}$$

We now pass in the given space-time region to a special coordinate system, choosing four solutions of equation (2.1) as the new x^σs:

$$\Box x^\sigma = \Gamma^\sigma = \frac{1}{\sqrt{-g}}(\sqrt{-g}\,g^{\sigma\beta})_{,\beta} = 0. \tag{2.7}$$

It is customary to refer to such systems as the above as harmonic coordinate systems. In this system equations (2.2) become

$$\frac{1}{2}g^{\alpha\beta}g_{\mu\nu,\alpha\beta} - L_{\mu\nu} = 0. \tag{2.8}$$

It is well known that the characteristics of a system of partial differential equations are determined exclusively by the coefficients of the higher derivatives. In our case it is the components of the metric tensor $g^{\alpha\beta}$ themselves that play this part. But the $g^{\alpha\beta}$ matrix can be reduced to the canonical form characterized by the signature $(+, -, -, -)$ by a nonsingular transformation of the coordinates at any point in space-time. This proves that the system of quasilinear equations (2.2) is hyperbolic (see /49/, p. 61).

2. Hadamard's discontinuity

In the classical theory of partial differential equations (see, for instance, /50/), wave propagation in space is characterized by Hadamard's discontinuity in the solution of the equations on the initial hypersurface S. We will show below that the hypersurface of discontinuity S of the field functions (of their derivatives), known as the wave-front surface, is the characteristic hypersurface of the field equations. Our next task is therefore to determine the characteristic manifolds ("characteristics") of Einstein's equations. However, before applying the concept of Hadamard's discontinuity directly to Einstein's equations, we will first illustrate it with the help of the scalar equation (2.1).

Assume that the function ψ is continuous in each of the regions 1 and 2 into which the surface S divides the space-time region under consideration, and that it tends to the limits $\psi_{(1)}^{(0)}$ and $\psi_{(2)}^{(0)}$ as x^α tends to a point $P_0(x_{(0)}^\alpha)$ on S from the regions 1 and 2, respectively. Then the following function of the point P_0 will be called the Hadamard discontinuity of the function ψ on the surface S:

$$[\psi]\,(P_0) \equiv \psi_{(1)}^{(0)} - \psi_{(2)}^{(0)}. \qquad (2.9)$$

Now let the function ψ be everywhere continuous near S while certain of its first derivatives $\psi_{,\alpha}$ have finite discontinuities on S:

$$[\psi] = 0, \quad [\psi_{,\alpha}] \neq 0 \qquad (2.10)$$

We construct the total differentials of $\psi_{(1)}$ and $\psi_{(2)}$ on S:

$$d\psi_{(1)} = \psi_{(1),\,\alpha}dx^{\alpha}, \quad d\psi_{(2)} = \psi_{(2),\,\alpha}dx^{\alpha}.$$

Their existence and continuity was demonstrated by Hadamard /51/ by considering the limits to S from regions 1 and 2. Subtracting the one from the other, we obtain, due to (2.10) and the continuity of $d\psi$ on S:

$$(\psi_{(1),\,\alpha} - \psi_{(2),\,\alpha})\,dx^{\alpha} = [\psi_{,\alpha}]\,dx^{\alpha} = 0. \qquad (2.11)$$

Let the surface S be given by $\varphi(x^z) = 0$. For $\partial_\alpha\varphi$ — the normal to the surface S — the relation

$$\varphi_{,\alpha}dx^{\alpha} = 0 \qquad (2.12)$$

holds if the increment dx^{α} belongs to the surface S. Comparing (2.11) and (2.12), we conclude that $[\psi_{,\alpha}]$ and $\varphi_{,\alpha}$ are proportional to each other:

$$[\psi_{,\alpha}] = \chi\varphi_{,\alpha}. \qquad (2.13)$$

If the first derivatives of the function ψ are continuous, it can be shown in a similar fashion that the discontinuities of the second derivatives are expressed by the formula

$$[\psi_{,\alpha\beta}] = \chi\varphi_{,\alpha}\varphi_{,\beta}, \qquad (2.14)$$

and so on (cf. Hadamard /51/, pp. 81 — 89).

Thus the problem of the investigation of gravitational waves as solutions of Einstein's equations must be linked to nonanalytic solutions of the Cauchy problem for a system of quasilinear hyperbolic partial differential equations; in other words, it is to be presumed that the coefficients of the equations, the initial data and the solution itself may be functions of a finite order of smoothness C^r while derivatives of these functions of orders higher than r may have Hadamard discontinuities on certain hypersurfaces. (The function ψ is said to be of class C^r if it has continuous partial derivatives up to the order r inclusive.) If ψ is of class C^{r-1} in the neighborhood of S while its r-th derivatives have Hadamard discontinuities on S, ψ is said to be a piecewise smooth function of class C^r, or piecewise* C^r.

The solution of Cauchy's problem will depend not only on the order of smoothness of the functions in which the initial data are given and the solution is sought, but also on the character of the initial hypersurface S. More specifically, the solutions to the problem will be substantially different depending on whether the hypersurface S is free or characteristic. **

For Einstein's equations (2.2), the important case from our standpoint, Cauchy's problem may be stated as follows:

Let the initial hypersurface S be given by an equation of the form

$$S: \quad \varphi(x^\alpha) = 0, \tag{2.15}$$

and let the functions $g_{\alpha\beta}(x^\circ)$ and their first derivatives $g_{\alpha\beta,\circ}(x^\circ)$ be given on it; determine functions $g_{\alpha\beta}(x^\circ)$ and their first derivatives which reduce to the initial data on S and satisfy equations (2.2) for $g_{\alpha\beta}$ outside S.

In Lichnerowicz's analysis of the Cauchy problem for Einstein's equations, the choice of a convenient coordinate system played an important role. We will henceforth assume that the coordinate system is harmonic so that equations (2.2) assume the form of (2.8) while the initial data obey the condition

$$\Gamma^\sigma = 0.$$

The exact solution of Cauchy's problem for Einstein's equations in harmonic coordinates has been given by Lichnerowicz in /54/, which we will be following henceforth.

Within the limits of the condition of harmonicity throughout the space-time region inside which the solution of Cauchy's problem is

---

* "Par morceaux" in Lichnerowicz's original terminology (see /52/, pp.27 – 35).

** A general formulation of Cauchy's problem and definitions of free and characteristic hypersurfaces will be found in the monographs of Petrovskii /49/ and Bers, John and Schechter /53/.

being sought, it is possible to choose local coordinates x^σ on S such that in these coordinates the equation for S reduces to

$$\varphi(x^\alpha) = x^0 = 0. \tag{2.16}$$

It is easily seen from the formulation of Cauchy's problem that the solutions of interest for the problem of gravitational waves are functions of class C^1 (piecewise C^2) for sufficiently smooth (but nonanalytic) initial data. In other words, $g_{\mu\nu}$ and their first derivatives $g_{\mu\nu,\sigma}$ will be continuous on the hypersurface S, while certain second derivatives $g_{\mu\nu,\rho\sigma}$ will have Hadamard discontinuities on S. Let us determine which of the second derivatives of $g_{\mu\nu}$ can have a discontinuity on the hypersurface S given by equation (2.16). According to Hadamard's formula (2.14), discontinuities of second derivatives can be expressed as

$$[g_{\mu\nu,\alpha\beta}] = a_{\mu\nu}\varphi_{,\alpha}\varphi_{,\beta}, \tag{2.17}$$

where $a_{\mu\nu}$ are the so-called "coefficients of discontinuity" (see also the works of Trautman /55/ and Bel /56/). From this it follows that of all the second derivatives of $g_{\mu\nu}$ on S, only $g_{\mu\nu,00}$ can have a discontinuity:

$$[g_{\mu\nu,00}] = a_{\mu\nu}. \tag{2.18}$$

But of these, the derivatives of $g_{0\alpha}$ do not appear in Einstein's equations. Therefore the important point for us is that of all the derivatives of $g_{\mu\nu}$ entering into equation (2.2), only second derivatives of the form $g_{ij,00}$ can be discontinuous in the hypersurface S. In this case Cauchy's data for the problem (2.2) reduce to specification on S only of the values of the functions $g_{\mu\nu}$ and $g_{\mu\nu,0}$, which we assume to be thrice and twice continuously differentiable with respect to the x^i coordinates, respectively. The remaining first derivatives of $g_{\mu\nu}$, as well as the second derivatives of g_{00} and g_{0i}, are uniquely determined by differentiation with respect to x^i of the previously known Cauchy data on S.

The following question arises in this connection: when do Einstein's equations (2.2), together with the Cauchy data, uniquely determine the derivatives $g_{ij,00}$ as well?

As Lichnerowicz shows (/52/, pp. 31 − 33; see also /57/, p.264), the system (2.2) in the harmonic coordinate system is equivalent to a system of the form

$$\frac{1}{2} g^{00} g_{ij,00} + \Omega_{ij} = 0, \tag{2.19}$$

$$S^0_\alpha = 0, \quad \Gamma^\alpha = 0, \tag{2.20}$$

where

$$S_\beta^\alpha = R_\beta^\alpha - \frac{1}{2} R\delta_\beta^\alpha;$$

(2.21)

here Ω_{ij}, S_α^0 and Γ^α do not contain derivatives of the form $g_{ij,00}$ and hence are completely determined by the Cauchy data. Fulfillment of conditions (2.20) on the hypersurface S guarantees their fulfillment in the neighborhood of S as well, provided equations (2.19) hold on S and outside it (Lichnerowicz's theorem regarding involution of the system of differential equations /52/).

This means that conditions (2.20) serve only for determining the Cauchy data, which cannot, therefore, be arbitrary. At the same time, system (2.19) serves for integration of the system (2.2) over x^0, i.e., for determining the unknown functions $g_{\mu\nu}$. Thus in empty space Cauchy's problem for Einstein's equations breaks down into two parts: 1) determination of the Cauchy data that satisfy equations (2.2); 2) integration of the system of equations (2.19) over x^0.

Let us assume that we have Cauchy data satisfying the conditions (2.20). Then under the condition $g^{00} \neq 0$ equations (2.2) admit of a solution which does not have the Hadamard discontinuity on S; this corresponds to the case where equations (2.19) taken together with the Cauchy data uniquely determine the derivatives $g_{ij,00}$ as well. On the other hand, if $g^{00} = 0$ in the neighborhood of S, then the second derivatives $g_{ij,00}$ — and therefore also the curvature tensor components R_{0i0j} — cannot be uniquely determined on S by the Cauchy data and the field equations, i.e., they have the Hadamard discontinuity on S. *

3. Characteristic hypersurfaces of Einstein's equations

The condition $g^{00} = 0$ governing the Hadamard discontinuity for the curvature tensor on the initial hypersurface S, specified in the form (2.16), can be formulated in generally covariant form. Indeed, passing to arbitrary coordinates in which $x^0 = \varphi(x'^\alpha)$, let us write

---

* By definition, discontinuity of the derivatives of functions expressing the solution of Cauchy's problem for a certain system of equations subject to continuity of the solution itself is known as weak discontinuity of the solution of the given system of equations. Thus the condition $g^{00} = 0$ denotes a weak discontinuity of the first order for the solution of the system of equations (2.2).

down the condition

$$g^{00} = \frac{\partial x^0}{\partial x'^\alpha} \frac{\partial x_0}{\partial x'^\beta} g'^{\alpha\beta} = 0$$

in the form of a general equation for the hypersurface S admitting a weak discontinuity in the solution of the system (2.2) (primes have been omitted):

$$g^{\alpha\beta}\varphi_{,\alpha}\varphi_{,\beta} = 0, \tag{2.22}$$

i. e., the **e i k o n a l e q u a t i o n** from geometrical optics (/16/, p. 173).

But equation (2.22) is a necessary and sufficient condition for isotropy of the hypersurfaces S (see /58/, p. 57). Consequently, first-order weak discontinuity in the solution of the system of equations (2.2) (Hadamard's discontinuity in the curvature tensor) is possible only if the initial hypersurface S is isotropic.

We see that the solution of Cauchy's problem for Einstein's equations in empty space depends radically on the nature of the initial hypersurface S. If the hypersurface S specified by the equation $\varphi(x^\alpha) = 0$ does not satisfy the condition (2.22),

$$g^{\alpha\beta}\varphi_{,\alpha}\varphi_{,\beta} \neq 0, \tag{2.23}$$

it is called **f r e e**, and Cauchy's problem for equations (2.2) in functions of class C^1 (piecewise C^2) admits of a unique solution. But if S does satisfy condition (2.22) it is termed **c h a r a c t e r i s t i c**, and the uniqueness theorem of the solution of Cauchy's problem does not hold.

4. Leray's theorem

It is also possible to tell something of the solution of Cauchy's problem from the general existence and uniqueness theorems for a solution of a system of quasilinear hyperbolic partial differential equations. Thus if the coefficients entering into the equations are all analytic and the solution is sought in analytic functions, then given analytic initial data on a free hypersurface the Cauchy problem has a solution and moreover a unique one (Cauchy-Kowalevski theorem; see /53/, p. 56). However, in the case of interest to us — the solution of Cauchy's problem in C^1 (piecewise C^2) functions — the Cauchy-Kowalevski theorem is inapplicable.

As Lichnerowicz points out /54/, in our case it is possible to use Leray's theorem /59/ according to which a system of quasi-linear hyperbolic partial differential equations will have a nonanalytic and moreover a unique solution provided that the initial hypersurface S is free (spacelike) and that the Cauchy data on this hypersurface are given by sufficiently smooth functions. With regard to equations (2.2) all the conditions of Leray's theorem are satisfied if one uses harmonic coordinates in which Einstein's equations assume the form (2.8) and the initial data are determined by the solution of the system of equations (2.20).

The following important result follows from Leray's theorem:

The Riemann tensor $R_{\alpha\beta\gamma\delta}$ in empty space-time can have an Hadamard discontinuity only on the characteristic hypersurface S of Einstein's equations (2.2), which is determined by the eikonal equation (2.22).

Indeed, the presence of an Hadamard discontinuity in a Riemann tensor on a certain hypersurface S is evidence that some at least of the second derivatives $g_{\mu\nu,\rho\sigma}$ cannot be determined uniquely from the field equations in the neighborhood of S from the initial data specified upon it. This in turn means that the hypersurface cannot be free.

5. Bicharacteristics of the equations of gravitation

We saw that in the Riemannian space V_4 of signature -2 the characteristic manifold of Einstein's equations in the absence of matter

$$R_{\mu\nu} = 0 \qquad\qquad (2.24)$$

is the isotropic three-dimensional hypersurface V_3 (2.15), the function φ satisfying the eikonal equation (2.22).

The envelope of the tangent planes to the characteristics passing through a given point is called the characteristic cone /50/ at this point. And as the characteristic hypersurface of Einstein's equations is isotropic (i.e., the metric is degenerate), the characteristic cone of the system of equations (2.2) coincides with the light cone at the given point (/52/, pp. 33—35). Equation (2.22) as a characteristic equation for the system (2.1) was first considered by Finzi /59/.

According to the definition of bicharacteristics (also known as rays) for a system of quasilinear second-order equations (see /50/, p. 551), the bicharacteristics of Einstein's equations (2.2) are identical with the flow lines of the isotropic vector field l^α orthogonal to the characteristic hypersurface S,

$$l^\alpha = g^{\alpha\beta}\,\varphi_{,\beta},\tag{2.25}$$

and may be expressed by the equations

$$\frac{dx^\alpha}{d\tau} = g^{\alpha\beta}\varphi_{,\beta},\tag{2.26}$$

where τ is a parameter on the curve. From (2.26) it obviously also follows that

$$l_\beta = g_{\beta\alpha}\frac{dx^\alpha}{d\tau}\,.\tag{2.27}$$

The functions $x^\alpha(\tau)$ and $l_\alpha(\tau)$ can be specified by the canonical system of equations

$$\frac{dx^\alpha}{d\tau} = \frac{\partial H}{\partial l_\alpha},\qquad \frac{\partial l_\alpha}{\partial \tau} = -\frac{\partial H}{\partial x^\alpha},\tag{2.28}$$

where the Hamiltonian

$$H(x^\alpha, l_\beta) = \frac{1}{2}\,g_{\alpha\beta}x^\alpha l^\beta\tag{2.29}$$

is identical with the characteristic form of Einstein's equations in empty space /50/. Both the solutions $x^\alpha(\tau)$ of the canonical system (2.28) determine the extremals of the Lagrangian

$$L = \frac{1}{2}\,g_{\alpha\beta}\frac{dx^\alpha}{d\tau}\frac{dx^\beta}{d\tau}\,.$$

In actual fact, passing from the variables $\left(x^\alpha, \dfrac{dx^\alpha}{d\tau}\right)$ to the variables $(x^\alpha,\,l^\beta)$, we obtain the classical relation between L and H:

$$H = \left(\frac{dx^\alpha}{d\tau}\right)\frac{\partial L}{\partial\left(\dfrac{dx^\alpha}{d\tau}\right)} - L.$$

Since the first integral of the system (2.28) is $2L = C = $ const, these solutions will be extremals for

$$\sqrt{2L} = \sqrt{g_{\alpha\beta} \frac{dx^\alpha}{d\tau} \frac{dx^\beta}{d\tau}}$$

as well, i. e., they will be geodesics of the Riemannian space V_4 with metric $g_{\alpha\beta}$ (/52/, pp. 33 −35).

As we know from the theory of partial differential equations /50/, bicharacteristics belong to the characteristic surface, i. e., the tangents to them are the generators of the characteristic cone. But, as we saw earlier, the characteristic cone for Einstein's equations is identical with the light cone. Consequently, the bicharacteristics of Einstein's equations are iso-tropic geodesics.

6. The Cauchy problem for the Einstein-Maxwell equations

In analyzing the definition of gravitational waves it may be of considerable benefit to make use of the experience acquired in the investigation of electromagnetic waves, which are described by the energy-momentum tensor

$$\tau_{\alpha\beta} = \frac{1}{4} g_{\alpha\beta} F_{\lambda\mu} F^{\lambda\mu} - F_\alpha^\rho F_{\beta\rho}, \tag{2.30}$$

where $F_{\alpha\beta}$ is the Maxwell stress tensor. It is therefore useful to examine Cauchy's problem for the Maxwell equations in the Rie-mannian space-time of the general theory of relativity. The general solution of this problem has been investigated by Lich-nerowicz (/52/, pp. 43 −52).

The self-consistent system of Einstein-Maxwell equations has the form

$$D_\alpha \equiv g^{\alpha\beta} F_{\alpha\gamma;\beta} = 0, \tag{2.31}$$

$$E^\alpha \equiv \frac{1}{2} \eta^{\beta\gamma\delta\alpha} F_{\gamma\delta;\beta} = 0, \tag{2.32}$$

$$Q_{\alpha\beta} \equiv R_{\alpha\beta} - \frac{1}{2} R g_{\alpha\beta} + \lambda \tau_{\alpha\beta} = 0, \tag{2.33}$$

where $\eta^{\alpha\beta\gamma\delta}$ is the discriminant tensor*

---

* More precisely a x i a l tensor, since under coordinate transformation its sign will depend on the sign of the Jacobian of the transformation (see, for instance, /60/, p. 11).

$$\eta^{\alpha\beta\gamma\delta} = \frac{1}{\sqrt{-g}} \, \varepsilon^{\alpha\beta\gamma\delta}, \qquad \eta_{\alpha\beta\gamma\delta} = -\sqrt{-g} \, \varepsilon_{\alpha\beta\gamma\delta}, \tag{2.34}$$

and $\varepsilon_{\mu\nu\gamma\delta}$ is the wholly antisymmetric Levi-Civita symbol, equal to $+1$ for ε_{1234} and all even permutations of the indices, to -1 for all odd permutations and to 0 for the remaining cases.

Let us assume that the field $F_{\alpha\beta}$ is of class C^0 (piecewise C^2). Then Cauchy's problem for the Einstein-Maxwell equations (2.31) — (2.33) may be formulated as follows: let the gravitational and electromagnetic fields be specified on the initial hypersurface (2.15); find the fields outside S if they satisfy equations (2.31) — (2.33).

In the coordinate system in which the equation for S has the form (2.16), the Cauchy's data consist of $g_{\alpha\beta}$ (continuously differentiable with respect to x^i at least three times), $g_{\alpha\beta,0}$ and $F_{\alpha\beta}$ (twice differentiable with respect to these coordinates). Only the derivatives $g_{\alpha\beta,00}$ and $F_{\alpha\beta,0}$ may be discontinuous on S. Separating the index 0 for convenience's sake, we can write equations (2.31) in the form

$$D_i \equiv g^{00} F_{0i,0} + g^{0k} F_{ki,0} + \ldots = 0, \tag{2.35}$$
$$D_0 \equiv g^{0i} F_{i0,0} + \ldots = 0 \tag{2.36}$$

(henceforth the three dots are employed so as to avoid writing out explicitly those terms which are uniquely determined by the Cauchy data).

Lichnerowicz shows that the system (2.35) — (2.36) is equivalent to the system comprising equations (2.35) and

$$D^0 = 0, \tag{2.37}$$

where the quantity $D^0 \; (\equiv g^{0i}D_i + g^{00}D_0)$, as is evident from equations (2.35) — (2.36), is uniquely determined by the Cauchy data. Similarly, equations (2.32) are equivalent to the system

$$E_i \equiv \frac{1}{2} \, \eta^{0jki} F_{jk,0} + \ldots = 0, \tag{2.38}$$

$$E^0 \equiv \frac{1}{2} \, \eta^{jklo} F_{kl,j} = 0, \tag{2.39}$$

where E^0 is determined by the Cauchy data. Lastly, equations (2.33) are equivalent to the system

$$Q_{ij} \equiv R_{ij} - \frac{1}{2} \, R g_{ij} + \lambda \tau_{ij} = 0, \tag{2.40}$$

$$Q_\alpha^0 \equiv R_\alpha^0 - \frac{1}{2} \, R \delta_\alpha^0 + \lambda \tau_\alpha^0 = 0, \tag{2.41}$$

where Q_α^0 is given by the Cauchy data. (We recall that outside of the sources the trace of the energy-momentum tensor $\tau_\alpha^\alpha \equiv 0$.) Thus Cauchy's problem may be broken down into two parts: 1) determination of the Cauchy data satisfying conditions (2.37), (2.39) and (2.41) on S; 2) integration of the system of equations (2.35), (2.38) and (2.40) with respect to the coordinate x^0 for the obtained initial data.

We assume from the first that $g^{00} \neq 0$ throughout S. Then $F_{ik,0}$ is uniquely determined from equation (2.38), $F_{0i,0}$ is uniquely determined from (2.35) and $g_{ij,00}$ is uniquely determined from (2.40). Thus all the second derivatives of $g_{\alpha\beta}$ and all the first derivatives of $F_{\alpha\beta}$ are uniquely determined by the initial data and initial system, and therefore the latter has a unique solution.

Now let $g^{00} = 0$ on S. Then $g_{ij,00}$ and $F_{0i,0}$ may be discontinuous on S and consequently S is a characteristic manifold of Maxwell's equations. The characteristic equation, as we know, has the form (2.22); in other words, the characteristic manifold of Maxwell's equations is identical with the characteristic manifold of Einstein's equations.

Thus we have proved Lichnerowicz's theorem (/52/, pp. 50−52):

The characteristic manifolds (2.15) of Einstein's equations and of Maxwell's equations in V_4 are identical and are determined by the solutions of the eikonal equation (2.22).

An immediate consequence of this theorem is the fact that the bicharacteristics of Einstein's equations are identical with those of Maxwell's equations.

7. Gravitational wave front and "rays" of gravitation

On the basis of the foregoing it may be stated that the characteristic manifold of Einstein's equations is the hypersurface on which the Riemann tensor has a Hadamard discontinuity, i.e., this hypersurface plays the role of a wave front understood as the surface of discontinuity of $R_{\alpha\beta\gamma\delta}$ /55, 59/. The bicharacteristics of Einstein's equations, on the other hand, are the trajectories of an isotropic vector orthogonal to the characteristic hypersurface (wave front) and therefore play the part of wave vector. Since the characteristic manifold and the bicharacteristics are invariants of coordinate transformation (/50/, p. 555), the three-dimensional characteristic hypersurface of Einstein's equations can be regarded as invariantly determined gravitational wave front while the bicharacteristics of Einstein's equations can be regarded as invariantly determined gravitational rays, i.e., the trajectories of propagation of the wave front.

Similarly, the electromagnetic wave front in the space V_4 is determined by the characteristic hypersurface of Maxwell's equations; by Lichnerowicz's theorem it is identical with the gravitational wave front. The trajectories of electromagnetic wave propagation — the electromagnetic rays — can be defined as bicharacteristics of Maxwell's equations; they are identical with gravitational rays.

Chapter 3

GRAVITATIONAL WAVES: SUBSTANCE OF THE PROBLEM

1. Various aspects of the problem

From the standpoint of the results given in Chapter 2, fields describing free gravitational waves are determined by the solutions of Einstein's equations (2.2) for initial data on a characteristic hypersurface. As a rule, however, partial solutions of Einstein's equations are obtained without specifying definite boundary conditions, and thus the wave character of a concrete solution may not be apparent. Yet when studying gravitational fields we have only partial solutions of Einstein's equations at our disposal. Hence the problem arises of determining in a generally covariant manner the class of gravitational field corresponding to Hadamard's discontinuity in solutions of Einstein's equations with initial data on the characteristic manifold.

No definite solution of this problem exists, despite numerous variants which will be reviewed in the following sections. From the point of view of the theory of differential equations, the difficulty of the problem arises from the complexity of the nonlinear structure of Einstein's equations and the absence for the latter of universal boundary conditions. From the differential-geometric standpoint the difficulty resides in the absence of a generally covariant d'Alembert operator explicitly following from Einstein's equations. Lastly, from the physical standpoint the problem is that the absence of a generally covariant expression for the gravitational field energy in the general theory of relativity makes it difficult to tackle the question of the possibility of energy transfer by gravitational waves, as well as to describe the waves themselves in terms of the free transfer of field energy.

Like all physical problems the problem of gravitational waves calls for experimental as well as theoretical treatment. In other words, gravitational waves can and should be viewed as an aspect of physical reality susceptible of experimental measurement. But if the experimental data are to be given a correct theoretical interpretation, the physical theory must contain a few general premises independent of concrete experiments. Only then will the theory be whole and closed, i.e., possess an intrinsic logical base (see, for example, /61/). Otherwise any comparison between the theory and the data of a given experiment would be tautological.

In this sense the general theory of relativity is exceptional among physical theories. The rigorous geometric foundation on which Einstein's theory of gravitation rests allows us to hope that it will be possible to arrive at a general and rigorous substantiation of the concept of gravitational radiation. It is to elucidate this possibility that we undertook to discuss the Cauchy problem for the equations of the gravitational field in the preceding chapter. There we found that the solution of Cauchy's problem for Einstein's equations of gravitation exhibits profound similarity at a number of important points with the solution of the corresponding problem for the equations of the electromagnetic field. In particular, the characteristic manifolds and bicharacteristics of Einstein's equations and those of Maxwell's equations in the space-time V_4 are identical. In classical electrodynamics the characteristic manifold of Maxwell's equations describes the electromagnetic wave front, and the bicharacteristics of Maxwell's equations describe the trajectories of propagation of electromagnetic radiation. In the light of this analogy one is justified in assuming that a gravitational wave front can be defined theoretically in terms of the characteristic manifold of Einstein's equation and its propagation trajectories in terms of the bicharacteristics.

The basic problem, however, remains that of defining the field of gravitational radiation, or the gravitational wave zone. The foregoing considerations do not rule out the possibility of finding a satisfactory definition. The search for initial premises could clearly proceed along the lines of further pursuit of the analogy between the gravitational and the electromagnetic field. It should obviously be borne in mind that this analogy cannot be pursued indefinitely. Nevertheless all the methods for describing gravitational radiation discussed below make some use of the analogy between the electromagnetic and gravitational fields.

This analogy is detectable by a variety of methods. The first of these follows directly from comparison of the differential structure of the equations of gravitation with that of the equations of electromagnetism, i.e., from comparative analysis of the solution of Cauchy's problem for Einstein's and Maxwell's equations. This analysis is easiest to perform if one takes the curvature tensor of the space-time V_4 to be analogous to the electromagnetic tensor $F_{\mu\nu}$ in the gravitational equations. Einstein's equations

$$R_{\alpha\beta} = -\lambda U_{\alpha\beta} \qquad \left(U_{\alpha\beta} \equiv T_{\alpha\beta} - \frac{1}{2} T g_{\alpha\beta} \right) \qquad (3.1)$$

and Bianchi's identities

$$R_{\alpha\beta\gamma\delta;\sigma} + R_{\alpha\beta\sigma\gamma;\delta} + R_{\alpha\beta\delta\sigma;\gamma} = 0 \tag{3.2}$$

yield the relations* /60, 62/

$$R_{\alpha\beta\gamma.;\delta}^{\cdots\delta} = -2\lambda U_{\gamma[\alpha;\beta]} \qquad (2U_{\gamma[\alpha;\beta]} \equiv U_{\gamma\alpha;\beta} - U_{\gamma\beta;\alpha}). \tag{3.3}$$

Relations (3.2) and (3.3) exhibit a striking analogy with Maxwell's equations

$$F_{\mu\nu;\sigma} + F_{\sigma\mu;\nu} + F_{\nu\sigma;\mu} = 0, \tag{3.4}$$

$$F_{\mu;\nu}^{\nu} = -j_{\mu}, \tag{3.5}$$

and the tensor

$$J_{\gamma\alpha\beta} = 2\lambda U_{\gamma[\alpha;\beta]} \tag{3.6}$$

can be interpreted as the gravitational analog of the electro-magnetic current. However, if (3.2) and (3.3) are regarded as equations for the components $R_{\alpha\beta\gamma\delta}$, a problem arises: under what conditions will Einstein's equations (3.1) follow from equations (3.2) and (3.3)? The problem can be formulated with greater rigor as follows: what conditions must the initial data of equations (3.2) and (3.3) satisfy in order for the complete class of their solutions to define the set of all gravitational fields of Einstein's theory?

This question has been resolved by Lichnerowicz, who shows /62/ that if, on an initial hypersurface S oriented in space, the initial data of equations (3.2) and (3.3) (i.e., the components of the Riemann tensor) satisfy relations (3.1), the latter will also be satisfied in the neighborhood of S. ** In other words, equations (3.2) and (3.3) are completely equivalent to Einstein's equations of gravitation if the Cauchy data for equations (3.2) and (3.3) on the spacelike initial hypersurface S are coupled by the conditions (3.1). In this case equations (3.2) − (3.3) are called quasi-Maxwell equations of gravitation /63/.

However, the "quasi-Maxwellian approach" leads to fundamental difficulties in the description of gravitational fields of the wave

---

* Here and below square brackets denote antisymmetrization with respect to the indices they enclose; correspondingly, parentheses denote symmetrization.

** This theorem is the analog of the theorem concerning the involution of Einstein's system of equations, discussed in the preceding chapter.

type which are defined by initial data on a characteristic (isotropic) hypersurface. Thus it is possible to construct for the gravitational field a wave equation corresponding to the equation for the electromagnetic field tensor $F_{\mu\nu}$ which follows from Maxwell's equations in Riemannian space-time (Tolman /63/). However, this analog turns out to be an identity for the Riemann tensor $R_{\alpha\beta\gamma\delta}$ and thus cannot serve to separate wave fields as a special class of gravitational field.

Aside from differential methods, the analogy between the gravitational and electromagnetic fields can also be detected algebraically. This makes it possible to construct a definition of fields of gravitational waves based on the similarity in algebraic structure between the electromagentic field tensor $F_{\mu\nu}$ and the Riemann tensor $R_{\alpha\beta\gamma\delta}$. As we will show in the next chapter, a characteristic trait of fields of electromagnetic radiation which sets them apart from the set of all electromagnetic fields can be expressed by purely algebraic conditions, namely the vanishing of the invariants of the electromagnetic field tensor $F_{\mu\nu}$. From this point of view the definition of electromagnetic radiation is based on the algebraic subdivision of all electromagnetic fields into two types, interpretable physically as wave and nonwave fields. This suggests the application of algebraic classification to the definition of gravitational wave fields as well. However, here it is immediately seen that the algebraic analogy between the electromagnetic and gravitational fields is not complete.

Indeed, due to differences in algebraic structure between the electromagnetic field tensor $F_{\mu\nu}$ and the space-time curvature tensor $R_{\alpha\beta\gamma\delta}$, gravitational fields subdivide not into two types (as do electromagnetic fields) but rather into five algebraically distinct types, defined by Petrov's classification (three basic types, of which two can be both degenerate and nondegenerate). As a result the gravitational wave field possesses diverse algebraic properties and correspondingly there is a multiplicity of algebraic criteria for distinguishing wavelike gravitational fields from all gravitational fields. This is another difficulty accounting for the fact that the problem of gravitational waves in the general theory of relativity has yet to receive a universally accepted theoretical solution. Petrov's algebraic classification of gravitational fields /64, 65/, however, has a very important role to play in what follows. It is therefore useful to consider it in some detail.

2. Algebraic classification of gravitational fields. Einstein spaces

Let a given Riemann space V_4 be an Einstein space, i.e., let it be described by the equations

$$R_{\alpha\beta} = \varkappa g_{\alpha\beta}. \qquad (3.7)$$

It is easily shown that one will then have

$$\varkappa = \frac{1}{4} R = \text{const}.$$

Proceeding according to Petrov's method (/65/, pp. 113−117), we map the Einstein space at every point on the centered affine bi-vector space B_N of dimensionality

$$N = C_n^2 = \frac{1}{2} n(n-1) = 6 \qquad (n = 4),$$

placing a single collective index in the space B_N in correspondence with each antisymmetric pair of indices of an arbitrary tensor in the Einstein space. Then to an arbitrary bi-tensor (i.e., tensor whose indices subdivide into antisymmetric pairs) belonging to the Einstein space there corresponds a tensor of half the valency in the space B_6.

We metrize the bi-vector space B_6, introducing into it the tensor $g_{ab}(a, b = 1, 2, 3, 4, 5, 6)$ as the image of a fourth-rank tensor in the Einstein space:

$$g_{ab} \to g_{\alpha\beta\gamma\delta} \equiv g_{\alpha\gamma} g_{\beta\delta} - g_{\alpha\delta} g_{\beta\gamma}, \qquad (3.8)$$

$$(\alpha\beta) \to a, \qquad (\gamma\delta) \to b.$$

Assuming that V_4 has the signature −2 (i.e., +, −, −, −) and fixing the enumeration of the bi-vector space indices

$$10 \to 1,\ 20 \to 2,\ 30 \to 3,\ 23 \to 4,\ 31 \to 5,\ 12 \to 6, \qquad (3.9)$$

we obtain the canonical form of the metric of the space R_6 in the chosen orthogonal frame

$$g_{ab} = \begin{pmatrix} -\tilde{\varepsilon} & 0 \\ 0 & \tilde{\varepsilon} \end{pmatrix}, \qquad (3.10)$$

where $\widetilde{\varepsilon}$ is a unit 3×3 matrix. From this follows, in particular, the nondegeneracy of the matrix $\|g_{ab}\|$.

Writing down equations (3.7) in the orthogonal frame we arrive at the conclusion that in Einstein spaces the matrix $\|R_{ab}\|$ of the curvature tensor is block-symmetric:

$$(R_{ab}) = \begin{pmatrix} \mathscr{E} & \mathscr{H} \\ \mathscr{H} & -\mathscr{E} \end{pmatrix},$$

(3.11)

where the blocks $\mathscr{E}$ and $\mathscr{H}$ are symmetric 3×3 matrices the elements of which satisfy the relations

$$\sum_{s=1}^{3} e_{ss} = -\varkappa, \quad \sum_{s=1}^{3} h_{ss} = 0.$$

(3.12)

Then, decomposing a λ-matrix of form $\|R_{ab} - \lambda g_{ab}\|$ into two three-dimensional complex conjugate matrices, we arrive at Petrov's fundamental theorem: there are three and only three types of gravitational field, defined in R_6 by the characteristics of the λ-matrix of the curvature tensor:

Type 1	Type 2	Type 3	
$[111, \overline{111}]$	$[21, \overline{21}]$	$[3, 3]$	(3.13)

respectively. Here the bar indicates elementary divisors with complex conjugate bases. For type 3 the elementary divisors have real bases (no bar). All spaces of constant curvature defined by a characteristic of the form $[(111, 111)]$ belong to type 1 (/65/, p. 119).

Petrov shows (/65/, p. §19) that the matrix $\|R_{ab}\|$ of the curvature tensor in a canonical nonholonomic orthogonal frame is reducible to the form (3.11), where for type 1 fields

$$\mathscr{E} = \begin{pmatrix} \alpha_1 & 0 & 0 \\ 0 & \alpha_2 & 0 \\ 0 & 0 & \alpha_3 \end{pmatrix}, \quad \mathscr{H} = \begin{pmatrix} \beta_1 & 0 & 0 \\ 0 & \beta_2 & 0 \\ 0 & 0 & \beta_3 \end{pmatrix},$$

(3.14)

$$\sum \alpha_i = -\varkappa, \quad \sum \beta_i = 0;$$

(3.15)

for type 2 fields

$$\mathscr{E} = \begin{pmatrix} \alpha_1 & 0 & 0 \\ 0 & \alpha_2 + 1 & 0 \\ 0 & 0 & \alpha_2 - 1 \end{pmatrix}, \quad \mathscr{H} = \begin{pmatrix} \beta_1 & 0 & 0 \\ 0 & \beta_2 & 1 \\ 0 & 1 & \beta_2 \end{pmatrix},$$

(3.16)

$$\alpha_1 + 2\alpha_2 = -\varkappa, \quad \beta_1 + 2\beta_2 = 0;$$

(3.17)

and for type 3 fields

$$\mathscr{E} = \begin{pmatrix} -\frac{1}{3}\varkappa & 1 & 0 \\ 1 & -\frac{1}{3}\varkappa & 0 \\ 0 & 0 & -\frac{1}{3}\varkappa \end{pmatrix}, \quad \mathscr{H} = \begin{pmatrix} 0 & 0 & 0 \\ 0 & 0 & -1 \\ 0 & -1 & 0 \end{pmatrix}. \quad (3.18)$$

Here α_s and β_s are respectively the real and imaginary parts of the bases of the elementary divisors

$$\sigma_s = \alpha_s + i\beta_s \quad (s = 1, 2, 3), \quad (3.19)$$

which are identical with the eigenvalues of the matrix $\|R_{ab}\|$.

Since there are three types of Einstein spaces, let us agree to designate them by $*T_i$, where $i = 1, 2, 3$ denotes the type of gravitational field. An empty space-time $R_{\alpha\beta} = 0$, i.e., the space $*T_i$ for $\varkappa = 0$, will be denoted by T_i. Petrov's classification was subsequently formulated within the frameworks of other formalisms used in gravitational wave research. Thus Debever gives a detailed description of types and subtypes of fields after Petrov which is based on the mutual orientation of isotropic vector fields in physical space-time /66/, while Penrose investigates the spinor properties of the Riemann tensor from the standpoint of the algebraic classification according to Petrov /67/. Penrose gives the following diagrammatic representation of Petrov's systematics:*

$$
\begin{array}{c}
\rightarrow \text{I} \\
\downarrow \quad \uparrow \\
\rightarrow \text{II} \leftrightarrow D \\
\downarrow \qquad \uparrow \\
\text{III} \leftrightarrow N \leftrightarrow O \\
*T_3 \quad *T_2 \quad *T_1
\end{array}
\qquad (3.20)
$$

Here I, D, O are subtypes of $*T_1$, distinguishable by the following properties: for I the three eigenvalues in the blocks of the matrix $\|R_{ab}\|$ are all different; for D two eigenvalues out of the three are identical, e.g.,

$$\alpha_2 = \alpha_3, \quad \beta_2 = \beta_3; \quad (3.21)$$

* Inasmuch as Penrose's notation has achieved wide currency in works on Petrov's classification thanks to the clarity of diagram (3.20), we will henceforth treat the field types I, D, O, II, N and III as if they were simply the corresponding Petrov types, without calling attention to departures from Petrov's original terminology /65/.

for O the three eigenvalues are identical and, due to (3.15) are real:

$$\alpha_1 = \alpha_2 = \alpha_3 = -\frac{1}{3}\varkappa, \qquad \beta_1 = \beta_2 = \beta_3 = 0 \qquad (3.22)$$

(for $\varkappa = 0$ type O contains only flat space-time).

In the second column of diagram (3.20), II and N are subtypes of $*T_2$; II is the "nondegenerate second type," for which the eigenvalues σ_1 and σ_2 are different, and N is the "degenerate second type," for which σ_1 and σ_2 are identical and, from (3.17), real:[*]

$$\alpha_1 = \alpha_2 = -\frac{1}{3}\varkappa, \qquad \beta_1 = \beta_2 = 0. \qquad (3.23)$$

The only eigenvalue, always real, in both blocks of the matrix $\|R_{ab}\|$ for $*T_3$ is given by $-\frac{1}{3}\varkappa$.

3. Classification of gravitational fields of general form

In view of the fact that the classification of Einstein spaces $*T_i$ rests entirely on the algebraic properties of the curvature tensor, it is expedient to use Weyl's conformal curvature tensor (see /58/, p. 115) to classify general gravitational fields $(R_{\alpha\beta} \neq \varkappa g_{\alpha\beta})$:

$$C_{\alpha\beta\mu\nu} = R_{\alpha\beta\mu\nu} - \frac{1}{2}(g_{\mu\varkappa}R_{\beta\nu} - g_{\alpha\nu}R_{\beta\mu} + g_{\beta\nu}R_{\alpha\mu} - g_{\beta\mu}R_{\alpha\nu}) +$$
$$+ \frac{1}{6}R(g_{\mu\alpha}g_{\beta\nu} - g_{\nu\alpha}g_{\beta\mu}). \qquad (3.24)$$

It possesses all the algebraic properties of the Riemann tensor:

$$C_{\alpha\beta\mu\nu} = -C_{\beta\alpha\mu\nu} = -C_{\alpha\beta\nu\mu} = C_{\mu\nu\alpha\beta}, \qquad C_{\alpha[\beta\mu\nu]} = 0. \qquad (3.25)$$

It is easily shown that

$$C_{\alpha\mu} \equiv C_{\alpha\beta\mu\nu}g^{\beta\nu} = 0, \qquad (3.26)$$

i.e., algebraically, the Weyl tensor of an arbitrary space V_4

---

[*] We note that Bel /68/ employs a somewhat different notation: types I, D, II, III and N are spoken of respectively as cas 1, cas 2a, cas 2b, cas 3a and cas 3b.

behaves like a Riemann tensor in empty space, and it is identical with the latter in the case (2.2). Determining the characteristic of the λ-matrix $\| C_{ab} - \lambda g_{ab} \|$ of the Weyl tensor in the bi-vector space R_6 and repeating the arguments of the preceding section, we conclude that there exist three and only three types of V_4 of general form, corresponding to the characteristics (3.13). One can show (/65/, § 20) that the matrix $\| C_{ab} \|$ in the canonical orthogonal frame assumes the same form (3.11), (3.14) − (3.18) as $\| R_{ab} \|$, it now being necessary to set $\varkappa = 0$ throughout.

Penrose's diagram (3.20) remains unaltered for the matrix $\| C_{ab} \|$ as well. Type 0 obviously represents conformally flat spaces V_4, for which $C_{\alpha\beta\mu\nu} = 0$ always, while type N is described by the matrices (3.16) for

$$\alpha_1 = \alpha_2 = 0, \qquad \beta_1 = \beta_2 = 0.$$

4. Petrov's classification and isotropic vector fields

Debever shows /66/ that the Riemann space V_4 of signature −2 admits of the canonical form of the matrix $\| C_{ab} \|$ in the bi-vector space R_6 with respect to at least one and not more than four isotropic field vectors $l^\alpha \neq 0$ satisfying the equations

$$l_{[\lambda} C_{\alpha]\beta\gamma[\delta} l_{\sigma]} l^\beta l^\gamma = 0. \tag{3.27}$$

The formulation of Debever's theorem in the form of equations (3.27) is due to Sachs /110/. The importance of the researches of Debever and Sachs in what follows impels us to dwell on their results in somewhat greater detail.

Type I according to Petrov is characterized by the fact that all four vectors $l^\alpha_{(N)}$ N 1, 2, 3, 4) are different; for type D they are identical in pairs (two independent vectors), for type II there are three independent vectors (two out of four are identical), for type type III there are two independent vectors (three out of four are identical) and, lastly, type N is characterized by the fact that all four vectors are identical, i.e., they determine the same direction.* To see this it is enough to verify equations (3.27) in the canonical orthogonal frame, specifying suitable values of the

---

* The vectors l^α in these equations are determined only up to collinearity (multiplication by an arbitrary scalar). Therefore a difference in the vectors $l^\alpha_{(N)}$ is interpreted as a difference in the isotropic directions specified by these vectors.

components l^α. Thus for type N one should take $l^\alpha = \delta_0^\alpha + \delta_1^\alpha$. We will refer to the vectors $l^\alpha_{(N)}$, which satisfy equations (3.27), as Debever vectors.

This brings us to a new invariant characterization of algebraic types of gravitational fields of general form. Designating the number of coincident (collinear) vectors $l^\alpha_{(N)}$ by a number in square brackets, one can systematize the foregoing considerations as follows:

Petrov type	I	D	II	N	III
Debever-Sachs symbol	[1111]	[22]	[211]	[4]	[31]

$$(3.28)$$

The above system can be used in the algebraic classification of gravitational fields according to Petrov as an alternative to diagram (3.20). In this formulation of Petrov's classification the types of gravitational field are distinguished by the mutual orientation of the Debever vectors in actual physical space-time.

The type of mutual orientation of the Debever vectors is determined by the specific form of equations (3.27); the most general form of these equations characterizes the "most general" case of vector orientation, i.e., type I. For the other types equations (3.27) transform into more stringent relations. The complete list for all the types in system (3.28) is as follows:

Petrov type	Equations for Debever vectors	
N or [4]	$C_{\alpha\beta\gamma\delta}l^\alpha = 0$	(3.29)
III or [31]	$C_{\alpha\beta\gamma[\delta}l^\gamma l_{\lambda]} = 0$	(3.30)
II, D or [211], [22]	$C_{\alpha\beta\gamma[\delta}l_{\lambda]}l^\beta l^\gamma = 0$	(3.31)
I or [1111]	$l_{[\rho}C_{\alpha]\beta\gamma[\delta}l_{\lambda]}l^\beta l^\gamma = 0$	(3.32)

It is easily shown that a vector $l^\alpha_{(N)}$ satisfying any one of equations (3.29) − (3.32) will automatically satisfy all the following equations as well. The assignment of a gravitational field to a given type is therefore governed by two factors: 1) the Debever vector $l^\alpha_{(N)}$ satisfies the given equation of the series (3.29) − (3.32), and 2) this vector satisfies none of the preceding equations in the series.

So far we have been considering general gravitational fields, the classification of which is characterized by the algebraic structure of the Weyl tensor $C_{\alpha\beta\gamma\delta}$. In empty space-time the Weyl tensor is identical with the Riemann tensor $R_{\alpha\beta\gamma\delta}$; accordingly, $R_{\alpha\beta\gamma\delta}$ will occur in the classification (3.28) −(3.32) in place of $C_{\alpha\beta\gamma\delta}$.

Henceforth we will refer to type I fields, corresponding to the maximally general form of mutual orientation of the Debever vectors, as a l g e b r a i c a l l y g e n e r a l, and to fields belonging to the other types — D, II, N and III — as a l g e b r a i c a l l y s p e c i a l. The meaning of these terms is evident from the Debever-Sachs approach.

Chapter 4

PIRANI'S CRITERION

1. Isotropic electromagnetic field — null field

The first attempt at a generally covariant geometric definition of the concept of gravitational waves in empty space based on Petrov's classification is due to Pirani (1957 /262/; see also his works /69 — 71/). Pirani's definition is based on two postulates in conformity with the concept of a wave in terms of Hadamard's discontinuity:

1) the state of free gravitational waves is completely characterized by the Riemann tensor;

2) the front of a gravitational wave manifests itself as a discontinuity in the Riemann tensor on an isotropic three-dimensional hypersurface.

The first postulate merely means that in Pirani's approach the Riemann tensor $R_{\alpha\beta\gamma\delta}$ acts as field function (intensity) of the gravitational field, whereas the metric tensor $g_{\alpha\beta}$, often associated with the gravitational field potential, does not play a primary role in the analysis of gravitational waves. From the physical standpoint the second postulate, according to which the gravitational wave front lies on the characteristic hypersurface of Einstein's equations, means that gravitational waves in empty space propagate with the fundamental velocity.

Pirani's definition presupposes an analogy between electromagnetic and gravitational waves. As a third postulate — not explicitly formulated — it is assumed that in gravitation as in electrodynamics wave fields can only be isotropic. In this connection Pirani gives an extension of the concept of isotropic electromagnetic fields to the case of gravitational fields.

We know that the energy-momentum tensor $\tau_{\mu\nu}$ of the electromagnetic field (2.30) has four pairwise equal eigenvalues: $k, k, -k, -k$. Moreover,

$$4k^2 = \Phi^2 + \Psi^2, \tag{4.1}$$

where

$$\Phi = F_{\mu\nu}F^{\mu\nu}, \quad \Psi = F^*_{\mu\nu}F^{\mu\nu}, \tag{4.2}$$

and $*F_{\mu\nu}$ is a tensor dual to the Maxwell tensor:

$$^*F_{\mu\nu} = \frac{1}{2}\,\eta_{\mu\nu\rho\sigma}F^{\rho\sigma}. \tag{4.3}$$

The electromagnetic field is termed isotropic (null field) if the eigenvalues of the tensor $\tau_{\mu\nu}$ are zero: $k = 0$, i.e., $\Phi = \Psi = 0$. From the physical standpoint an isotropic electromagnetic field corresponds to wave propagation of electromagnetic energy with the fundamental velocity, as here the observer is unable to track the field. By definition an observer will be able to track the electromagnetic field if for him the flux of the Poynting vector

$$P_\alpha = (\delta^\beta_\alpha - v_\alpha v^\beta)\,\tau_{\beta\sigma}v^\sigma \tag{4.4}$$

equals zero across all possible two-dimensional surfaces (here v^σ is the timelike velocity 4-vector of the observer). But in order for the flux of P^α to be zero at all times, it is necessary that the vector P^α itself be zero. According to (4.4), this means that

$$\tau_{\alpha\sigma}v^\sigma = (\tau_{\rho\sigma}v^\rho v^\sigma)\,v_\alpha \tag{4.5}$$

From condition (4.5) it follows that if the observer tracks the field, his velocity 4-vector will be the eigenvector of the matrix $\|\tau_{\mu\nu}\|$. However, as is known /62/, the eigenvectors of the tensor $\tau_{\mu\nu}$ of an isotropic electromagnetic field can be isotropic (and moreover identical) or spacelike, but they cannot be timelike. Hence it is impossible to make P^α vanish in the case of the isotropic field, and in order for an observer to track the field his velocity 4-vector must degenerate into an isotropic one, i.e., the observer must travel at the speed of light.

Thus one can give the following definition of an isotropic electromagnetic field: an electromagnetic field is termed isotropic if the matrix $\|\tau_{\mu\nu}\|$ has no timelike eigenvectors.

2. Principal Riemannian vectors.
Tracking the gravitational field

Pirani's definition is based on an extension of the notion of an isotropic field (in its latest formulation for the electromagnetic field) to the case of gravitational fields. Such a generalization is difficult to accomplish directly, however, as Einstein's theory of gravitation lacks a true energy-momentum tensor for the gravitational field. To remove this difficulty Pirani defines the concept of tracking of the gravitational field in a way which differs in principle from electromagnetism, introducing the so-called principal Riemannian vectors.

The principal vectors of the Riemann tensor $R_{\alpha\beta\gamma\delta}$ are the directions of intersection of pairs of two-dimensional surfaces defined by the eigenvectors of the tensor R_{ab} (a, $b = 1$, 2, ..., 6) in the bi-vector space R_6 (and therefore by the bi-vectors in the physical space V_4). The number and orientation of the principal Riemannian vectors can be determined if one knows the eigendirections of the tensor R_{ab} in R_6. Thus for type I of Penrose's diagram (3.20) there exists a single (timelike) principal vector; for type D there are two isotropic and one timelike principal vector; and for types II, III and N there exists a single (isotropic) principal vector.

We now introduce the following definition, in accordance with Pirani: an observer will be tracking the gravitational field if his velocity 4-vector coincides with a timelike principal Riemannian vector.

Obviously, an observer can only track a gravitational field the principal vector of which is timelike, i.e., a field of type I or D. As to type II, III and N fields, an observer tracking such gravitational fields would have to have an isotropic velocity 4-vector, i.e., he would have to travel at the speed of light.

We can now take the following definition of an isotropic gravitational field: a gravitational field is isotropic if the curvature tensor $R_{\alpha\beta\gamma\delta}$ has no timelike principal Riemannian vectors.

It follows from the foregoing that isotropic gravitational fields comprise fields belonging to types II, III and N, and only to these. We now come to the formulation of the criterion for the existence of gravitational waves according to Pirani.

Pirani's criterion. In a given region of empty space-time V_4 free gravitational waves are present if within this region the Riemann tensor belongs to type II, N or III of diagram (3.20); otherwise gravitational waves are absent.

3. Example. Wyman-Trollope gravitational wave fields

Thus the definition of the state of a free gravitational wave field based on Pirani's criterion (and on other criteria which will be discussed later) is closely linked to the determination of the type to which a given gravitational field belongs within Petrov's classification. It is therefore worthwhile to examine those known solutions of Einstein's equations in empty space which belong to types II, N and III.

Of these solutions a considerable number (those of Peres, Takeno, Petrov, Robinson and Trautman, Kundt et al.) will be discussed in subsequent chapters when we analyze other suggested criteria for gravitational waves (in a vacuum, or in a medium filled with electromagnetic radiation). To illustrate Pirani's criterion, let us look at a class of solutions of Einstein's equations, recently obtained by Wyman and Trollope /72, 73/, which does not coincide with the above-mentioned solutions or generalizes them considerably.

To the Wyman-Trollope class of solutions corresponds the metric

$$g_{\alpha\beta} = \begin{Vmatrix} 2\alpha & 1 & \beta & \gamma \\ 1 & 0 & 0 & 0 \\ \beta & 0 & e^{-\tau} & 0 \\ \gamma & 0 & 0 & e^{-\tau} \end{Vmatrix}, \tag{4.6}$$

where

$$\beta = \xi x^2 + \xi_0, \qquad \gamma = \eta x^2 + \eta_0,$$

and $\xi, \eta, \xi_0, \eta_0, \alpha$ and τ are functions of the coordinates x^0, x^1, x^3; β is a function harmonic in x^1 and x^3:

$$\beta_{,11} + \beta_{,33} = 0,$$

and γ is a function harmonically conjugated to β. The metric (4.6) was obtained by using the expansion of $g_{\alpha\beta}$ in the orthogonal frame along four real vectors (see, for instance, /74/), one of which — the isotropic vector l^α — is assumed to be harmonic.

Wyman and Trollope succeeded in integrating the field equation in empty space (2.2) with the metric (4.6) for a number of special cases. They single out three special cases:

A. $\xi^2 + \eta^2 = 0$,
B. $\xi^2 + \eta^2 \neq 0$, $\alpha_{,22} = 0$,
C. $\xi^2 + \eta^2 \neq 0$, $\tau_{,11} + \tau_{,33} = 0$.

It can be shown * that cases A and C correspond to type III fields in Penrose's diagram, and case B to type II fields. If the functions ξ and η are such that β and γ are independent of x^2, the given metric (in a vacuum) belongs to type N (degenerate type 2, according to Petrov's classification); in this case l^α coincides with the Killing vector, which defines the group of motions of this space-time along the coordinate lines x^2. Geometrically the trajectories of this vector are interpreted as bicharacteristics of Einstein's equations.

* The corresponding calculations have been carried out by L.B.Grigor'eva. She demonstrates that the metric discussed in Trollope's work /73/ and corresponding to the case of a nonharmonic propagation vector l^α is identical with the well-known Robinson-Trautman metric (see Chapter 9).

Chapter 5

BEL'S CRITERIA

1. Superenergy tensor

The criterion for the existence of gravitational waves proposed by Bel /56, 68, 76 − 80/ (see also Debever /81/), like Pirani's criterion, is based on an analogy with the theory of electromagnetic waves. But unlike Pirani's criterion, Bel's first criterion, to which this section is devoted, rests on the definition of the "energy tensor" (more precisely the "superenergy tensor") of the gravitational field. By analogy with the energy-momentum tensor of the electromagnetic field (2.30), such a "superenergy tensor" should obviously be quadratic in the Riemann tensor $R_{\alpha\beta\gamma\delta}$.

Let the given V_4, then, be an empty space-time − so that Einstein's equations have the form (2.2) − and let the indices $\alpha\beta$ and $\gamma\delta$ be the antisymmetric pairs of the tensor $R_{\alpha\beta\gamma\delta}$. We introduce two new tensors, duals of the tensor $R_{\alpha\beta\gamma\delta}$:

$$^{*}R_{\alpha\beta\gamma\delta} = \frac{1}{2}\,\eta_{\alpha\beta\rho\sigma}\,R^{\rho\sigma\cdot\cdot}_{\cdot\cdot\gamma\delta}, \qquad \overset{*}{R}_{\alpha\beta\gamma\delta} = \frac{1}{2}\,\eta_{\gamma\delta\rho\sigma}\,R^{\rho\sigma\cdot\cdot}_{\cdot\cdot\alpha\beta}. \qquad (5.1)$$

It can be shown that in Einstein spaces (3.7)

$$^{*}R_{\alpha\beta\gamma\delta} = R^{*}_{\alpha\beta\gamma\delta} \overset{\text{def}}{=} \overset{*}{R}_{\alpha\beta\gamma\delta} \qquad (5.2)$$

(see Appendix I, Theorem 1).

We now define B e l ' s s u p e r e n e r g y t e n s o r /76/ as the fourth-rank tensor

$$T^{\alpha\beta\lambda\mu} = \frac{1}{2}\,(R^{\alpha\rho\lambda\sigma}\,R^{\beta\cdot\mu\cdot}_{\cdot\rho\cdot\sigma} + \overset{*}{R}{}^{\alpha\rho\lambda\sigma}\overset{*}{R}{}^{\beta\cdot\mu\cdot}_{\cdot\rho\cdot\sigma}). \qquad (5.3)$$

47

It is easily seen that in its properties the superenergy tensor (5.3) in empty space exhibits a close analogy to the electromagnetic field tensor $\tau_{\mu\nu}$. First of all, it is completely symmetric, thanks to the fact that the tensor $\overset{\bullet}{R}_{\alpha\beta\gamma\delta}$ in empty V_4 is symmetric with respect to the index pairs $\alpha\beta$ and $\gamma\delta$. Secondly, as in the case of the tensor $\tau_{\mu\nu}$, it gives zero upon contraction with the metric tensor: $g_{\alpha\beta}T^{\alpha\beta\mu\nu} = 0$. Thirdly, it satisfies the covariant equation of continuity, which is analogous to the equation of continuity for the tensor $\tau_{\mu\nu}$ in a space-time without sources /80/:

$$T^{\alpha}_{\cdot\beta\mu\nu;\alpha} = 0. \tag{5.4}$$

Fourthly, the analogy between the tensors $T^{\alpha\beta\mu\nu}$ and $\tau_{\mu\nu}$ also emerges when one compares the eigenvalues of $\tau^{\mu\nu}$ and the invariants of $T^{\alpha\beta\mu\nu}$. Tensor $\tau_{\mu\nu}$ satisfies the relation /81/

$$\tau^{\beta}_{\alpha}\tau_{\beta\gamma} = \frac{1}{4} k^2 g_{\alpha\gamma}, \tag{5.5}$$

where k is the eigenvalue of the tensor $\tau_{\alpha\beta}$, having the form (4.1). One can show /81/ that the superenergy tensor satisfies the analogous relation

$$T_{\alpha\beta\lambda\mu}T^{\cdot\beta\lambda\mu}_{\gamma\cdots} = \frac{1}{4} K^2 g_{\alpha\gamma}, \tag{5.6}$$

where

$$K^2 = (R_{\alpha\beta\gamma\delta}R^{\alpha\beta\gamma\delta})^2 + (R_{\alpha\beta\gamma\delta}\overset{\bullet}{R}^{\alpha\beta\gamma\delta})^2. \tag{5.7}$$

The close algebraic analogy between Bel's tensor and the energy-momentum tensor of the electromagnetic field can be employed to define the "energy and momentum density" of the gravitational field. Let a timelike unit 4-vector u^{α} be specified at every point M of space-time. We construct the scalar

$$W = T^{\alpha\beta\lambda\mu}u_{\alpha}u_{\beta}u_{\lambda}u_{\mu}. \tag{5.8}$$

It is easily shown /80/ that this scalar can be expressed as

$$W(u^{\alpha}) = \frac{1}{2}(\mathcal{E}_{\alpha\beta}\mathcal{E}^{\alpha\beta} + \mathcal{H}_{\alpha\beta}\mathcal{H}^{\alpha\beta}), \tag{5.9}$$

where the symmetric tensors $\mathcal{E}_{\alpha\beta}$ and $\mathcal{H}_{\alpha\beta}$, introduced by Matte

/82/, are defined as

$$\mathcal{E}_{\alpha\lambda} = R_{\alpha\beta\lambda\mu}u^{\beta}u^{\mu}, \tag{5.10}$$

$$\mathcal{H}_{\alpha\lambda} = -\overset{*}{R}_{\alpha\beta\lambda\mu}u^{\beta}u^{\mu}. \tag{5.11}$$

These tensors are obviously oriented in space, in the sense that the timelike vector u^{α} is their eigenvector (corresponding to zero eigenvalue). Hence it is easily shown that the square of each of these tensors is nonnegative:

$$\mathcal{E}_{\alpha\beta}\mathcal{E}^{\alpha\beta} \geqslant 0, \quad \mathcal{H}_{\alpha\beta}\mathcal{H}^{\alpha\beta} \geqslant 0, \tag{5.12}$$

the equality holding only when the tensor is zero.

It is moreover possible to prove the following theorem /80/: if for a certain vector u^{α} the quantities $\mathcal{E}_{\alpha\beta}$ and $\mathcal{H}_{\alpha\beta}$ are simultaneously zero, it follows in a necessary and sufficient manner that $R_{\alpha\beta\gamma\delta} \equiv 0$, i.e., the space-time is flat.* Indeed, let the following equalities hold:

$$R_{\alpha\beta\lambda\mu}u^{\beta}u^{\mu} = 0, \quad \overset{*}{R}_{\alpha\beta\lambda\mu}u^{\beta}u^{\mu} = 0.$$

According to the lemma proved in Appendix I, the second of these is equivalent to the relations

$$(u_{\nu}R_{\alpha\beta\lambda\mu} + u_{\lambda}R_{\alpha\beta\mu\nu} + u_{\mu}R_{\alpha\beta\nu\lambda})u^{\beta} = 0.$$

Multiplying them by u^{ν} and exploiting the condition $u^2 = 1$, we obtain

$$R_{\alpha\beta\lambda\mu}u^{\beta} = 0. \tag{5.13}$$

From this follows (for Einstein spaces) the equality

$$\overset{*}{R}_{\alpha\beta\lambda\mu}u^{\beta} = \overset{*}{R}_{\alpha\beta\lambda\mu}u^{\beta} = 0,$$

which, in turn, is equivalent to the relation

$$u_{\gamma}R_{\alpha\beta\lambda\mu} + u_{\alpha}R_{\beta\gamma\lambda\mu} + u_{\beta}R_{\gamma\alpha\lambda\mu} = 0. \tag{5.14}$$

* We note that in /82/ Matte writes down the equations of the gravitational field in an empty space in the language of the quantities (5.10) and (5.11), so that in the first approximation they are analogous to Maxwell's equations, in which it is the quantities $\mathcal{E}$ and $\mathcal{H}$ that play the role of electric and magnetic field strengths. From Matte's point of view this analogy is sufficient demonstration of the reality of gravitational waves.

Multiplying (5.14) by u^γ and using (5.13), we obtain $R_{\alpha\beta\lambda\mu} \equiv 0$, which proves the theorem.

2.   Energy and momentum of the gravitational field

While discussing the concept of gravitational waves from the standpoint of energy transport by them, Synge /83/ formulates two necessary conditions which must be satisfied by the function $F(u^\alpha)$ expressing the energy density of the gravitational field: 1) $F(u^\alpha) \geqslant 0$, and 2) if $F(u^\alpha) = 0$, then $R_{\alpha\beta\gamma\delta} = 0$, i.e., the field energy vanishes only in the absence of the field itself. It is easy to show that the scalar $W(u^\alpha)$ satisfies both these conditions: the first is satisfied due to relations (5.9) and (5.12), the second by virtue of the theorem proved above.

Thus the scalar $W(u^\alpha)$ can be taken to be the definition of the "energy density" of the gravitational field. * As the vector u^α is timelike, one can choose a local coordinate system in which $u^\alpha = \delta_0^\alpha$. In this system, obviously, $W = T^{0000}$, just as the concept of nongravitational energy is linked to the component T^{00} of the energy-momentum tensor of "matter" in Einstein's equations.

Consider now the vector /76, 84/

$$P^\alpha = \left(\delta_\rho^\alpha - u_\rho u^\alpha\right) T^{\rho\beta\lambda\mu} u_\beta u_\lambda u_\mu, \tag{5.15}$$

which can be termed, by analogy with Poynting's electromagnetic vector (4.4), the Poynting vector (or superenergy flux density) of the gravitational field.

In the same coordinate system, obviously,

$$P^0 = 0, \qquad P^i = T^{i000}.$$

As Bel shows /76/, in the linear approximation the following relation holds at every point:

$$W_{,0} = -P^i_{,i}, \tag{5.16}$$

whence from Gauss's theorem

---

* With allowance, of course, for the density properties required for correct application of such concepts (the energy density according to Bel, say, would be — in the physical sense — the quantity $\sqrt{-g}\, W$).

$$\partial_0 \int_V W \, dV = - \int_\Sigma P^i n_i \, d\Sigma, \qquad\qquad (5.17)$$

where Σ is the two-dimensional boundary of the given three-dimensional volume V and n^i is the unit vector of the outward normal to Σ. Formula (5.17) means* that the gravitational super-energy flux across an element $d\Sigma$ is proportional to $P^i n_i$. Consequently, in order for the superenergy flux across any surface Σ surrounding a given point to be zero, it is necessary and sufficient that $P^i(u^\alpha) = 0$. Thus we come to the formulation of the criterion for the existence of gravitational waves according to Bel.

Bel's first criterion. The presence of a superenergy flux is necessary and sufficient for the existence of free gravitational waves. Consequently, gravitational waves are present in the neighborhood of an arbitrary point of empty space-time V_4 if, for any timelike unit vector u^α at this point, $P^\alpha(u^\alpha) \neq 0$. If $P^\alpha(u^\alpha) = 0$, there are no gravitational waves in the neighborhood of this point.

3. Equivalence of the Pirani and Bel criteria

We will now prove the rigorous equivalence of the first Bel criterion and Pirani's criterion (this proof was obtained by Bel /80/). Thanks to their covariant character, it is sufficient to do so in the local coordinate system used above, where $u^\alpha = \delta_0^\alpha$. In this system, obviously,

$$P^i = R^{i \cdot 0 \cdot}_{\cdot j \cdot k} R^{0j0k} = - \sum_{j,k} R_{ijok} R_{ojok}, \qquad P^0 = 0,$$

or, differently expressed,

$$P^i = \tfrac{1}{2} C_{jm} \varepsilon^{jmi},$$

---

* Strictly speaking the partition (5.16) is noncovariant and therefore all further statements should be qualified by the phrase "in the given coordinate system."

where ε^{jmi} is the three-dimensional Levi-Civita symbol. The three-dimensional antisymmetric tensor C_{jm} has the form

$$C_{jm} = \sum_k (\mathscr{E}_{jk}\mathscr{H}_{km} - \mathscr{E}_{mk}\mathscr{H}_{kj}).$$

As Bel shows, in a bi-vector space with basis bi-vectors constructed on the natural unit vectors of the coordinate system chosen by us (the enumeration of the indices in the bi-vector space corresponds to the choice (3.9)),

$$\hat{\mathscr{E}}_{(1)} = e_{(1)} \wedge e_{(0)}, \quad \hat{\mathscr{E}}_{(2)} = e_{(2)} \wedge e_{(0)}, \quad \hat{\mathscr{E}}_{(3)} = e_{(3)} \wedge e_{(0)},$$

$$\hat{\mathscr{E}}_{(4)} = e_{(2)} \wedge e_{(3)}, \quad \hat{\mathscr{E}}_{(5)} = e_{(3)} \wedge e_{(1)}, \quad \hat{\mathscr{E}}_{(6)} = e_{(1)} \wedge e_{(2)},$$

the matrix of the curvature tensor can be expressed as

$$R_{ab} = \begin{pmatrix} -\mathscr{E} & \mathscr{H} \\ \mathscr{H} & \mathscr{E} \end{pmatrix},$$

where $\mathscr{E}$ and $\mathscr{H}$ are the matrices $\|\mathscr{E}_{ik}\|$ and $\|\mathscr{H}_{ik}\|$ of the spatial components of the tensors (5.10) and (5.11). Obviously, if $P^{\mu}(u^{\alpha}) \equiv 0$, then $P^i = 0$ and therefore $C_{jm} = 0$, i.e., the matrices $\|\mathscr{E}_{ik}\|$ and $\|\mathscr{H}_{ik}\|$ commute. But in order for two three-dimensional matrices to commute, it is necessary and sufficient for them to reduce simultaneously to the diagonal form in a certain basis. Thus it follows necessarily from the condition $P^{\alpha} = 0$ and from formulas (3.14) that the corresponding field $R_{\alpha\beta\gamma\delta}$ is of Petrov type 1. Conversely, if $P^{\mu}(u^{\alpha}) \neq 0$, i.e., the corresponding gravitational field describes gravitational waves according to Bel's first criterion, it will belong to type 2 or 3, i.e., it also satisfies Pirani's criterion. This proves our claim.

4. Invariants of the curvature tensor in an empty space

Bel's second criterion, formulated by him in /68/, is based — like Pirani's — on an extension of the concept of isotropic fields, known from electromagnetism, to the case of gravitational fields. Unlike Pirani, however, Bel arrived at the definition of the isotropic gravitational field by generalizing the concept of an isotropic field as one whose invariants vanish, rather than by generalizing the concept of tracking the field.

Whereas the number of functionally independent scalars which can be formed from Maxwell's tensor is two, from the Riemann tensor it is possible to form 14 of which only four are nonzero in empty space /85, 86/:

$$A = \frac{1}{8} R^{\alpha\beta\cdot\cdot}_{\cdot\cdot\lambda\mu} R^{\lambda\mu\cdot\cdot}_{\cdot\cdot\alpha\beta}, \qquad\qquad B = \frac{1}{8} R^{\alpha\beta\cdot\cdot}_{\cdot\cdot\lambda\mu} \overset{*}{R}^{\lambda\mu\cdot\cdot}_{\cdot\cdot\alpha\beta},$$

$$C = \frac{1}{16} R^{\alpha\beta\cdot\cdot}_{\cdot\cdot\lambda\mu} R^{\lambda\mu\cdot\cdot}_{\cdot\cdot\rho\sigma} R^{\rho\sigma\cdot\cdot}_{\cdot\cdot\alpha\beta}, \qquad D = \frac{1}{16} R^{\alpha\beta\cdot\cdot}_{\cdot\cdot\lambda\mu} R^{\lambda\mu\cdot\cdot}_{\cdot\cdot\rho\sigma} \overset{*}{R}^{\rho\sigma\cdot\cdot}_{\cdot\cdot\alpha\beta};$$

(5.18)

these Bel calls fundamental scalars. Then, defining the isotropic gravitational field by the condition

$$A = B = C = D = 0, \tag{5.19}$$

we obtain a new criterion for the existence of gravitational waves.

Bel's second criterion. The field of free gravitational waves is identical with the isotropic gravitational fields defined by condition (5.19) for $R_{\alpha\beta\gamma\delta} \neq 0$. An empty space-time with Riemann tensor $R_{\alpha\beta\gamma\delta} \neq 0$ will describe free gravitational waves if all four fundamental scalars (5.18) vanish. Otherwise free gravitational waves are absent.

Let us now determine which Petrov types of gravitational fields satisfy Bel's second criterion. Writing down the conditions (5.19) in bi-vector space and using the canonical form of the curvature tensor matrix (3.11), (3.14) − (3.18), we see that conditions (5.19) are satisfied by three out of the six types in Penrose's diagram: $0, N$ and III. Dropping type 0, which is trivial ($R_{\alpha\beta\gamma\delta} \equiv 0$), we see that Bel's second criterion is satisfied by all gravitational fields belonging to types N and III of Penrose's diagram and only by these.

5. Debever vectors and Bel's second criterion

Types $0, N$ and III in Penrose's diagram in empty space (for which the eigenvalues of the tensor R_{ab} equal zero) are known as degenerate types of gravitational fields. In Bel's classification /68/ they constitute the single type he calls cas 3.

As Debever shows /81/, in order for an empty V_4 to belong to Bel's type 3, it is necessary and sufficient that it admit of the existence of a vector l^α satisfying the equations

$$R_{\alpha\beta\gamma\delta}l^{\alpha}l^{\gamma} = 0,$$
$$\overset{*}{R}_{\alpha\beta\gamma\delta}l^{\alpha}l^{\gamma} = 0. \tag{5.20}$$

The vector field l^{α} (Debever vector) is unitary and isotropic. Thus Bel's second criterion admits of the following equivalent formulations /75/:

Bel's second criterion (new formulation). An empty space-time with Riemann tensor $R_{\alpha\beta\gamma\delta} \neq 0$ describes free gravitational waves if and only if it admits of the existence of an isotropic vector field l^{α} satisfying equations (5.20).

Chapter 6

LICHNEROWICZ'S CRITERION

1. Bilinear degenerate form of Maxwell's tensor

The criterion for the existence of gravitational waves proposed by Lichnerowicz /87 −90/ (for a comprehensive exposition see /62/) is also based on an analogy with the method for determining the state of electromagnetic radiation. The latter rests on the solution of Cauchy's problem for the Einstein-Maxwell equations in the space-time V_4. Let us briefly consider the salient points of Lichnerowicz's approach to this problem.

Let the electromagnetic field tensor $F_{\alpha\beta}$ belong to class C^0 (piecewise C^2). According to Hadamard's formula (2.13), the discontinuities in the first derivatives of $F_{\alpha\beta}$ on the characteristic hypersurface $\varphi(x^\alpha)$ are given by

$$[F_{\alpha\beta,\gamma}] = f_{\alpha\beta}l_\gamma \qquad (l_\gamma \equiv \varphi_{,\gamma}), \tag{6.1}$$

where $f_{\alpha\beta}$ are the discontinuity coefficients for the tensor $F_{\alpha\beta}$. It then follows from the first group of Maxwell's equations that the discontinuity coefficients satisfy the equations

$$l_\alpha f_{\beta\gamma} + l_\beta f_{\gamma\alpha} + l_\gamma f_{\alpha\beta} = 0, \tag{6.2}$$

and from the second group of Maxwell's equations that

$$l^\alpha f_{\alpha\beta} = 0. \tag{6.3}$$

Our main assumption will be that the discontinuities in the electromagnetic field tensor along the wave front are proportional to the field itself, i.e., that $f_{\alpha\beta} \sim F_{\alpha\beta}$. Then the tensor $F_{\alpha\beta}$ obviously satisfies equations of the type (6.2) and (6.3)

$$l_{[\alpha} F_{\beta\gamma]} = 0, \qquad l^\alpha F_{\alpha\beta} = 0, \tag{6.4}$$

whence it follows necessarily that the vector l^{α} is isotropic: $l_{\alpha}l^{\alpha} = 0$. A second characteristic property of the vector l^{α} which satisfies equations (6.4) is that the lines of the vector field form a congruence of isotropic geodesics /260, 261/.

In conformity with Lichnerowicz, we will refer to the bilinear antisymmetric form satisfying equations (6.4) as a s i n g u l a r (or d e g e n e r a t e) f o r m of second order.* One can then formulate the following theorem (Lichnerowicz /62/, §7): the coefficients $F_{\alpha\beta}$ of a singular bilinear form in a V_4 of signature -2 are given by

$$F_{\alpha\beta} = l_{\alpha}b_{\beta} - l_{\beta}b_{\alpha}, \tag{6.5}$$

where b_{α} is a certain vector orthogonal to l_{α} ($b_{\alpha}l^{\alpha} = 0$). An obvious consequence of this is that if the components of Maxwell's tensor $F_{\alpha\beta}$ are coefficients of a singular bilinear form, they define an isotropic electromagnetic field. Conversely, an isotropic electromagnetic field $F_{\mu\nu}$ is the coefficient of a singular bilinear form.

Earlier it was shown (Ch. 4) that the electromagnetic radiation field can be defined as the isotropic field corresponding to the vanishing of the invariants of the Maxwell tensor. Now we see that an isotropic electromagnetic field can be defined in turn as the field of the Maxwell tensor whose components $F_{\mu\nu}$ are the coefficients of a singular bilinear form. This establishes the following definition (equivalent to that given in Chapter 4): M a x w e l l ' s t e n s o r $F_{\mu\nu} \neq 0$ d e s c r i b e s e l e c t r o m a g n e t i c r a d i a t i o n i f t h e r e e x i s t s a (n e c e s s a r i l y i s o t r o p i c) v e c t o r f i e l d l^{α} s a t i s f y i n g e q u a t i o n s (6.4).

2. Degenerate double form of the Riemann tensor

Let all functions in the metric $g_{\alpha\beta}(x^{\sigma})$ belong to class C^1(piecewise C^3). According to Hadamard's formula (2.14), the discontinuities in the second derivatives of $g_{\alpha\beta}$ on the characteristic hypersurface (2.15) are given by

$$[g_{\alpha\beta,\rho\sigma}] = a_{\alpha\beta}l_{\rho}l_{\sigma}. \tag{6.6}$$

Inserting (6.6) in the expression for the Riemann tensor

$$R_{\alpha\beta\lambda\mu} = \frac{1}{2}(g_{\alpha\lambda,\beta\mu} + g_{\beta\mu,\alpha\lambda} - g_{\alpha\mu,\beta\lambda} - g_{\beta\lambda,\alpha\mu}) + K_{\alpha\beta\lambda\mu},$$

---

* 2-forme singulière, according to Lichnerowicz's original terminology /62/.

where $K_{\alpha\beta\lambda\mu}$ does not contain second derivatives of the metric and hence has no discontinuity on S, it is easy to obtain the expression for the discontinuities of $R_{\alpha\beta\lambda\mu}$:

$$[R_{q\beta\lambda\mu}] = \frac{1}{2}\ (a_{\alpha\lambda}l_\beta l_\mu + a_{\beta\mu}l_\alpha l_\lambda - a_{\alpha\mu}l_\beta l_\lambda - a_{\beta\lambda}l_\alpha l_\mu). \qquad (6.7)$$

It obviously follows from here that

$$l_\alpha[R_{\beta\gamma\lambda\mu}] + l_\beta\,[R_{\gamma\alpha\lambda\mu}] + l_\gamma\,[R_{\alpha\beta\lambda\mu}] = 0. \qquad (6.8)$$

If we assume further that there is no discontinuity at S in the energy-momentum tensor $T_{\alpha\beta}$ appearing on the right in the Einstein equations and that therefore, by virtue of (1.1), $[R_{\alpha\beta}] = 0$, then, according to Lichnerowicz $(/62/,\ \S20)$,

$$l^\alpha\,[R_{\alpha\beta\lambda\mu}] = 0. \qquad (6.9)$$

Let us make the following fundamental assumption: let the discontinuities of the gravitational field described by the tensor $R_{\alpha\beta\gamma\delta}$ on the wave front S be proportional to the field components:

$$[R_{\alpha\beta\gamma\delta}] \sim R_{\alpha\beta\gamma\delta}.$$

Then the curvature tensor should satisfy equations of the form

$$l_\lambda R_{\alpha\beta\gamma\delta} + l_\alpha R_{\beta\lambda\gamma\delta} + l_\beta R_{\lambda\alpha\gamma\delta} = 0, \qquad (6.10)$$

$$l^\alpha R_{\alpha\beta\gamma\delta} = 0, \qquad (6.11)$$

from which it follows that the vector l^α is isotropic for $R_{\alpha\beta\gamma\delta} \neq 0$. Indeed, contracting equations (6.10) with l^α and taking (6.11) into account, we obtain

$$(l^\alpha l_\lambda)\,R_{\rho\beta\lambda\sigma} = 0,$$

which proves our claim.

We now introduce the following definition $/88/$: we will say that every tensor

$$H_{\alpha\beta\lambda\mu}(= -H_{\beta\alpha\lambda\mu} = -H_{\alpha\beta\mu\lambda} = H_{\lambda\mu\alpha\beta})$$

defines a d e g e n e r a t e   d o u b l e   f o r m* if there exists a

---

* D o u b l e - f o r m e   s i n g u l i è r e   in Lichnerowicz's original terminology.

vector l^α such that $H_{\alpha\beta\lambda\mu} \neq 0$ satisfies the equations

$$l_{[\rho}H_{\alpha\beta]\gamma\delta} = 0, \qquad l^\alpha H_{\alpha\beta\lambda\mu} = 0. \tag{6.12}$$

Lichnerowicz draws the following three consequences from equations (6.12):

1) l^α is isotropic (the proof is analogous to the preceding one);

2) $l^\alpha l^\beta_{;\alpha} = 0$, i.e., the vector field l^α defines a congruence of isotropic geodesics;

3) the tensor $H_{\alpha\beta\gamma\delta}$ can be expressed in the form

$$H_{\alpha\beta\lambda\mu} = b_{\alpha\lambda}l_\beta l_\mu + b_{\beta\mu}l_\alpha l_\lambda - b_{\alpha\mu}l_\beta l_\lambda - b_{\beta\lambda}l_\alpha l_\mu, \tag{6.13}$$

where

$$b_{\alpha\lambda} = b_{\lambda\alpha}, \qquad b_{\alpha\lambda}l^\lambda = 0.$$

Then, contracting expression (6.13) with $g^{\beta\mu}$, we find that the tensor $H_{\alpha\lambda} = H_{\alpha\beta\lambda\mu}g^{\beta\mu}$ has the form

$$H_{\alpha\lambda} = \tau l_\alpha l_\lambda \qquad (\tau = b^\alpha_\alpha). \tag{6.14}$$

On the basis of the foregoing results, one can formulate the Lichnerowicz criterion for the existence of gravitational waves as follows.

Lichnerowicz criterion. The space-time V_4 describes the state of the total gravitational radiation if its Riemann tensor $R_{\alpha\beta\gamma\delta} (\neq 0)$ forms the coefficients of a singular double form, i.e., there exists an (isotropic) vector $l^\alpha \neq 0$, satisfying equations (6.10) — (6.11). If no such vector exists, there is no gravitational radiation.

The Ricci tensor for a gravitational field satisfying the Lichnerowicz criterion should, from (6.14), have the form

$$R_{\alpha\beta} = \tau l_\alpha l_\beta. \tag{6.15}$$

Conversely, conditions (6.11) and the isotropy of the vector l^α follow from conditions (6.15) and (6.10). Correspondingly, (6.10) follows from (6.15), (6.11) and the isotropy condition for l^α /62/.

3. The Lichnerowicz criterion and Petrov's classification

It is evident from formula (6.15) that for $\tau = 0$ the Lichnerowicz criterion defines gravitational waves in empty space-time ("purely wavelike" gravitational field). Then (see Appendix I) equations (6.10) and (6.11) become equivalent, the one following uniquely from the other:

$$l_{[\lambda}R_{\alpha\beta]\gamma\delta} = 0 \leftrightarrow l^{\alpha}R_{\alpha\beta\gamma\delta} = 0. \tag{6.16}$$

This means that a purely wavelike gravitational field is uniquely defined by any one of these systems of equations.

As is known (/62/, §21; /68/, §6), an empty V_4 belongs to type N of Penrose's diagram if and only if there exists a vector field l^{α} satisfying one of the systems (6.16). Thus all spaces V_4 of type N define purely wavelike gravitational fields; conversely, all purely wavelike fields are of type N.

For $\tau \neq 0$ in (6.15) we obtain the case of so-called total gravitational radiation.* In this case classification of gravitational fields is based on the Weyl tensor (3.24), which was mentioned in Section 3 of Chapter 3. In order to determine what situation in this classification is occupied by fields of total gravitational radiation according to Lichnerowicz, we will prove the following auxiliary statement: if in a V_4 of signature -2 there is a vector l^{α} satisfying the Lichnerowicz conditions (6.10) $-$ (6.11), then this vector also satisfies the equations

$$l_{[\lambda}C_{\alpha\beta]\gamma\delta} = 0,$$
$$l^{\alpha}C_{\alpha\beta\lambda\mu} = 0, \tag{6.17}$$

i. e., the Weyl tensor in the given V_4 defines a singular double form. Indeed, inserting expression (6.15) in the Weyl tensor (3.24) and making use of (6.10) and (6.11), as well as of the isotropy of the vector l^{α}, after a direct check we are convinced of the validity of equations (6.17).

One can show (Lichnerowicz /62/, §21) that if a certain tensor $H_{\alpha\beta\gamma\delta}$ having all the algebraic properties of the curvature tensor in empty space,

$$H_{\alpha\beta\gamma\delta} = -H_{\beta\alpha\gamma\delta} = -H_{\alpha\beta\delta\gamma} = H_{\gamma\delta\alpha\beta},$$
$$H_{\alpha[\beta\gamma\delta]} = 0, \qquad H_{\alpha\beta\gamma\delta}g^{\beta\delta} = 0, \tag{6.18}$$

*Radiation totale in Lichnerowicz's terminology.

defines a singular double form, then in the bi-vector space R_6 the matrix $\| H_{ab} \|$ of this tensor reduces to the canonical form characteristic of type N in Penrose's diagram (degenerate type 2 in the Petrov classification).

Let a space V_4 satisfy the Lichnerowicz criterion. Then from the foregoing proof it admits of the existence of a vector l^α satisfying equations (6.17). Taking the algebraic properties of the Weyl tensor (3.25) — (3.26) into account and making use of Lichnerowicz's results, we arrive at the conclusion that the tensor $C_{\alpha\beta\gamma\delta}$ belongs to the degenerate type 2 according to Petrov's classification. Thus we obtain the following theorem: a s p a c e - t i m e V_4 s a t i s f y i n g t h e L i c h n e r o w i c z c r i t e r i o n o f t o t a l g r a v i t a t i o n a l r a d i a t i o n b e l o n g s t o t h e d e g e n e r a t e t y p e 2 a s r e g a r d s t h e a l g e b r a i c s t r u c t u r e o f t h e B a y l e y t e n s o r /91/.

4. Conformal representation of gravitational wave fields

To illustrate the applicability of the Lichnerowicz criterion, we will consider a study undertaken by Konopleva /92, 93/ of the conformal representation of purely wavelike gravitational fields. Let V_4 be the space-time defined by the conditions

$$R^\mu_{[\tau;\lambda]} = 0,$$
$$R^\nu_\mu = -4\lambda^2 C^\nu_{.\tau\lambda\mu} R^{\tau\lambda},$$

where λ is the gravitational constant, and $C^\nu_{.\tau\lambda\mu}$ is the Weyl conformal curvature tensor.* As the Einstein spaces (3.7) satisfy these conditions trivially, we will assume that the given V_4 is a non-Einstein space conformal to a certain Einstein space V'_4. The conditions for feasibility of such a representation can be reduced to

$$R^\mu_{[\tau;\lambda]} = 2e^{-2\sigma} R'^{..\mu\nu}_{.\tau\lambda..} \sigma_\nu,$$

---

* These relations were obtained by the method of compensating fields of the Yang-Mills type in the theory of gravitation with the Lagrangian

$$L = R + \frac{\lambda^2}{4\pi} R_{\mu\nu\tau\lambda} R^{\mu\nu\tau\lambda}.$$

In the Einstein theory they are to be interpreted not as field equations but rather as conditions for distinguishing a certain class of gravitational fields (including, in particular, all Einstein spaces).

where $R'_{\tau\lambda\mu\nu}$ is the Riemann tensor for the space V'_4 and $\sigma_\nu \equiv \partial_\nu\sigma$. Hence V'_4 satisfies the condition

$$R'^{\cdots\mu\nu}_{\tau\lambda\cdots}\sigma_\nu = 0,$$

i.e., V'_4 is an Einstein space of the Petrov degenerate type 2, satisfying the Lichnerowicz criterion for pure gravitational radiation; σ_ν is an isotropic vector describing the propagation of the gravitational wave front.

Just as in electrodynamics the equations

$$F_{[\mu\nu;\tau]} = 0$$

enable one to express Maxwell's tensor $F_{\mu\nu}$ in terms of the vector potential A_μ and its first derivatives, so the initial equations

$$R_{\mu[\tau;\lambda]} \equiv \frac{1}{2} R^{\cdots\cdot\sigma}_{\tau\lambda\mu\cdot;\sigma} = 0$$

make it possible to express the Ricci tensor in terms of the vector σ_λ and its first derivatives:

$$R_{\mu\lambda} = -2\sigma_{\lambda;\mu} + 2\sigma_\mu\sigma_\lambda + \frac{1}{3}\varkappa g_{\mu\lambda}.$$

In view of the fact that the vector σ_μ is a gradient and making use, by analogy with electrodynamics, of the Lorentz-type condition $\sigma^\mu_{;\mu} = 2\varkappa/3$, we obtain the wave equation for the vector σ_μ:

$$g^{\alpha\beta}\sigma_{\mu;\alpha\beta} = 0.$$

Thus in the Einstein space V'_4 the vector σ_λ satisfies the Lichnerowicz condition for a purely wavelike gravitational field, while in the original V_4 conformal to it, it describes gravitational waves in the same sense in which the vector potential of the electromagnetic field satisfies the covariant wave equation.

Chapter 7

THE ZEL'MANOV CRITERION

1. Generalized wave operator

The criterion for the existence of gravitational waves formulated in /94/* on the basis of a general idea of Zel'manov presupposes the use of the following c o v a r i a n t   g e n e r a l i z a t i o n   o f   t h e   w a v e   o p e r a t o r:

$$\mathbf{D} \equiv - g^{\rho\sigma}\nabla_\rho\nabla_\sigma.$$ (7.1)

The generally covariant wave equation for an arbitrary tensor field $Q^{\alpha\cdots}_{\lambda\cdots}$ will then be

$$\mathbf{D}Q^{\alpha\cdots}_{\lambda\cdots} = K^{\alpha\cdots}_{\lambda\cdots},$$ (7.2)

where $K^{\alpha\cdots}_{\lambda\cdots}$ is a tensor containing no derivatives higher than the first of $Q^{\alpha\cdots}_{\lambda\cdots}$. An equation of the form of (7.2) was used by Tolman /63/ to describe electromagnetic waves in Riemannian space-time.

It is evident that a homogeneous equation of the type of (7.2) is trivial for the metric tensor $g_{\alpha\beta}$, and that in the case of Einstein spaces it is trivial for the Ricci tensor $R_{\alpha\beta}$ too. Hence the idea of writing such an equation for the Riemann tensor $R_{\alpha\beta\gamma\delta}$, which is what A. L. Zel'manov suggested. Note, however, that equation (7.2) for tensor $R_{\alpha\beta\gamma\delta}$,

$$\mathbf{D}R_{\alpha\beta\gamma\delta} = K_{\alpha\beta\gamma\delta},$$ (7.3)

---

* The earliest work on gravitational waves based on the wave operator (7.1) dates back to 1962 (see Ivanenko's foreword to the Russian translation of the book by Weber /95/). Subsequently Roy and Radhakrishna independently suggested /96/ defining gravitational waves by means of the application of the operator (7.1) to the curvature tensor.

is also trivial (i.e., becomes an identity) in the case of symmetric spaces, for which the Riemann tensor is covariantly constant, $R_{\alpha\beta\gamma\delta;\sigma} = 0$ (in this case, of course, one must have $K_{\alpha\beta\gamma\delta} = 0$). Equation (7.3), moreover, can also become an identity for certain special choices of the tensor $K_{\alpha\beta\gamma\delta} \neq 0$. Thus if we take

$$K_{\alpha\beta\gamma\delta} = \frac{1}{2}\, R \cdot R_{\alpha\beta\gamma\delta} - R_{\alpha\beta\sigma}^{\cdots\rho}\, R_{\gamma\delta\rho}^{\cdots\sigma} - 2\,(R_{\sigma\delta\alpha}^{\cdots\rho}R_{\beta\rho\gamma}^{\cdots\sigma} + R_{\gamma\sigma\alpha}^{\cdots\rho}\,R_{\beta\rho\delta}^{\cdots\sigma}),$$

then equation (7.3) is satisfied identically for all Einstein spaces (3.7) /97/ (see also Appendix I, Theorem 3).

Thus if one approaches the concept of gravitational waves on the basis of equation (7.3), it is necessary to demand, first, that the space-time V_4 not be symmetric, and second, that it be specified by a choice of the tensor $K_{\alpha\beta\gamma\delta}$. The Zel'manov criterion is based on the assumption* that $K_{\alpha\beta\gamma\delta} = 0$.

Zel'manov criterion. The space-time V_4 describes gravitational waves if and only if its Riemann tensor $R_{\alpha\beta\gamma\delta}$: 1) is not covariantly constant, i.e., $R_{\alpha\beta\gamma\delta;\sigma} \neq 0$, 2) satisfies the generally covariant wave equation:

$$\mathbf{D}R_{\alpha\beta\gamma\delta} = 0. \qquad (7.4)$$

2. Characteristics of the generalized wave equation

In order to establish the physical base of the Zel'manov criterion — which might seem at first glance to be somewhat formal and artificial — it is important to investigate the characteristics of the tensor equations (7.4) as a system of differential equations of second order in which the unknowns, strictly speaking, are the components of the curvature tensor $R_{\alpha\beta\gamma\delta}$.

As Savel'eva shows /99/, the left-hand side of equations (7.4) can be reduced by identity transformations to the form

$$g^{\rho\sigma}R_{\alpha\beta\gamma\delta;\,\rho\sigma} = g^{\rho\sigma}\partial_{\rho\sigma}R_{\alpha\beta\gamma\delta} + L_{\alpha\beta\gamma\delta}(\Gamma^{\sigma}) + \Omega_{\alpha\beta\gamma\delta}\,(\Gamma^{\tau}_{\rho\sigma}) + Q_{\alpha\beta\gamma\delta}(R^{\sigma}_{\rho}), \qquad (7.5)$$

where the following notation has been introduced:

---

* In /98/, equation (7.3) is discussed under the assumption that $K_{\alpha\beta\gamma\delta} \neq 0$.

$$L_{\alpha\beta\gamma\delta}(\Gamma^\sigma) = -\left[(\Gamma^\sigma_{,\gamma} - \Gamma^\rho\Gamma^\sigma_{\rho\gamma})R_{\alpha\beta\sigma\delta} + (\Gamma^\sigma_{,\alpha} - \Gamma^\rho\Gamma^\sigma_{\rho\alpha})R_{\sigma\beta\gamma\delta} + \right.$$
$$\left. + (\Gamma^\sigma_{,\beta} - \Gamma^\rho\Gamma^\sigma_{\rho\beta})R_{\alpha\sigma\gamma\delta} + (\Gamma^\sigma_{,\delta} - \Gamma^\rho\Gamma^\sigma_{\rho\delta})R_{\alpha\beta\gamma\sigma} + \Gamma^\sigma R_{\alpha\beta\gamma\delta,\sigma}\right],$$

$$\Omega_{\alpha\beta\gamma\delta}(\Gamma^\tau_{\rho\sigma}) = (\Gamma^\sigma_{\mu\nu}g^{\mu\nu}_{,\gamma} - g^{\mu\nu}\Gamma^\rho_{\mu\gamma}\Gamma^\sigma_{\rho\nu})R_{\alpha\beta\sigma\delta} + $$
$$+ (\Gamma^\sigma_{\mu\nu}g^{\mu\nu}_{,\alpha} - g^{\mu\nu}\Gamma^\rho_{\mu\alpha}\Gamma^\sigma_{\rho\nu})R_{\sigma\beta\gamma\delta} + (\Gamma^\sigma_{\mu\nu}g^{\mu\nu}_{,\beta} - g^{\mu\nu}\Gamma^\rho_{\mu\beta}\Gamma^\sigma_{\rho\nu})R_{\sigma\sigma\gamma\delta} + $$
$$+ (\Gamma^\sigma_{\mu\nu}g^{\mu\nu}_{,\delta} - g^{\mu\nu}\Gamma^\rho_{\mu\delta}\Gamma^\sigma_{\rho\nu})R_{\alpha\beta\gamma\sigma} - g^{\mu\nu}(\Gamma^\sigma_{\mu\gamma}R_{\alpha\beta\sigma\delta,\nu} + $$
$$+ \Gamma^\sigma_{\mu\alpha}R_{\alpha\beta\gamma\delta,\nu} + \Gamma^\sigma_{\mu\sigma}R_{\alpha\beta\gamma\delta,\nu}) + \Gamma^\sigma_{\mu\sigma}R_{\alpha\beta\gamma\sigma,\nu}) - $$
$$- g^{\mu\nu}(\Gamma^\sigma_{\nu\gamma}R_{\alpha\beta\sigma\delta,\mu} + \Gamma^\sigma_{\nu\alpha}R_{\sigma\beta\gamma\delta,\mu} + \Gamma^\sigma_{\nu\beta}R_{\alpha\sigma\gamma\delta,\mu} + \Gamma^\sigma_{\nu\delta}R_{\alpha\beta\gamma\sigma,\mu}),$$

$$Q_{\alpha\beta\gamma\delta}(R^\sigma_\rho) = -[R^\sigma_\gamma R_{\alpha\beta\sigma\delta} + R^\sigma_\alpha R_{\sigma\beta\gamma\delta} + R^\sigma_\beta R_{\alpha\sigma\gamma\delta} + R^\sigma_\delta R_{\alpha\beta\gamma\sigma}].$$

Here, as earlier, $\Gamma^\sigma = -g^{\alpha\beta}\Gamma^\sigma_{\alpha\beta}$. We see that in the identity (7.5) the term $L_{\alpha\beta\gamma\delta}$ is expressed algebraically in terms of the quantities Γ^σ and their derivatives and that it therefore vanishes for $\Gamma^\sigma = 0$, i.e., in the harmonic coordinate system. The term $\Omega_{\alpha\beta\gamma\delta}$ is expressed algebraically in terms of the Christoffel symbols $\Gamma^\sigma_{\mu\nu}$ and therefore can be made to vanish at any specified point in space-time. The term $Q_{\alpha\beta\gamma\delta}$ is identically zero in empty space-time ($R_{\alpha\beta} = 0$).

Let a harmonic coordinate system be introduced in the region of empty space-time under consideration. Then the terms $L_{\alpha\beta\gamma\delta}$ and $Q_{\alpha\beta\gamma\delta}$ in expressions (7.5) vanish identically. Let us further assume that the chosen coordinate system is locally geodesic at a certain specified point M. Then at M, firstly, the term $\Omega_{\alpha\beta\gamma\delta}$ vanishes; secondly, the matrix $\|g^{\rho\sigma}\|$ assumes the canonical form for the signature $(+, -, -, -)$. Thus equation (7.4), considered as a system of second-order partial differential equations for the components of the curvature tensor $R_{\alpha\beta\gamma\delta}$, is hyperbolic.

Examining the Cauchy problem with given initial data $R_{\alpha\beta\gamma\delta}$ and $R_{\alpha\beta\gamma\delta,0}$ on a hypersurface S of the form (2.16) (in a locally chosen coordinate system), we reduce the system of equations (7.4) to the form

$$g^{00}R_{\alpha\beta\gamma\delta,00} + \cdots = 0,$$

where the dots denote terms not containing derivatives $R_{\alpha\beta\gamma\delta,00}$ and therefore completely determined by the initial data. Hence the characteristic equation for the system (7.4) in the given coordinate system is the equation $g^{00} = 0$. Writing it in general coordinates (as was done for Einstein's equations in empty space in Chapter 2), we arrive at the conclusion that the characteristic hypersurface of the system of wave equations (7.4) is identical with the characteristic hypersurface of Einstein's equation (2.15), where the function φ satisfies the eikonal equation (2.22).

Consequently, the generally covariant wave equations (7.4) in empty space describe the propagation of the discontinuities of the second derivatives of the Riemann tensor $R_{\alpha\beta\gamma\delta}$ along the bicharacteristics (isotropic geodesics) of Einstein's equations.

Furthermore, from the notation (7.5) it can be concluded that in empty space, in a certain coordinate system (namely the harmonic system) the generally covariant system (7.4) becomes an ordinary system of wave equations for each component of the Riemann tensor in the neighborhood of any point M:

$$g^{\rho\sigma}R_{\alpha\beta\gamma\delta,\,\rho\sigma} = 0. \tag{7.6}$$

This links the Zel'manov criterion directly to the ordinary meaning of "local waves of curvature" in the neighborhood of a point M.

3.   Zel'manov criterion and Petrov's classification

In order to determine the Petrov type of the gravitational fields satisfying the Zel'manov criterion, we will confine ourselves to the case of the Einstein spaces $*T_i$:

$$R_{\alpha\beta} = \varkappa g_{\alpha\beta}. \tag{7.7}$$

In spaces $*T_i$, as is known, the following identity holds /97/:

$$g^{\rho\sigma}R_{\alpha\beta\gamma\delta;\,\rho\sigma} + R_{\alpha\beta\sigma}^{\cdots\rho}.R_{\gamma\delta\rho}^{\cdots\sigma}. +2\,(R_{\delta\sigma\alpha}^{\cdots\rho}.R_{\beta\rho\gamma}^{\cdots\sigma}. - R_{\delta\sigma\beta}^{\cdots\rho}.R_{\alpha\rho\gamma}^{\cdots\sigma}. + \varkappa R_{\alpha\beta\gamma\delta}) = 0 \tag{7.8}$$

(see Appendix I, Theorem 3). From (7.8) follows an obvious result: in order for the Riemann tensor of the space $*T_i$ to satisfy equations (7.4), it is necessary and sufficient that it satisfy the conditions

$$R_{\alpha\beta\sigma}^{\cdots\rho}.R_{\gamma\delta\rho}^{\cdots\sigma}. + 2\,(R_{\delta\sigma\alpha}^{\cdots\rho}.R_{\beta\rho\gamma}^{\cdots\sigma}. - R_{\delta\sigma\beta}^{\cdots\rho}.R_{\alpha\rho\gamma}^{\cdots\sigma}. + \varkappa R_{\alpha\beta\gamma\delta}) = 0. \tag{7.9}$$

Writing conditions (7.9) in the bi-vector space R_6 in a canonical nonholonomic orthogonal frame and making use of the canonical form of the matrix of the curvature tensor (3.11), (3.14) − (3.18), we arrive at the following conclusions /100, 101/. For the spaces $*T_1$ conditions (7.9) lead to the system of equations

$$\alpha_1\,(\alpha_2 - \alpha_3) - \beta_1\,(\beta_2 - \beta_3) = 0,$$
$$\beta_1\,(\alpha_2 - \alpha_3) + \alpha_1\,(\beta_2 - \beta_3) = 0$$

and four more equations, obtained from the above by cyclic permutations of the indices 1, 2, 3. These equations are the integrability conditions, written down in R_6, of the equations

$$R_{\alpha\beta\gamma\delta,\,\sigma} = 0, \tag{7.10}$$

which define symmetric spaces (/65/, p. 399). The new system of equations obtained by covariant differentiation of the integrability conditions is identically satisfied by virtue of the initial equations (7.10). Consequently, any space $*T_1$ defined by conditions (7.9) is a symmetric space.

For the spaces $*T_2$ relations (7.9) can be written in the canonical orthogonal frame as a system of equations /101/ which are consistent only under conditions

$$\alpha_1 = \alpha_2 = 0, \qquad \beta_1 = \beta_2 = 0, \qquad \varkappa = 0. \tag{7.11}$$

As we saw, these conditions define an empty space T_2 of the degenerate second type (type N on Penrose's diagram). Consequently, the spaces $*T_2$ defined by relations (7.9) can only be T_2 spaces ($\varkappa = 0$) of type N.

Conversely, it we write down relations (7.9) in the canonical orthogonal frame in the bi-vector space R_6 and recall conditions (7.11), we see that relations (7.9) are satisfied identically, i.e., any Einstein space T_2 of type N will satisfy conditions (7.9).

Finally, writing down conditions (7.9) in the canonical orthogonal frame for the spaces $*T_3$, we see that for any $\varkappa$ they lead to a contradiction. This means that the spaces $*T_3$ cannot satisfy conditions (7.9).

As Petrov shows /57/, there exist only two symmetric spaces $*T_2$; they belong to the degenerate type 2 of spaces T_2 ($\varkappa = 0$) and in the special coordinate system they are described by the metrics

$$ds^2 = 2dx^0 dx^1 - \operatorname{sh}^2 x^0 dx^{2\,2} - \sin^2(x^0 + k)\, dx^{3\,2}$$
$$ds^2 = 2dx^0 dx^1 + \operatorname{ch}^2 x^0 dx^{2\,2} + \cos^2(x^0 + k)\, dx^{3\,2} \tag{7.12}$$
$$(k = \text{const}).$$

Thus, Einstein spaces satisfying the Zel'manov criterion can only be empty spaces V_4 ($\varkappa = 0$) of Petrov type N. Conversely, any empty space-time of type N — except for the two symmetric spaces (7.12) — will satisfy the Zel'manov criterion.

4. Relationship between the Zel'manov and Lichnerowicz criteria. Examples

The relationship between the Zel'manov and Lichnerowicz criteria in the case of empty V_4 is easily determined on the basis of Petrov's algebraic classification. We already know that free gravitational waves in Lichnerowicz's sense of the term correspond to type N fields on Penrose's diagram. Consequently, any empty V_4 satisfying the Zel'manov criterion will also satisfy the Lichnerowicz criterion. Conversely, any empty V_4 satisfying the Lichnerowicz criterion — except for the two spaces (7.12) — also satisfies the Zel'manov criterion.

For general V_4 spaces $(R_{\alpha\beta} \neq \varkappa g_{\alpha\beta})$, the general relationship between the Zel'manov criterion and Petrov's classification — and also between it and the Lichnerowicz criterion — still remains unclear. However, one can already state that there exist gravitational fields of the form $R_{\alpha\beta} \neq \varkappa g_{\alpha\beta}$ that satisfy the Zel'manov criterion. A number of such solutions of Einstein's equations with a nonzero right-hand side

$$R_{\alpha\beta} - \frac{1}{2} R g_{\alpha\beta} = -\lambda\tau_{\alpha\beta}, \qquad (7.13)$$

interpretable as the energy-momentum tensor of an isotropic electromagnetic field, are given in /102, 103/.

The isotropy condition for the electromagnetic field $F_{\mu\nu}$ formulated in Chapter 4 imposes a rigorous restriction on the energy-momentum tensor $\tau_{\alpha\beta}$, and therefore also — due to the field equations (7.13) — on the Ricci tensor. In order for the metric $g_{\mu\nu}$ to describe a gravitational field with the energy-momentum tensor of an isotropic electromagnetic field, it is necessary and sufficient that the corresponding Ricci tensor $R_{\mu\nu}$ satisfy the following set of conditions: the Rainich-Wheeler algebraic conditions /36/

$$R = 0, \quad R_{\alpha\rho}R^{\rho\beta} = \frac{1}{4} \delta_{\alpha}^{\beta} (R_{\mu\nu}R^{\mu\nu}) = 0 \qquad (7.14)$$

and the Nordtvedt-Pagels differential conditions /104/

$$\eta^{\alpha\mu\nu\sigma} (R_{\beta\nu;\,\sigma} R_{\mu\gamma} - R_{\beta\mu;\,\sigma} R_{\nu\gamma}) = 0. \qquad (7.15)$$

In turn, in a number of cases /103, 105/ the existence of the electromagnetic wave front leads to an additional symmetry property of the space-time V_4, interpretable in terms of groups of motions of the given V_4 (continuous groups of coordinate transformations preserving the functional form of the metric; see, for example, /58, 106/). That is, the metrics of these V_4 admit of 5-parametric groups of motions G_r ($1 \leqslant r \leqslant 6$) which leave unaltered the isotropic three-dimensional hypersurfaces $*V_3$ that act as the wave front surfaces. If any point of a certain surface in V_4 can be shifted via transformations of the group G_r to any other point of this surface, the latter is called a surface of transitivity of the group G_r. Thus the isotropic surfaces of transitivity of the groups of motions acting in such gravitational fields either are identical with electromagnetic wave fronts of (for $r < 3$) belong to to them.

Let us look at a few metrics satisfying conditions (7.14) $-$ (7.15), i. e., describing gravitational fields generated by electromagnetic radiation and accordingly admitting the group of motions $G_r (r > 3)$, which acts transitively on the isotropic hypersurface of the wave front /103/:

1) the space-time described by the interval

$$ds^2 = 2dx^0 dx^1 + \alpha(x^0)\, dx^{2^2} + 2\beta(x^0)\, dx^2 dx^3 + \gamma(x^0)\, dx^{3\,2} \qquad (7.16)$$

admits of the group of motions G_3, G_4 and G_5 acting transitively on the isotropic three-dimensional hypersurfaces $*V_3$ (here $\alpha\gamma - \beta^2 > 0$).

2) The space-time described by the interval

$$ds^2 = dx^{0\,2} - dx^{1\,2} - 2x^3 dx^2 (dx^0 + dx^1) + \alpha(x^0 + x^1)(dx^{2^2} + dx^{3^2}), \qquad (7.17)$$

admits of the group of motions G_4 acting transitively on the isotropic hypersurface $*V_3$. The requirement that the density-pressure of electromagnetic radiation be positive $- R_{00} < 0 -$ imposes the following condition on the function α for a Lorentz signature at the point:

$$\alpha < 0, \quad \left(\frac{\partial\alpha}{\partial u}\right)^2 - 2\alpha\frac{\partial^2\alpha}{\partial u^2} > -1 \quad (u = x^0 + x^1).$$

3) The space-time described by the interval

$$ds^2 = du\, dv - 2x^3 du\, dx^2 + \alpha(u)\, dx^{2^2} + 2\beta(u)\, dx^2 dx^3 + \gamma(u)\, dx^{3^2}, \qquad (7.18)$$

in other words, the space time with the metric tensor

$$g_{\mu\nu} = \begin{pmatrix} 1 & 0 & -x^3 & 0 \\ 0 & -1 & -x^3 & 0 \\ -x^3 & -x^3 & \alpha & \beta \\ 0 & 0 & \beta & \gamma \end{pmatrix},$$

(7.19)

admits of the group of motions G_3 acting transitively on the isotropic hypersurface $*V_3$. The requirement that $R_{00} < 0$ for a Lorentz signature reduces to the following conditions upon the functions entering in (7.19):

$$\alpha < 0, \quad m > 0,$$

$$2m\left[\frac{\partial^2 m}{\partial u^2} + \left(\frac{\partial \beta}{\partial u}\right)^2 - \frac{\partial \alpha}{\partial u}\frac{\partial \gamma}{\partial u} - 1\right] - \left(\frac{\partial m}{\partial u}\right)^2 < 0,$$

where $m = \alpha\gamma - \beta^2$. Obviously, these conditions are easily satisfied by choosing suitable functions α, β and γ.

A direct check easily shows that the metrics (7.16) − (7.19) satisfy the Zel'manov criterion. Moreover, as shown in /107/, the spaces V_4 with these metrics admit of an isotropic field $l^\alpha = \delta_1^\alpha$ satisfying the equations (6.10) − (6.11), i. e., they describe gravitational waves in Lichnerowicz's sense as well.

However, there are solutions of the gravitational equation (7.13) with $\tau_{\alpha\beta} \neq 0$ which satisfy the Lichnerowicz criterion but not the Zel'manov criterion. Examples of this kind − obtained in /91, 107, 108/ − will be discussed in Chapter 10.

Chapter 8

OTHER CRITERIA FOR GRAVITATIONAL FIELDS

1. The Debever criterion

Debever's approach to the question of the wave properties of gravitational fields is based on their relationship in empty space-time with the isotropic vector fields.

As we know from the works of Debever /66, 81, 109/, Bel /80/, Sachs /110/ et al., in an empty V_4 one can associate with the Riemann tensor two isotropic two-dimensional hypersurfaces, which are jointly spanned at every point by four isotropic vectors: $l^{\alpha}_{(N)}$ ($N = 1$, 2, 3, 4). Making use of the canonical form of the matrix of the curvature tensor in bi-vector space $\| R_{ab} \|$, one can show that in every empty V_4 there exists at least one and at most four isotropic vector fields $l^{\alpha}_{(N)} \neq 0$ satisfying the equations

$$l_{[\lambda} R_{\alpha] \beta\gamma [\delta} l_{\sigma]} l^{\beta} l^{\gamma} = 0 \tag{8.1}$$

(Debever's theorem /66/ in the formulation of Sachs /110/).

Let us define, in accordance with Debever, the s u p e r e n e r g y t e n s o r

$$V_{\alpha\beta\lambda\mu} = \frac{1}{8} \rho \left[(g_{\alpha\beta} P_{\lambda\mu} + g_{\lambda\mu} P_{\alpha\beta} + g_{\alpha\lambda} P_{\beta\mu} + g_{\beta\mu} P_{\alpha\lambda} + \right. $$
$$\left. + g_{\beta\lambda} P_{\alpha\mu} + g_{\alpha\mu} P_{\beta\lambda}) - \frac{96}{L} L_{\alpha\beta\lambda\mu} \right], \tag{8.2}$$

where ρ is an arbitrary nonzero scalar and we have introduced the completely symmetric tensor

$$L_{\alpha\beta\lambda\mu} = \frac{1}{24} \underset{(L, M, N, Q)}{P} l^{L}_{\alpha} l^{M}_{\beta} l^{N}_{\lambda} l^{Q}_{\mu}, \tag{8.3}$$

in which P denotes summation over all permutations of the indices. Moreover, in (8.2) we find the quantities

$$L = L_\lambda^\lambda, \qquad L_{\lambda\mu} = L_{\alpha\cdot\lambda\mu}^{\cdot\alpha\cdot\cdot}, \qquad p_{\lambda\mu} = \frac{12}{L} L_{\lambda\mu} - g_{\lambda\mu},$$

and it is assumed that $L \neq 0$.

The Debever tensor (8.2) in empty space-time has the following properties /81/: 1) it is completely symmetric; 2) all its contractions with the metric tensor vanish:

$$g^{\alpha\beta} V_{\alpha\beta\lambda\mu} = 0; \qquad (8.4)$$

3) the tensor $V_{\alpha\beta\lambda\mu}$ is conserved:

$$V_{\beta\lambda\mu;\,\alpha}^\alpha = 0; \qquad (8.5)$$

4) the tensor $V_{\alpha\beta\lambda\mu}$ satisfies the algebraic identity

$$V_{\alpha\beta\lambda\mu} V^{\gamma\beta\lambda\mu} = \frac{9}{4}\, \rho^2\, (1 - 3\sigma)\, \delta_\alpha^\gamma, \qquad (8.6)$$

where

$$\sigma = 1 - 2\, \frac{(l_{23})^2\,(l_{14})^2 + (l_{13})^2\,(l_{24})^2 + (l_{12})^2\,(l_{34})^2}{(l_{23}l_{14} + l_{13}l_{24} + l_{12}l_{34})^2}\,,$$

$$l_{(MN)} = g_{\alpha\beta}\, l_{(M)}^\alpha l_{(N)}^\beta.$$

We can easily see that the properties of the Debever tensor (8.2) reveal its profound similarity to the Bel superenergy tensor (5.3). Going over to the canonical orthogonal frame and taking the concrete form of the isotropic vectors l^α, we can show that, up to a scalar factor, the two tensors are identical:

$$V_{\alpha\beta\lambda\mu} \cong T_{\alpha\beta\lambda\mu}.$$

Hence the Debever tensor, like the Bel tensor, can serve as a basis for defining the "superenergy flux" of the gravitational field. Thus the Debever criterion is completely equivalent to the first Bel criterion.

2. Gravitational waves of the integrable type (Hély and Zund-Levine criteria)

In the works of Hély /111 — 117/, and also of Zund and Levine /118 — 120/, gravitational waves are defined according to Lichnerowicz but with certain additional restrictions upon the space-time metric. Carrying into effect the idea of Lichnerowicz /62/, Hély examines gravitational fields satisfying the criterion of "gravitational waves of the integrable type."*

By definition, the space-time V_4 describes gravitational waves of the integrable type if it admits of a vector field l^α which satisfies, in addition to equations (6.10) − 6.11), and the isotropy condition for l^α which follows from them, the following gradient condition as well:

$$l_\alpha = \partial_\alpha l, \qquad (8.7)$$

where l is a scalar function of the coordinates.

An example of free gravitational waves of the integrable type is the gravitational field described by the metric /113/

$$g_{\alpha\beta} = \overset{(00)}{g_{\alpha\beta}} + 2q\chi l_\alpha l_\beta, \qquad (8.8)$$

where $\overset{(00)}{g_{\alpha\beta}}$ is the flat space-time metric,

$$l_\alpha = f_\alpha/\chi, \qquad \chi = \frac{d\psi}{dl} + x^\gamma \frac{\partial f_\gamma}{\partial l},$$
$$l^\alpha l_\alpha = 0, \qquad l^\alpha_{;\alpha} = 0, \qquad (8.9)$$

ψ and f_γ are five arbitrary functions of the argument l and q is a scalar.

An example of a gravitational field corresponding to the case of total gravitational radiation of the integrable type is considered in /114, 115/. The corresponding metric is written as follows:

$$g_{\alpha\beta} = \overset{(00)}{g_{\alpha\beta}} + l_\alpha u_\beta + l_\beta u_\alpha, \qquad (8.10)$$

where the vectors u_α and l_α (8.7) satisfy a certain system of differential equations which follow from equations (6.10) − (6.11).

Zund and Levine /119/ introduced a definition of "total gravitational radiation of special type": the space-time V_4 corresponds to the case of total gravitational radiation of special type if it 1) is conformally flat and 2) admits of a covariantly constant vector field l^α satisfying the Lichnerowicz conditions (6.10) − (6.11),

---

* "De type intégrable" in the Hély-Lichnerowicz terminology.

as well as the equations

$$l_\alpha = (\ln \tau)_{,\alpha}, \tag{8.11}$$

where τ is a scalar defined by the system of equations (6.15) which follows from equations (6.10) $-$ (6.11).

The class of gravitational fields satisfying this definition is considerably narrower than the class of fields describing total gravitational radiation of the integrable type according to Lichnerowicz. Indeed it is easy to show that the metrics which describe total gravitational radiation of the special type should be representable as /119/

$$g_{\alpha\beta} = a^{-2}\varphi^2(\lambda)\overset{(00)}{g_{\alpha\beta}}, \tag{8.12}$$
$$\lambda = x^0 + x^1, \quad a^2 = \text{const} \neq 0,$$

where the function $\varphi(\lambda)$ satisfies the condition

$$\varphi(\lambda) \neq (\alpha\lambda^2 + 2\beta\lambda + \gamma)^{-2},$$

and α, β and γ are numerical coefficients. The components of the vector l^α are of the form (8.11), the scalar τ has the form

$$\tau = 2\varphi^{-6}[2(\varphi')^2 - \varphi\varphi''] \neq \text{const}, \tag{8.13}$$

and the prime designates differentiation with respect to λ.

As Zund and Levine point out, not all gravitational fields which are fields of total gravitational radiation in Lichnerowicz's sense and the sense of equations (6.10) $-$ (6.11) satisfy the Zel'manov criterion and equation (7.4). However, every total gravitational radiation of the special type in the sense of Zund and Levine, as one can demonstrate /119/, automatically satisfies the Zel'manov criterion. This point has a bearing on the question of the relationship between the Zel'manov and Lichnerowicz criteria in the case of nonempty space-time.

3. The Maldybaeva criterion

The criterion for gravitational waves proposed by Maldybaeva /121/, like the Zel'manov criterion, is based on a generally covariant generalization of the d'Alembertian. Instead of the operator (7.1), however, the gravitational waves are described with the help of the de Rahm operator /42/

$$\Delta = d\delta + \delta d, \tag{8.14}$$

where d is the operator of exterior differentiation (see /122/) and δ the operator of co-differentiation (see /42/), i.e., for taking the divergence of skew differential forms.

Due to its structure, the operator (8.14) is applicable only to polylinear skew differential forms. Consider, for instance, its application to the bilinear skew form

$$F = \frac{1}{2} F_{\alpha\beta} dx^\alpha \wedge dx^\beta, \tag{8.15}$$

where $F_{\alpha\beta}$ is the electromagnetic field tensor. Maxwell's equations for the electromagnetic field in a region free of sources can be written in the form of two groups of equations /123/:

$$dF = 0, \qquad \delta F = 0, \tag{8.16}$$

from which it follows that the 2-form F satisfies the generalized wave equation

$$\Delta F = 0. \tag{8.17}$$

Equation (8.17) was first obtained by Tolman /63/. We note that, unlike the operator (7.1), the operator (8.14) has a number of fundamental topological /42/ and group /124/ properties. The idea of applying this operator to the study of gravitational wave fields was put forward by Lichnerowicz /43/.

To describe gravitational waves in terms of the Riemann tensor $R_{\alpha\beta\gamma\delta}$, one constructs a 4×4 square matrix $\| \Omega_{\alpha\beta} \|$, the elements of which are the bilinear skew forms

$$\Omega_{\alpha\beta} = \frac{1}{2} R_{\alpha\beta\gamma\delta} dx^\gamma \wedge dx^\delta \tag{8.18}$$

("curvature 2-form" in Lichnerowicz's terminology /125/).

According to Maldybaeva's definition, an empty space-time with the Riemann tensor $R_{\alpha\beta\gamma\delta}$ defines gravitational waves if the corresponding curvature 2-form $\Omega_{\alpha\beta}$ satisfies the generalized wave equation

$$\Delta\Omega_{\alpha\beta} = 0, \tag{8.19}$$

where the operator Δ is given by formula (8.14) and the 2-form $\Omega_{\alpha\beta}$ by formula (8.18).

Expressing the operator Δ in terms of the covariant derivatives with the help of the de Rahm formula /42/, we write equations (8.19) in the tensor form

$$\mathbf{D}R_{\alpha\beta\gamma\delta} + 2R_{\rho\gamma\delta\tau}\,R_{\alpha\beta..}^{..\rho\tau} = 0, \qquad\qquad (8.20)$$

where the operator $\mathbf{D}$ is given by formula (7.1).

Extending the arguments to the case of the Einstein spaces (3.7), we obtain the equations

$$\mathbf{D}R_{\alpha\beta\gamma\delta} + 2R_{\rho\gamma\delta\tau}\,R_{\alpha\beta..}^{..\rho\tau} - 2\varkappa R_{\alpha\beta\gamma\delta} = 0. \qquad\qquad (8.21)$$

Making use of the identity (7.8) and writing down equations (8.21) in the canonical orthogonal frame, we can show that they are satisfied if and only if the Riemann tensor belongs to Petrov's degenerate second type (type N of diagram (3.20) for $\varkappa = 0$, see /126/).

Thus the Maldybaeva criterion is satisfied by Einstein spaces of the degenerate second type T_2 and only by these. In Einstein spaces, therefore, the Zel'manov and Maldybaeva criteria demarcate the same class of gravitational fields; symmetrical spaces (7.12) of the type N, which satisfy the Maldybaeva criterion but not the Zel'manov criterion, constitute an exception.

4.   Misra-Singh criterion

The criterion for gravitational waves given by Misra and Singh /127, 128/ is based on the concept of an isotropic gravitational field definable with the help of the Matte symmetrical tensors (5.10) and (5.11) discussed above. It is easily seen, by passing to the coordinate system in which $l_\alpha = \delta_\alpha^0$ that the rank of each of the matrices $\| \mathscr{E}_{\alpha\lambda} \|$ and $\| \mathscr{H}_{\alpha\lambda} \|$ does not exceed 3. Further, the tensors $\mathscr{E}_{\alpha\lambda}$ and $\mathscr{H}_{\alpha\lambda}$ are oriented in space:

$$\begin{aligned} \mathscr{E}_{\alpha\lambda}\,u^\lambda &= 0, \\ \mathscr{H}_{\alpha\lambda}\,u^\lambda &= 0. \end{aligned} \qquad\qquad (8.22)$$

Thus in a certain sense the tensors $\mathscr{E}_{\alpha\beta}$ and $\mathscr{H}_{\alpha\beta}$ are analogous to the three-dimensional vectors E^i and H^i of the electric and magnetic fields /82/. It is therefore possible to construct a definition of isotropic gravitational fields based on the analogy with the isotropic electromagnetic field (Chapter 4).

In this approach the isotropic gravitational field is characterized, firstly, by identity of the eigenvalues of the matrices $\|\mathscr{E}_{\alpha\lambda}\|$ and $\|\mathscr{H}_{\alpha\lambda}\|$ (analogy with the identity of the moduli of the electric and magnetic field vectors) and, secondly, by the fact that one of the eigendirections is common to both matrices (analogy with the mutual orthogonality of the three-dimensional vectors E^i and H^i). Introducing a third requirement — that the eigenvalues of the matrices $\|\mathscr{E}_{\alpha\lambda}\|$ and $\|\mathscr{H}_{\alpha\lambda}\|$ equal zero — we arrive at the Misra-Singh criterion: an empty space-time V_4 having the Riemann tensor $R_{\alpha\beta\gamma\mu}$ describes gravitational waves if and only if the tensors (5.10) and (5.11) satisfy the relations

$$\mathscr{E}_{\alpha\lambda}\mathscr{E}^{\alpha\lambda} = \mathscr{H}_{\alpha\lambda}\mathscr{H}^{\alpha\lambda}, \tag{8.23}$$

$$\mathscr{E}_{\alpha\lambda}\mathscr{E}_{\beta}^{\lambda}\mathscr{E}^{\beta\gamma} = \mathscr{H}_{\alpha\lambda}\mathscr{H}_{\beta}^{\lambda}\mathscr{H}^{\beta\gamma} = 0. \tag{8.24}$$

In their study of the properties of gravitational fields in empty space satisfying the above criterion, Misra and Singh prove two important theorems. The first states that a space-time satisfying this criterion admits of the existence of the isotropic vector field l^α for which the following conditions are fulfilled:

$$R_{\alpha\beta\gamma[\delta}l_{\lambda]}l^\gamma = 0. \tag{8.25}$$

But according to the known result of Debever /66/ and Bel /80/ (see Chapter 3, Section 4), the empty space-time V_4 defined by condition (8.25) can only belong to types N or III of Penrose's diagram (3.20).

The second theorem states the following: in order for the space-time V_4 to describe gravitational waves in the Misra-Singh sense, it is necessary and sufficient that its Riemann tensor satisfy the equations

$$R_{\alpha\beta\gamma\delta}R^{\gamma\delta\mu\nu}R_{\mu\nu\rho\sigma} = 0. \tag{8.26}$$

By writing down these equations in the canonical orthogonal frame for the canonical form of the matrix of the Riemann tensor, we can again show that they are always satisfied for fields of types N and III of diagram (3.20) and only for these.

Thus in order for an empty space-time V_4 to satisfy the Misra-Singh criterion, it is necessary and sufficient that it belong to the Petrov type N or III.   The Misra-Singh criterion is therefore equivalent to the second Bel criterion.

The Misra-Singh criterion was extended by its authors /127/ to the case of nonempty space-times V_4 (fields of total gravitational radiation).   To arrive at this extension it is sufficient to formulate the definition of the isotropic gravitational field in terms of the Weyl tensor $C_{\alpha\beta\gamma\delta}$ (see Chapter 3, Section 3).   Indeed, by analogy with the Matte tensors $\mathscr{E}_{\alpha\lambda}$ and $\mathscr{H}_{\alpha\lambda}$, we introduce the symmetric tensors

$$\widetilde{\mathscr{E}}_{\alpha\lambda} = C_{\alpha\beta\lambda\mu}u^{\beta}u^{\mu}, \quad \widetilde{\mathscr{H}}_{\alpha\lambda} = -\dot{C}_{\alpha\beta\lambda\mu}u^{\beta}u^{\mu}.$$

Defining the isotropic gravitational field in the general case with the help of the tensors $\widetilde{\mathscr{E}}_{\alpha\lambda}$ and $\widetilde{\mathscr{H}}_{\alpha\lambda}$ in precisely the same way as we defined it for the empty gravitational field with the tensors $\mathscr{E}_{\alpha\lambda}$ and $\mathscr{H}_{\alpha\lambda}$, i.e., by means of the equation

$$C_{\alpha\beta\gamma\delta}C^{\gamma\delta\mu\nu}C_{\mu\nu\rho\sigma} = 0,$$

we can formulate the following theorem: in order for the space-time V_4 to satisfy the definition of total gravitational radiation of Misra and Singh, it is necessary and sufficient that it belong to type N or III as regards the algebraic structure of the Weyl tensor $C_{\alpha\beta\gamma\delta}$.

Chapter 9

PROPAGATION OF GRAVITATIONAL WAVES

1. Gravitational geometric optics

So far we have been chiefly concerned with generally covariant
formulations of concepts and criteria fundamental to the study of
gravitational wave fields. The question of the propagation of
gravitational waves, i.e., the analysis of definitions of wave front,
propagation trajectories (rays) and so on, has essentially been
disregarded.

By an analysis of the Cauchy problem for the system of equations
of the gravitational and electromagnetic fields in the Riemannian
space-time V_4 it was shown (Chapter 2) that the fundamental ideas
of geometrical optics are common to the electromagnetic and the
gravitational field. Indeed, as in the theory of electromagnetic
waves in Maxwell's electrodynamics, the law of propagation of
gravitational waves is determined by the eikonal equation (2.22).

The solution of this fundamental equation —
the scalar function $\varphi(x^\sigma)$ known as the eikonal —
defines the hypersurface of the gravitational
wave front (2.15), as well as the trajectories of wave propagation,
which form a congruence of lines of flow of the isotropic vector l^α
(2.25). The vector l^α will be termed the wave vector of a
gravitational wave.

To different solutions of the eikonal equation there obviously
correspond different wave front types, which in turn physically
define distinct types of gravitational waves. Hence the problem
arises of establishing a generally covariant classification of gravitational wave types based on the properties of the wave front.

Although there exists as yet no universally accepted definitive
solution of this problem, in a number of instances it has proved
possible to give a generally covariant description of gravitational
wave types based on certain specific wave front properties definable
in terms of the wave vector l^α. Indeed, by specifying in a

space-time V_4 an isotropic vector field which guarantees the
existence of a solution of the eikonal equation — i.e., which is a
gradient field as in (2.25) — we can classify gravitational waves
according to the properties of this vector field. Our task is made
easier by the fact that the solution of the problem of the existence
of isotropic fields (Debever vector fields in particular) in the
space-time V_4 is in many instances helpful in establishing the
algebraic type of the space-time V_4 according to the Petrov
classification.

Two types of gravitational waves, plane and spherical,
have been determined in this way. The names themselves are
determined by the geometric analogy with plane and spherical
electromagnetic waves, based on the similarity between the laws of
geometrical optics for gravitational and for the electromagnetic
fields. We will be making extensive use of this analogy in the
physical interpretation of corresponding types of gravitational waves.

2. Spherical gravitational waves.   Examples.

According to the Robinson-Trautman definition /129 — 131/, the
metric of a space-time V_4 describes a field of spherical gravitational waves if the given V_4 admits of an isotropic vector field l^α
satisfying the equations

$$l_{[\alpha;\beta]} = 0, \tag{9.1}$$

$$l_{(\alpha;\beta)}l^{\alpha;\beta} - \frac{1}{2}(l^\alpha_{;\alpha})^2 = 0, \tag{9.2}$$

$$l^\alpha_{;\alpha} \neq 0. \tag{9.3}$$

The first of these conditions means /57/ that the vector field l^α
is a gradient field, i.e., that it can be represented in the form
(2.25). Then, due to the isotropy of l^α, the equation $\varphi(x^\alpha) = a$,
where a is a parametric constant, describes the family of
characteristic manifolds of Einstein equations satisfying the eikonal
equation (2.22).

As we saw earlier (Chapter 2), the trajectories of the vector
field l^α satisfying equations (2.22) and (2.25) constitute a family of
bicharacteristics of the Einstein equations and are therefore isotropic geodesics in the space-time V_4 with the metric $g_{\alpha\beta}$. Then
from the physical point of view condition (9.2) means the absence of
distortion of the form of the shadow thrown upon a screen by an
opaque object illuminated by light rays moving along the

trajectories of the vector l^α /131 — 134/. Condition (9.3), in turn, implies magnification or reduction of the shadow compared with the object itself (unlike the case of plane electromagnetic waves, for which $l^\alpha_{;\alpha} = 0$ always /135/).

Indeed, let a given congruence of isotropic geodesics with the tangent vector l^α define the trajectories of propagation of light. Consider a small opaque object illuminated by the light rays and casting a shadow on a screen placed orthogonally to the rays. It can be shown /110/ that all parts of the shadow reach the screen simultaneously. We now shift the object by parallel displacement along the rays to the position occupied by the screen and compare its dimensions with those of the shadow. If the screen is placed at a distance dr from the object, its shadow will be subjected to the rotation $\omega\, dr$, the shear or distortion $|\sigma|\, dr$ and dilation or contraction $\varepsilon\, dr$; the scalars ε, ω and σ are given by /71, 136/

$$\varepsilon = \frac{1}{2}\, l^\alpha_{;\alpha}, \qquad \omega^2 = \frac{1}{2}\, l_{[\alpha;\,\beta]} l^{\alpha;\,\beta}, \qquad \sigma^2 = \frac{1}{2}\, l_{(\alpha;\,\beta)} l^{\alpha;\,\beta} - \varepsilon^2.$$

The interpretation of the "optical scalars" ε, ω and σ is based on the following hydrodynamic analogy. Let u^α be the field of the timelike unit vector by means of which we specify the 4-velocity of an ideal fluid. Then the kinematics of an infinitesimal volume element of the fluid will be described by the coefficients of the following expansion of the covariant derivative of the 4-velocity:

$$u_{\alpha;\,\beta} = \omega_{\alpha\beta} + \sigma_{\alpha\beta} + \frac{1}{3}\, \tilde{\varepsilon}\eta_{\alpha\beta} - a_\alpha u_\beta.$$

Here

$$\eta_{\alpha\beta} = -\, g_{\alpha\beta} + u_\alpha u_\beta,$$

$a_\alpha = u_{\alpha;\beta} u^\beta$ is the so-called "4-acceleration vector" (equal to zero for geodesic congruence), $\tilde{\varepsilon} = u^\sigma_{;\sigma}$, and the tensors

$$\omega_{\alpha\beta} = \eta^\sigma_{[\alpha}\eta^\tau_{\beta]} u_{\sigma;\,\tau}, \qquad \sigma_{\alpha\beta} = \eta^\sigma_{(\alpha}\eta^\tau_{\beta)} u_{\sigma;\,\tau}$$

are respectively the tensors of the angular rotation velocity and shear rate of the volume element in the geodesic coordinate system (Fermi system) fixed along the trajectories of vector u^α. The scalars of rotation $\tilde{\omega}$ and shear (distortion) $\tilde{\sigma}$ of the trajectories u^α are defined in terms of the tensors $\omega_{\alpha\beta}$ and $\sigma_{\alpha\beta}$:

$$\widetilde{\omega}^2 = \frac{1}{2}\,\omega_{\alpha\beta}\omega^{\alpha\beta}, \quad \widetilde{\sigma}^2 = \frac{1}{2}\,\sigma_{\alpha\beta}\sigma^{\alpha\beta}.$$

As Kundt shows /137/, the condition $\omega=0$ is not only necessary but also sufficient for the fulfillment of condition (9.1), i.e., specification of a congruence of isotropic geodesics without rotation is equivalent to specification of the wave front surface.

Robinson and Trautman /130/ have obtained the class of exact solutions of the Einstein equations in empty space describing spherical gravitational waves and comprising — as Foster and Newman demonstrate /138/ — all algebraically special gravitational fields, i.e., fields of Petrov types D, II, N and III. This class of solutions is represented by the metric

$$ds^2 = 2dx^0\,dx^1 + \left(K - 2Hx^1 - \frac{2M}{x^1}\right)dx^{0^2} -$$
$$- x^{1^2}P^{-2}\{[dx^2 + Q_{,3}\,dx^0]^2 + [dx^3 + Q_{,3}\,dx^0]^2\},$$
$$M = M(x^0), \; P = P\,(x^0,\,x^2,\,x^3), \; Q = Q\,(x^0,\,x^2,\,x^3), \qquad (9.4)$$

where the functions H and K are given by the formulas

$$H = P^{-1}P_{,0} + P\,(P^{-1}Q)_{,23} - PQ\,(P^{-1})_{,23},$$
$$K = P\,(P_{,22} + P_{,33}) - (P_{,2})^2 - (P_{,3})^2.$$

In this coordinate system, the gravitational wave front is expressed by the equation $x^0=$const while the isotropic vector l^α orthogonal to it is given by $l^\alpha = \delta_1^\alpha$, so that the trajectories of the gravitational wave (gravitational rays) are identical with the coordinate lines x^1.

The field equations (2.2) with respect to the metric (9.4) reduce to two relations:

$$Q_{,22} - Q_{,33} = 0,$$
$$K_{,22} - K_{,33} = 4P^{-2}\,(M_{,0} - 3HM). \qquad (9.5)$$

The former allows one to make Q vanish by a coordinate transformation (conserving the form of the metric), so that in the new coordinate system the field equations reduce to the single (second) relation in (9.5).

Studying the Robinson-Trautman metric (9.4) in a coordinate system in which $Q=0$, Bartrum /135/ demonstrates that it may be extended to the case of nonempty space-time, and more specifically to the case where an electromagnetic field is present. It can be shown, further, that the electromagnetic field is isotropic, i.e., both invariants (4.2) of the Maxwell tensor $F_{\mu\nu}$ vanish.

For the Robinson-Trautman metric, only one of the components $T_{\mu\nu}$ is nonzero:

$$T_{00} = E^2/\rho^2,$$

where

$$\lambda E^2 = \frac{1}{2} P^2 (K_{,22} - K_{,33}) - 2M_{,0} + (QM/P) P_{,0}.$$

Making use of the theorem which he himself had proved earlier /139/ regarding the differential properties of the wave vector l^α, Bartrum obtained a particular solution describing a self-consistent system of spherical gravitational and electromagnetic waves propagating along general trajectories — the lines of the vector field l^α:

$$ds^2 = (2 - A)\, dr^2 + Br^2\, (d\varphi^2 + \sin^2\varphi\, d\theta^2) -$$
$$- 2\, (1 - A)\, dr\, dt - A\, dt^2, \qquad (9.6)$$

where

$$A = \left(\frac{M}{m}\right)^{2/3} \left(2\, \mathrm{tg}\, \frac{\varphi}{2}\right)^{2n} - \frac{2r}{3m}\, M_{,0} - \frac{2M}{r},$$
$$B = \left(\frac{M}{m}\right)^{-2/3} \left(2\, \mathrm{tg}\, \frac{\varphi}{2}\right)^{-2n}, \qquad m = \text{const}, \qquad M = M\,(x^0), \qquad (9.7)$$

n is an integer and the spherical coordinates r, φ, θ, t are related to the "Cartesian" coordinates, in which Q has dropped out, by the usual transformation. A remarkable point is that in empty space for $m = m_0$ the metric (9.6) — (9.7) transforms into the Schwarzschild metric.

The Kerr-Schild solution /140, 141/ in empty space-time may also serve as an example of a gravitational field admitting of interpretation in terms of spherical gravitational waves:

$$g_{\mu\nu} = \overset{(00)}{g_{\mu\nu}} + 2Hl_\mu l_\nu. \qquad (9.8)$$

Here l_μ is an isotropic vector field: $g_{\mu\nu}\, l^\mu l^\nu = 0$, whence follows also the condition $\overset{(00)}{g_{\mu\nu}} l^\mu l^\nu = 0$, and conversely; the function $H(x^\alpha)$ together with the vector l^α satisfies the field equations

$$a_{(\alpha} l_{\beta)} + (\dot{H} + 2H\varepsilon)\, l_{(\alpha;\, \beta)} - H g^{\sigma\rho} l_{\alpha;\, \rho} l_{\beta;\, \sigma} + \frac{1}{2}\, bl_\alpha l_\beta = 0, \qquad (9.9)$$

where we have used the notation

$$a_\alpha = (\dot{H} + 2H\varepsilon)_{,\alpha} - 2H_{,\rho}l^{;\rho}_{\alpha;} - Hl^{;\;\rho\cdot}_{\alpha;\;\rho} ,$$

$$b = 2H\ddot{H} - g^{\alpha\beta}H_{;\alpha\beta}, \quad \varepsilon = \frac{1}{2}l^{\alpha}_{;\alpha}, \quad \dot{H} = l^{\alpha}H_{,\alpha}.$$

From the field equation (9.9) it follows /141/ that the vector l^{α} is tangent to the congruence of geodesics of zero shear: $\sigma = 0$. Assuming further that this congruence has zero rotation, i.e., demanding that the vector l^{α} be normal ($l_{[\alpha;\beta]} = 0$), we obtain an empty gravitational field with gravitational waves propagating along the congruence l^{α}.

In order for this gravitational field to correspond to spherical gravitational waves (i. e., in order for the condition $\varepsilon \neq 0$ to be satisfied), it is necessary and sufficient that it belong to Petrov type II or D (Mas /142/). If this condition holds, the metric (9.8) becomes

$$g_{\mu\nu} = \overset{(00)}{g_{\mu\nu}} + 2\varepsilon l_\mu l_\nu.$$

On the other hand, in the case $\varepsilon = 0$ the corresponding gravitational field belongs to type N or III. This follows from the result of Kerr and Schild /141/, who demonstrated that the following relation is fulfilled for the metric (9.8):

$$R_{\alpha\beta\gamma\delta}\, l^{\alpha}l^{\delta} = \ddot{H}l_\beta l_\gamma.$$

Moreover, from condition $\varepsilon = 0$ it follows that $\ddot{H} = 0$ and thus the metric (9.8) satisfies the Bel criterion (5.20). In this last case, as we will see below, the Kerr-Schild metric describes plane gravitational waves.

3. Plane gravitational waves. The Kundt definition

A generally covariant definition of plane gravitational waves was given in two different ways by Bondi-Pirani-Robinson /143/, Penrose /144/ and Kundt /137, 145—147/.

According to the Kundt definition, the metric of a space-time V_4 will describe a field of plane (or "plane-front") gravitational waves if the given V_4 admits of an isotropic vector field l^{α} satisfying equations $(9.1) - (9.2)$ and the condition

$$l^\alpha_{;\alpha} = 0. \tag{9.10}$$

As we already know, these requirements reduce to the following: that the trajectories of the vector l^α are isotropic geodesics. Here the first requirement, expressed by equation (9.1) (condition of existence of a wave front), means that the shape of the shadow cast by an object on a screen orthogonal to the rays (to the trajectories of l^α) is not deformed as it would have been had the object undergone a rotation with respect to its true position. The second requirement, expressed by equation (9.2), means that it is not deformed as it would have been had the object undergone a displacement. Lastly, the third requirement, i.e., condition (9.10), means that the shadow is neither magnified nor reduced by comparison with the object itself (see /71, 131, 148/).

Thus in his definition Kundt accounts for the main properties familiar to us from the study of plane electromagnetic waves in the Minkowski space-time, where the front of a plane wave travels parallel to itself along trajectories of propagation of light orthogonal to it, without any distortion.

Chevreton /149/ has shown that a field of plane gravitational waves satisfying the Kundt definition in an empty space V_4 can only belong to Petrov type O (trivial case, $R_{\alpha\beta\gamma\delta} = 0$), type N or type III. If it belongs to type N, the vector l^α will be covariantly constant: $l^\alpha_{;\beta} = 0$.

All empty spaces V_4 of type N admitting of a covariantly constant vector field l^α are known /105, 150/, and they constitute a class of solutions of the Einstein equations which have been determined up to the integration of a certain system of differential equations. Plane-wave solutions of this type will be discussed in detail in the next chapter.

Kundt also obtains another class of solutions of the field equations in empty space /137/, corresponding to plane waves in the sense of the definition which he introduced. Included among solutions of this class are fields of Petrov type N and type III.

The Kundt metric was obtained in an isotropic tetrad, i.e., an isotropic quasiorthogonal frame $\{t^\alpha, \bar{t}^\alpha, l^\alpha, m^\alpha\}$, of which the vectors l^α and m^α are real and the vectors t^α and $\bar{t}^\alpha$ complex conjugates; further, $l^\alpha m_\alpha = \bar{t}^\alpha t_\alpha = 1$:

$$ds^2 = |\, dz + B du \,|^2 + 2\, dv\, du + H\, du^2, \tag{9.11}$$

where $z = x + iy$, and B and H are real functions of the coordinates, such that

$$B_{,v} = 0, \ B_{,xx} + B_{,yy} = 0, \quad H = -vB_{,x} + A, \quad A_{,v} = 0,$$
$$A_{,xx} + A_{,yy} + 2\,BB_{,xx} + 3\,B_{,x}B_{,x} - 2\,B_{,xu} + B_{,y}\,B_{,y} = 2\,\tau. \tag{9.12}$$

Here the lines u are timelike and the scalar τ is given by equations (6.15). In a vacuum $\tau = 0$, whence it follows, in view of the isotropy of l_α, that for a nonempty space-time the metric (9.11) corresponds to the case of electromagnetic radiation. The general trajectories of propagation of electromagnetic and gravitational waves (lines of flow of the isotropic vector field l^α) coincide with the coordinate lines v; in other words, if the v-coordinate is chosen as affine parameter on the congruence of the isotropic geodesics, the latter are given by the equations

$$\frac{dx^\alpha}{dv} = l^\alpha, \tag{9.13}$$

and the wave front is given by the hypersurface $u = \text{const.}$

The Kundt metric (9.11) is a special case of the class of metrics obtained by him in /137/. This class, according to Kundt, describes plane-front gravitational waves corresponding to more general conditions in which the vector l^α is not necessarily normal, i. e., is not bound by the requirement that $l_{[\alpha;\,\beta]} = 0$.

In the case $\tau = 0$ (empty space-time), the Kundt metric belongs to Petrov type N if $B = 0$. According to the Chevreton theorem considered earlier, for $B = 0$ the Kundt metric describes a space-time which admits of a covariantly constant vector field l^α. Such spaces V_4 will be discussed in detail in the next chapter.

4. Plane gravitational waves.
Bondi-Pirani-Robinson definition

As Goldberg and Kerr have shown /151, 152/, the asymptotic behavior of gravitational fields set up by isolated sources is very similar to the behavior of plane electromagnetic waves in the Minkowski space-time.

This result may be regarded as the motivation which led Bondi, Pirani and Robinson /143/ to attempt to give a rigorously group definition of the concept of plane gravitational waves in empty space as a metric field satisfying two postulates: 1) the field is the same at any point of the wave front; 2) the metric tensor, like the vector potential of plane electromagnetic waves, has a definite symmetry group. The group of motions G_5, which leaves the isotropic hypersurface in V_4 unaltered, is such a group. The equation of this hypersurface (which describes the wave front) is given, in a certain coordinate system, by

$$x^1 - x^0 = \text{const.} \tag{9.14}$$

Petrov shows /57/ that there exists only one space V_4 of signature 2 admitting of a group of motions G_5 which acts transitively on the isotropic three-dimensional hypersurface. In the coordinate system of (9.14) its interval is written as follows:

$$ds^2 = - A\, dx^{1^2} - 2D\, dx^1 dx^2 - B\, dx^{2^2} - C\, dx^{3^2} + C\, dx^{0^2}, \tag{9.15}$$

where A, B, C and D are functions of the retarded argument $x^1 - x^0$ that satisfy the differential equation

$$M'' - \frac{1}{2} M' (\ln M)' - M' (\ln C)' - A'B' - (D')^2 = 0,$$

in which $M = AB - D^2 > 0$ and the prime denotes differentiation with respect to $x^1 - x^0$.

Starting from results obtained by Takeno /153/, Johari /154/ extended the Bondi-Pirani-Robinson definition to the case of non-empty spaces V_4 satisfying equations (7.13). Hély /112/ and Johari /154/ examined the concept of plane-polarized gravitational waves and defined the parameters of polarization. (Problems of this kind had been discussed earlier by Rosen /155/, as well as Boardman and Bergmann /156/.) In this connection an interesting work which stands alone is that of Avez /157/, in which a definition is given of monochromatic gravitational waves. We will now consider this work in some detail.

5. Monochromatic gravitational waves. The Avez definition

Pursuing the general electromagnetic analogy, Avez /157/ calls a gravitational wave m o n o c h r o m a t i c   i f   t h e   c o r r e s p o n d - i n g   w a v e   v e c t o r (2.25) is harmonic, i.e., satisfies the equation

$$(\sqrt{-g}\, l^\alpha)_{,\alpha} = (\sqrt{-g}\, g^{\alpha\beta}\varphi_{,\beta})_{,\alpha} = 0. \qquad (9.16)$$

In this case the complex function $U = \exp(i\varphi)$ is also harmonic:

$$(\sqrt{-g}\, g^{\alpha\beta}U_{,\beta})_{,\alpha} = 0; \qquad (9.17)$$

this fact is invariant under the substitution $\varphi \to f(\varphi)$, where f is any function of the class C^2. As a result Avez was able to study mono-chromatic gravitational waves as the field of a simple periodic function $U(x^\alpha)$.

Let the wave vector l^α satisfy the condition (9.1), and let, further, the isotropic geodesic congruence corresponding to it have zero dilation:

$$l^\alpha_{;\alpha} = 0. \qquad (9.18)$$

Then, obviously, it will satisfy equation (9.16) and be harmonic. The corresponding plane gravitational wave (in Kundt's sense) will be monochromatic.

Avez studied in greatest depth the spaces V_4 which admit of interpretation in terms of monochromatic gravitational waves. He started from the Einstein equations (1.1), taking the energy-momentum tensor of the ideal fluid plus electromagnetic field on the right (for $T_{\alpha\beta}$):

$$T_{\alpha\beta} = X\left[(\rho + p)u_\alpha u_\beta - pg_{\alpha\beta} + \frac{1}{4}F_{\lambda\mu}F^{\lambda\mu}g_{\alpha\beta} - F_{\alpha\rho}F^{\cdot\rho}_{\beta\cdot}\right] - \frac{1}{2}\Theta g_{\alpha\beta}. \qquad (9.19)$$

Here ρ, p and u_α are the density, pressure and 4-velocity, respectively, and X and Θ are constants representing the arbitrary nature of the choice of the energy-momentum tensor.

The solution of the problem is given by the following theorem of Avez: gravitational fields definable by the energy-momentum tensor (9.19) admit of monochromatic gravitational waves only if

1) $\rho = p = 0$ (i.e., the only source is the electromagnetic field);
2) the gravitational wave front $\varphi(x^\alpha)$ is defined by the condition

$$l_{\beta;\alpha} = l_\alpha\varepsilon_\beta + l_\beta\varepsilon_\alpha, \qquad (9.20)$$

where ε_α is a certain vector orthogonal to l_α;
3) the wave vector l^α is an eigenvector of the tensor $F_{\alpha\beta}$:

$$F_{\alpha\rho}l^\alpha = \lambda \cdot l_\rho. \qquad (9.21)$$

Noting that under these conditions

$$l^\delta R_{\alpha\beta\gamma\delta} = (\mu_{\alpha\beta} - \mu_{\beta\alpha})\, l_\gamma + l_\beta\mu_{\alpha\gamma} - l_\alpha\mu_{\beta\gamma},$$
$$\mu_{\alpha\beta} = \varepsilon_{\beta;\alpha} - \varepsilon_\alpha\varepsilon_\beta$$

and computing the quantities

$$R_{\alpha\beta\gamma\delta}l^\beta l^\delta, \quad \overset{*}{R}_{\alpha\beta\gamma\delta}l^\beta l^\delta,$$

in accordance with Debever, we see that in the case of an empty space-time ($T_{\alpha\beta} = 0$) they vanish, i.e., they satisfy equations (5.20). This means, according to the second Bel criterion, that the given gravitational field belongs to type N or III. Thus, an empty space-time describes monochromatic gravitational waves only if it belongs to Petrov type N or III.

To obtain exact solutions of the Einstein equations describing monochromatic gravitational waves, it is convenient to employ a coordinate system in which the components of the metric tensor are expressed explicitly in terms of the harmonic function

$$U(x^\alpha) = \exp(i\varphi). \tag{9.22}$$

Then the $g_{\mu\nu}$, which can be treated as the potentials of the gravitational field, are completely analogous to the vector potential of a plane monochromatic electromagnetic wave /151/:

$$A^\alpha = a^\alpha \exp i\,(\boldsymbol{k}\boldsymbol{r} - \omega t).$$

Let the solution be sought in the form, say,

$$g_{\mu\nu} = \overset{(00)}{g_{\mu\nu}} + 2a_{\mu\nu}U(x^\alpha), \tag{9.23}$$

where $a_{\mu\nu}$ is a constant symmetric tensor (analog of the amplitude of periodic oscillations). As "amplitude tensor" $a_{\mu\nu}$ we choose the tensor

$$a_{\mu\nu} = l_\mu\varepsilon_\nu + l_\nu\varepsilon_\mu, \tag{9.24}$$

where l_μ is a constant isotropic vector and ε_μ is a constant vector orthogonal to it. * Further, let the eikonal φ in the chosen

---

* In a coordinate system in which the metric $g_{\mu\nu}$ is given by (9.23), the relations expressing the covariant constancy and orthogonality of the vectors assume the simple form of the ordinary relations of constancy and orthogonality in a Galilean metric.

coordinate system be given by

$$\varphi = l_\alpha x^\alpha = \overset{(00)}{g_{\alpha\beta}} l^\alpha x^\beta,\tag{9.25}$$

so that

$$U(x^\alpha) = A_0 \cos(l_\alpha x^\alpha) + B_0 \sin(l_\alpha x^\alpha) \quad (A_0, \, B_0 = \text{const}).\tag{9.26}$$

By substitution in equations (2.2) it can now be shown /159/ that, under the given assumptions, the metric (9.23) − (9.26) describes an empty V_4 corresponding to plane monochromatic gravitational waves. The analogy between such a gravitational field and the field of plane monochromatic electromagnetic waves will become yet more striking if we express the metric (9.23) − (9.26) in the equivalent form /159/:

$$g_{\mu\nu} = \overset{(00)}{g_{\mu\nu}} + 2\sigma_{\mu\nu},\tag{9.27}$$

$$\sigma_{\mu\nu} = a_{\mu\nu} \exp[il_\alpha x^\alpha] + \overset{*}{a}_{\mu\nu} \exp[-il_\alpha x^\alpha],\tag{9.28}$$

$$a_{\mu\nu}, \, \overset{*}{a}_{\mu\nu} = \frac{1}{2}(l_\mu \varepsilon_\nu + l_\nu \varepsilon_\mu)(A_0 \mp iB_0).\tag{9.29}$$

The well-known Peres metric /160/

$$ds^2 = dx^{0\,2} - dx^{1\,2} - dx^{2\,2} - dx^{3\,2} - 2f(dx^0 + dx^3)^2\tag{9.30}$$

also belongs to the class of metrics (9.23) if one sets

$$\bar{x}^3 = z = f(x^1, \, x^2, \, u), \quad \bar{x}^0 = u = x^0 + x^3,$$
$$a_{33} = a_{00} = a_{03} = -1$$

(the remaining $a_{\mu\nu}$ components are equal to zero). The field equations (2.2) then reduce to a single condition of harmonicity of the function f in the arguments x^1 and x^2:

$$f_{,11} + f_{,22} = 0.\tag{9.31}$$

Chapter 10

PLANE GRAVITATIONAL WAVES DEFINED BY AN ABSOLUTELY PARALLEL VECTOR FIELD

1. Plane waves in empty space-time

As we already know from Chapter 9, the trajectories of propagation (rays) of a plane gravitational wave in the Kundt sense for type N fields in empty space are defined by the absolutely parallel — or, in other words, covariantly constant — isotropic vector field l^α.

The converse can also be proved /105/: every empty space-time admitting of an absolutely parallel vector field l^α belongs to the Petrov type N, where l^α is isotropic and unique. This follows from the conditions of integrability of the equations $l^\alpha_{;\beta} = 0$, given by (6.11), and from the Debever result (3.29).

Thus an absolutely parallel vector field in empty space defines a congruence of isotropic geodesics which represent the trajectories of propagation of plane gravitational waves according to Kundt.

As Eisenhart shows /161/ (see also Kruchkovich-Solodovnikov /162/), the metric tensor of a space V_4 admitting of the unique isotropic absolutely parallel vector field l^α can be written as

$$g_{\alpha\beta} = \begin{pmatrix} E & 1 & Q & F \\ 1 & 0 & 0 & 0 \\ Q & 0 & A & D \\ F & 0 & D & B \end{pmatrix}, \tag{10.1}$$

where A, B, D, E, F, Q are functions of the x^0, x^2, x^3 coordinates; the vector l^α in this same coordinate system is given by $l^\alpha = \delta^\alpha_1$.

For the metric (10.1) only six of the twenty significant components of the Riemann tensor are nonzero: R_{3230}, R_{3202}, R_{0202}, R_{3232}, R_{0303}, R_{0203}. Out of the ten field equations (2.2), six are identically satisfied, while of the remaining four three become

$$R_{3232} = R_{3230} = R_{3202} = 0, \tag{10.2}$$

where

$$R_{3223} = D_{,23} - \frac{1}{2}(A_{,33} + B_{,22}) - \frac{1}{4}\{A_{,3}(A_{,3}B - B_{,2}D) +$$
$$+ B_{,2}(B_{,2}A - A_{,3}D) + B_{,3}[A_{,2}D - A(2D_{,2} - A_{,3})] -$$
$$- (2D_{,3} - B_{,2})[A_{,2}B - D(2D_{,2} - A_{,3})]\},$$

$$R_{3220} = \frac{1}{2}(D_{,02} - A_{,03} + Q_{,23} - F_{,22}) + \frac{1}{4g}(D_{,0} + F_{,2} - Q_{,3}) \times$$
$$\times (A_{,3}D - AB_{,2}) + A_{,0}(A_{,3}B - B_{,2}D) + (B_{,3} + D_{,0} - F_{,2}) \times$$
$$\times [D(2D_{,2} - A_{,3}) - A_{,2}B] + B_{,0}[A_{,2}D + A(A_{,3} - 2D_{,2})],$$

$$R_{3230} = \frac{1}{2}(B_{,02} - D_{,03} - Q_{,33} - F_{,23}) +$$
$$+ \frac{1}{4g}\{(D_{,0} + Q_{,3} - F_{,2})(A_{,3}B - B_{,2}D) + B_{,0}(AB_{,2} - A_{,3}D) +$$
$$+ (D_{,0} + F_{,2} - Q_{,3})[D(B_{,2} - 2D_{,3}) - AB_{,3}] +$$
$$+ A_{,0}[B(2D_{,3} - B_{,2}) - B_{,3}D]\},$$

$$g = \det\|g_{\alpha\beta}\| = AB - D^2 < 0.$$

The last field equation links together the remaining components of the Riemann tensor:

$$AR_{0330} + BR_{0220} - 2DR_{0230} = 0, \tag{10.3}$$

where

$$R_{0220} = Q_{,02} - \frac{1}{2}(A_{,00} + E_{,22}) + \frac{1}{4g}\{(D_{,0} - F_{,2} - Q_{,3}) \times$$
$$\times [2A_{,0}D + A(Q_{,3} - F_{,2} - D_{,0})] - (A_{,0})^2 B + (E_{,3} - 2F_{,0}) \times$$
$$\times [A_{,2}D + A(A_{,3} - 2D_{,2})] + (E_{,2} - 2Q_{,2}) \times$$
$$\times [B_{,3}D + B(B_{,2} - 2D_{,3})]\},$$

$$R_{0330} = F_{,03} - \frac{1}{2}(B_{,00} + E_{,33}) + \frac{1}{4g}\{(D_{,0} + Q_{,3} - F_{,3}) \times$$
$$\times [2B_{,0}D + B(Q_{,3} + F_{,2} - D_{,0})] -$$
$$- A(B_{,0})^2 + (2F_{,0} - E_{,3})[AB_{,3} + D(B_{,2} - 2D_{,3})] +$$
$$+ (E_{,2} - 2Q_{,0})[B_{,3}D + B(B_{,2} - 2D_{,3})]\},$$

$$R_{0230} = \frac{1}{2}(F_{,02} + Q_{,03} - E_{,23} - D_{,00}) -$$
$$- \frac{1}{4g}\{(D_{,0} + B_{,3} - F_{,2})[BA_{,0} - D(D_{,0} + F_{,2} - Q_{,3})] +$$
$$+ B_{,0}[A(D_{,0} + F_{,2} - Q_{,3}) - DA_{,0}] + (2Q_{,0} - E_{,2}) \times$$
$$\times (DB_{,2} - BA_{,3}) + (2F_{,0} - E_{,3})(DA_{,3} - AB_{,2})\}.$$

Thus the general metric (10.1) which satisfies the four field equations (10.2) − (10.3) defines the class of exact solutions of the Einstein equations in empty space satisfying the Lichnerowicz and

Zel'manov wave criteria as well as the Kundt definition of plane gravitational waves. We can show that this class comprises a number of known solutions of the Einstein equations belonging to the degenerate Petrov type II, in particular the solutions of Takeno /153, 163/, Peres /160/ — (9.30), Petrov /57/ — (9.15), et al.

Thus the Peres metric (9.30) can be reduced by a simple coordinate transformation (rotation of the axes in the (x^0, x^3) plane) /164/ to the form

$$g_{\mu\nu} = \begin{pmatrix} 1 + f(x^0, x^2, x^3) & 1 & 0 & 0 \\ 1 & 0 & 0 & 0 \\ 0 & 0 & -1 & 0 \\ 0 & 0 & 0 & -1 \end{pmatrix}. \tag{10.4}$$

The metric (10.4) is obviously a special case of the metric (10.1) for

$$A = B = -1, \qquad D = Q = F = 0,$$
$$E = 1 + f(x^0, x^2, x^3).$$

Here the field equations (10.2) are satisfied identically and equation (10.3) reduces to the condition of harmonicity of the function f in the arguments x^2 and x^3:

$$f_{,22} + f_{,33} = 0.$$

The Takeno metric /153/ is

$$ds^2 = -A\, dx^{1^2} - 2D\, dx^1 dx^2 - B\, dx^{2^2} - (P - S)\, dx^{3^2} - 2S\, dx^3 dx^0 + (P + S)\, dx^{0^2}, \tag{10.5}$$

where A, B, D, P, S are functions of the argument $x^3 - x^0$ and the quadratic form

$$dl^2 = A\, dx^{1^2} + 2D\, dx^1 dx^2 + B\, dx^{2^2}$$

is positive definite and is a solution of equations (2.2) if

$$M_{,33} - (M_{,3})^2/2M - A_{,3}B_{,3}/(D_{,3})^2 = 0, \quad M \equiv AB - D^2.$$

It can be shown /165/ that, like the Petrov metric (9.15), the above metric is reducible by a coordinate transformation and trivial relabelling to the form

$$ds^2 = 2\,dx^0 dx^1 + A\,(x^0)\,dx^{2^{\,2}} + 2D\,(x^0)\,dx^2 dx^3 + B\,(x^0)\,dx^{3^{\,2}},$$

whence it follows that it is a special case of the metric (10.1) if we choose $E = Q = F = 0$ and if the functions A, B, D are regarded as dependent only on x^0.

Lastly, another Petrov solution /65/, represented by the metric

$$g_{\mu\nu} = \begin{pmatrix} 0 & 1 & -x^3 & 0 \\ 1 & 0 & 0 & 0 \\ -x^3 & 0 & A\,(x^0) & D\,(x^0) \\ 0 & 0 & D\,(x^0) & B\,(x^0) \end{pmatrix}, \tag{10.6}$$

is again a special case of (10.1). For this metric $AB - D^2 < 0$, A, $B \neq 0$, and among the field equations (2.2) the only nontrivial equation is (10.3).

It is natural to suppose that the arbitrariness inherent in the definition of the metric tensor (10.1) of the Einstein spaces admitting of an absolutely parallel vector field is somewhat fictitious, i.e., stems from the choice of coordinate system; there should exist, then, admissible coordinate transformations*

$$\begin{aligned} x^0 &= \tilde{x}^0, \\ x^1 &= \tilde{x}^1 + \chi\,(\tilde{x}^2, \tilde{x}^3, \tilde{x}^0), \\ x^2 &= \varphi\,(\tilde{x}^2, \tilde{x}^3, \tilde{x}^0), \\ x^3 &= \psi\,(\tilde{x}^2, \tilde{x}^3, \tilde{x}^0), \end{aligned} \tag{10.7}$$

which conserve the form of the metric $g_{\mu\nu}$ (10.1) and of the vector field $l^\alpha\ (= \delta_1^\alpha)$, and which may enable us to simplify the metric (10.1) and in particular to remove certain of the functions that enter into it. Moreover, the solution of the field equation (2.2) is itself defined by the form (10.1) only up to the integration of four second-order partial differential equations. This also reduces the number of independent arbitrary functions in the metric (10.1) quite considerably. In this connection it would be appropriate to attempt to integrate at least a few of the equations (10.2) − (10.3).

Both problems were recently solved by Kaigorodov and Pestov /166, 167/, who show that in the new coordinate system $(\tilde{x}^\alpha)$ the components $\tilde{g}_{23},\ \tilde{g}_{03},\ \tilde{g}_{33}$ can be assigned the values

$$\tilde{g}_{23} = 0, \quad \tilde{g}_{03} = 0, \quad \tilde{g}_{33} = -1$$

---

* The term admissible will be applied to transformations whose Jacobian does not vanish. Correspondingly, the arbitrariness of the functions χ, φ and ψ in (10.7) is restricted only by the following differential condition: $J = \varphi_{,2}\psi_{,3} - \psi_{,2}\varphi_{,3} \neq 0$.

for a suitable choice of the functions φ, ψ and χ in the transformation (10.7) (these functions are defined as integrals of a certain
system of equations of the Cauchy-Kowalevski type).

Thus in the general case the metric tensor of the Einstein space
admitting of an absolutely parallel vector field can be represented
as

$$g_{\alpha\beta} = \begin{pmatrix} E & 1 & Q & 0 \\ 1 & 0 & 0 & 0 \\ Q & 0 & A & 0 \\ 0 & 0 & 0 & -1 \end{pmatrix}, \tag{10.8}$$

where A, E, Q are functions of the coordinates x^0, x^2, x^3 satisfying
equations (10.2) — (10.3), and the equation (10.3) becomes

$$R_{0330} - R_{0220} = 0. \tag{10.9}$$

Making use of the necessary and sufficient conditions obtained
earlier for fields of the degenerate type 2 — which involve only
first derivatives of the vector fields, with the result that there is
further simplification of the field equations /74/ — Kaigorodov
reduces the arbitrariness in the definition of the functions E, Q and
A to a single second-order equation (10.9), which remains unin-
tegrated.

The final result of these investigations can be formulated as
follows: in order for an Einstein space to admit of
an isotropic absolutely parallel field l^{α}, it is
necessary and sufficient that in a certain coordi-
nate system the vector l^{α} be expressed as $l^{\alpha} = \delta^{\alpha}_1$,
and that the metric V_4 assume the form (10.8),
where the functions E, Q, A are given either by the
relations

$$A = -1, \quad Q = 2ex^3, \quad E_{,22} + E_{,33} = 4e \quad (e = 0, 1)$$

(first class of solutions) or by the relations

$$A = - [x^3 + a]^2, \quad B = 2b (x^{3^2} + 2ax^3),$$

$$E_{,22} + (x^3 + a)^2 E_{,33} - \frac{a_2}{x^3 + a} E_{,2} + (x^3 + a) E_{,3} +$$

$$+ \frac{2}{x^3 + a} [8\lambda^2 (x^3 + a)^3 - 4x^3 (x^3 + a) (\lambda a_2)_{,0} - (x^3 + a)^2 a_{,00} -$$

$$- 4x^3 a_{,20} (x^3 \lambda + a) + 4x^3 a_{,2} a_{,0} \lambda] = 0,$$

$$\lambda = \text{const}, \quad a = a (x^0, x^2), \quad b = b (x^0)$$

(second class of solutions).

It is easy to see that the above-mentioned wave solutions of Peres, Takeno and Petrov are special cases of the two classes of solutions singled out by Kaigorodov and Pestov, or that they reduce to the latter by admissible coordinate transformations.

2. Absolutely parallel vector field in a nonempty space-time

The class of solutions of form (10.1) admits of extension to the case of nonempty space-time /91/.

Let the space-time V_4 have a metric of the form (10.1) satisfying (aside from the condition $\partial g_{\mu\nu}/\partial x^1 = 0$) only the three equations (10.2). If one computes the components of the Ricci tensor $R_{\alpha\beta}$ one soon sees that nine of its ten components vanish identically and that the only nonzero component has the form

$$R_{00} = \frac{1}{g}(AR_{0330} + BR_{0220} - 2DR_{0230}).$$

A direct check will show that the Rainich-Wheeler conditions (7.14) and the Nordtvedt-Pagels conditions (7.15), which define the energy-momentum tensor of the isotropic electromagnetic field, are satisfied for this particular metric.

However, the solution of the gravitational equations thus obtained, since it satisfies the Lichnerowicz criterion for total gravitational radiation (Ch. 6), describes the propagation not just of electromagnetic waves but also of gravitational waves. Indeed, as the space V_4 with the metric tensor (10.1) admits of congruence of the lines of flow of the covariantly constant vector l^a, it follows that this vector satisfies the second Lichnerowicz condition (6.11). Next introducing the vector field $l_\alpha = \delta_\alpha^0$ and the expressions for the components of the Riemann tensor into the first system of Lichnerowicz conditions, (6.10), one can see that it is satisfied identically.

Thus this class of solutions of the Einstein-Maxwell equations describes a self-consistent system of free electromagnetic and gravitational waves in space-time without matter /91/. It comprises a number of known wave solutions of the Einstein-Maxwell equations; these include, to name a few, extensions of the solutions of Peres and Bondi-Pirani-Robinson to the case of nonempty space-time, known as "fields of type P and H" (according to Takeno's terminology /102, 168/).

Special cases of these solutions satisfying not only the Lichnerowicz but also the Zel'manov criterion were discussed in Chapter 7. However, it should be noted that in the general case these solutions of the Einstein-Maxwell equations describe a self-consistent system of electromagnetic and gravitational fields (nonempty space-time) in which the gravitational field satisfies the Lichnerowicz criterion but not, as a rule, the Zel'manov criterion. This last point is relevant to the question of the general relationship between these two criteria in the case of nonempty space-time.

As the class of solutions we have described satisfies the Lichnerowicz conditions (6.10) — (6.11), it follows, from the general theorem proved in Section 3 of Chapter 6, that they belong to the degenerate type 2 gravitational fields of general form.

As we saw in Chapter 2, the characteristic manifolds of the Einstein equations and Maxwell equations — like their bicharacteristics — are identical. Consequently, the trajectories of propagation of plane gravitational waves defined by an absolutely parallel vector field l^x, are at the same time the trajectories of light rays. At the same time, it follows from the coincidence of the gravitational and electromagnetic wave fronts that electromagnetic waves in a space-time admitting of an absolutely parallel vector field are also plane according to Kundt.

It can be shown /169, 170/ that the class of solutions described above always admits of a group of motions with a singular operator /106/, the trajectories of which are identical with those of wave propagation (with the rays). Moreover, if the given group of motions is intransitive /106/, then its (always isotropic) surface of transitivity will either belong to the wave front or coincide with it.

Chapter 11

THE ASYMPTOTIC PROPERTIES OF FIELDS
OF GRAVITATIONAL RADIATION

1. Gravitational radiation of axially symmetric isolated systems. Bondi information function

In studying the asymptotic behavior of fields of gravitational radiation, it is convenient to use the Bondi-Sachs method based on expansion of the quantities characterizing the field in powers of $1/r$, where r is a parameter playing the role of distance from an isolated system of sources. Assuming that such an expansion is possible, we choose a coordinate system such that, firstly, the form of the terms which dominate for large values of r is simplified to the maximum extent, and secondly, their wave character is brought out.

Bondi /20, 171/ analyzed the problem of the emission of gravitational waves by an axially symmetric system of bodies using the following space-time metric as initial metric:

$$ds^2 = g_{00}\,dx^{0^2} + 2g_{01}dx^0dx^1 + 2g_{02}dx^0dx^2 - g_{22}dx^{2^2} - g_{33}\,dx^{3^2}. \qquad (11.1)$$

The form of the metric (11.1) was determined from the following physical analogy with the model of radiation in a flat space-time.

Let a ray of light emerge from a certain point O, surrounded by a small sphere on which the angular polar coordinates φ and θ have been specified. We introduce the timelike coordinate u, analogous to the "retarded time" of the ordinary theory, and define the coordinates u, θ, φ of an event E to be the values of the corresponding coordinates of the point at which the ray OE intersects the sphere. As the coordinates u, θ, φ are constant along the ray, the trajectory of a ray of light in space-time is a coordinate line of the fourth coordinate r. The affine parameter r defined in this manner along the trajectory of the ray will be henceforth interpreted as the distance from the source O. In flat space-time, choosing $u = t - r$ to be the timelike coordinate, we can express the metric as

$$ds^2 = du^2 + 2\, du\, dr - r^2 (d\theta^2 + \sin^2 \theta\, d\varphi^2).\qquad (11.2)$$

For an asymptotically flat Riemann space-time, the immediate generalization of this metric is the metric (11.1). Moreover, by choosing a coordinate system of the type of (11.2), Bondi was able to remove the so-called "logarithmic term" of form $(\ln r)/r$ from the expansion of the Riemann tensor, the presence of which he regarded as a flaw in this approach. For the problem of radiation of an axially symmetric system, Bondi specifies the following components for the metric (11.1):

$$g_{00} = r^{-1} B \exp 2\beta - r^2 A^2 \exp 2\gamma,$$
$$g_{01} = \exp 2\beta, \; g_{02} = A r^2 \exp 2\gamma, \qquad (11.3)$$
$$g_{22} = - r^2 \exp 2\gamma, \; g_{33} = -r^2 \sin^2 \theta \exp (- 2\gamma).$$

Here β, γ, A and B are functions of r, θ, u and are independent of φ. In the coordinate system so chosen, the axially symmetric metric (11.1), (11.3), as we shall see, contains no logarithmic terms in the expansion in $1/r$.

Of the ten field equations (2.2) three are satisfied identically for the metric (11.3):

$$R_{03} = R_{13} = R_{23} = 0.$$

Of the remaining seven, four equations

$$R_{11} = R_{12} = R_{22} = R_{33} = 0 \qquad (11.4)$$

are independent, one equation,

$$R_{01} = 0$$

is satisfied owing to (11.4), and the components R_{02} and R_{00}, due to the Bianchi identities, satisfy the relations

$$(r^2 R_{02})_{,1} = 0, \quad (r^2 R_{00})_{,1} = 0, \qquad (11.5)$$

i.e., do not contain terms of order higher than the second in $1/r$.

The system of four equations (11.4) in the four unknowns β, γ, A, B ("fundamental equations," in Bondi's terminology) belongs to the group of equations $R_{ij} = 0$ which, as we saw in Chapter 2, determine the behavior of the solution in the neighborhood of the initial hypersurface S depending on the initial data upon it. The system of fundamental equations has the following remarkable property: it contains no second derivatives of the type $g_{ij,00}$, and contains only one derivative of the type $g_{jk,0i}$, namely $\gamma_{,01}$. This means that specification of the function $\gamma(r, \theta, u)$ on the initial hypersurface $u = \text{const}$,

$$\gamma(r, \theta) = \gamma(r, \theta, u)|_{u=\text{const}},$$

defines not only the functions γ, β, A and B themselves, it also defines the derivative $\gamma_{,0}$, i.e., the behavior of the solution in the neighborhood of the hypersurface $u = \text{const}$, apart from the arbitrariness in the choice of the integration functions. As the equations only contain derivatives in r of the sought functions, it follows that the five integration functions will depend only on the coordinates u and θ. One of these should be set equal to zero so as to satisfy the requirement of regularity of the metric for large r; a second function is eliminated by a coordinate transformation which conserves the form of the metric. As a result the expansion of the metric in powers of $1/r$,

$$\gamma = C(u, \theta)/r + C_{,0}(u, \theta)/r^2 + \ldots,$$
$$\beta = -C^2/4r^2 + \ldots,$$
$$U = -\frac{1}{r^2}(C_{,2} + 2C \operatorname{ctg} \theta) + \tag{11.6}$$
$$+ \frac{1}{r^3}[F(u, \theta) + 3CC_{,2} + 4C^2 \operatorname{ctg} \theta] + \ldots,$$
$$V = r + G(u, \theta) + \ldots,$$

is determined by three integration functions — C, F and G. Since these functions are related by the two supplementary relations (11.5)

$$G_{,0} = \frac{1}{2}(C_{,22} + 3C_{,2} \operatorname{ctg} \theta - 2C)_{,0} - (C_{,0})^2, \tag{11.7}$$

$$-3F_{,0} = G_{,2} + 3CC_{,02} + 4CC_{,0} \operatorname{ctg} \theta + C_{,0}C_{,2}, \tag{11.8}$$

only one of them can be regarded as independent, say $C(u, \theta)$. Thus the value of $C(u, \theta)$ and of its derivative $C_{,0}$ w. r. to the "retarded time" u on the hypersurface $u = a = \text{const}$ completely determines the solution in the neighborhood of the hypersurface, i.e., in a certain interval $(a \leqslant u \leqslant b)$. Thus every irreversible change in the system of sources is determined by the quantity

$$C_{,0} = \frac{\partial}{\partial u} C(u, \theta), \qquad (11.9)$$

which contains all the information concerning the behavior of the system with variation of u. The function $C_{,0}$ is called the information function* of the system /171/. The most important property of the information function is that it determined the fraction of mass of the system borne away by gravitational radiation.

Let a system of sources be stationary at all times until the instant $u = a$, and let it return to the stationary state after a period of nonstationarity — at the instant $u = b$. The definition of the information function makes it possible to obtain the mass lost by the system during the time interval $a \leqslant u \leqslant b$. The gravitational field described by the following Weyl metric is the stationary field corresponding to the axially symmetric metric (11.3) (see Synge /172/):

$$ds^2 = \exp(2\psi)dt^2 - \exp(-2\psi)[\exp(2\sigma)(d\rho^2 + dz^2) + \rho^2 d\varphi^2]. \qquad (11.10)$$

Expanding the function ψ in the multipole moments of the system of sources and writing down the metric (11.10) in the Bondi coordinates $u. r, \theta, \varphi$, we obtain the relation between the functions G and F and the multipole moments of an axially symmetric system:

$$G = 2M, \quad F = 2D \sin\theta. \qquad (11.11)$$

Here M is the mass of the system of sources ("monopole moment") and D is its dipole moment. Returning to the general metric (11.3), we can define the mass of the source system as the mean of $G(u, \theta)$ over the angle:

$$M(u) = \frac{1}{2} \int_0^\pi G(u, \theta) \sin\theta \, d\theta. \qquad (11.12)$$

Next, integrating the equation (11.7) we obtain the expression for the decrease of mass with time in terms of the information function:

$$M_{,0} \equiv \frac{dM}{du} = -\frac{1}{2} \int_0^\pi (C_{,0})^2 \sin\theta \, d\theta \leqslant 0. \qquad (11.13)$$

---

* A term in frequent use is "Bondi news function."

Formula (11.13) means that the mass of an isolated axially symmetric system of sources will be constant if and only if the information function of the system equals zero. Otherwise the mass decreases monotonically.

In view of this we can formulate the following criterion of gravitational radiation for axially symmetric isolated systems:

Bondi's criterion. The gravitational field of an isolated axially symmetric system of sources, defined by the metric (11.1), (11.3), is a field of gravitational radiation if the information function (11.9) of the system is nonzero. Otherwise, there is no gravitational radiation.*

2. Newman-Penrose formalism

By computing the components of the Riemann tensor $R_{\alpha\beta\gamma\delta}$ for the Bondi metric and expanding them in powers of $1/r$, it can be shown /171/ that they break down into three groups of equal components (up to a sign). In the first group, the expansion begins with a term of the third order, $2\,(G + CC_{,0})\,r^{-3}$, in the second group with a term of the second order, $(C_{,02} + 2C_{,0}\,\text{ctg}\,\theta)\,r^{-2}$, and in the third group with a term of the first order, $C_{,00}r^{-1}$. This means that for $C_{,00} \neq 0$ the gravitational field decreases in inverse proportion to r at large distances.

In an attempt to remove the element of arbitrariness in this result which stems from the choice of a "dominant" coordinate system, Newmann and Penrose undertook to study the tetrad components of the Riemann tensor in place of its coordinate components.

In order to do this we will use the Newman-Penrose formalism /174/ which, in addition, yields an invariant formulation of the "laws of conservation" of multipole moments.

---

* We note that the vanishing of the information function does not imply stationarity of the system. Indeed, from relation (11.8) it follows that for $C_{,0} = 0$ and $G_{,2} \neq 0$ the quantity $F_{,0}$ is nonzero, which, owing to the second formula of (11.11), means that the dipole moment of the system increases linearly with time. How much the monopole and dipole terms contribute to the energy and momentum lost by an isolated system is a nontrivial question which has attracted special attention. It was recently reviewed by Papapetrou within the framework of the linear approximation of Einstein's theory of gravitation /173/. It was found that the effective monopole and dipole terms which appear formally reduce in actual practice to the quadrupole moment of the source system (quadrupole moments of the so-called "electric" and "magnetic" types). At the same time, the quadrupole moment of a system cannot be regarded as an effective moment reducible to higher moments.

The Newman-Penrose method is based on the assumption that there exist in the chosen region of the manifold V_4 four isotropic differentiable vector fields* (as smooth as the components of the metric $g_{\mu\nu}$), two of which are conveniently chosen to be conjugate complex. In Bondi coordinates ($x^0 = u$, $x^1 = r$, $x^2 = \theta$, $x^3 = \varphi$) these vector fields can be specified as follows:

$$l^\mu = \delta_1^\mu, \qquad n^\mu = \delta_0^\mu - \delta_1^\mu,$$
$$m^\mu = \frac{1}{r}\left(\delta_2^\mu + \frac{i}{\sin\theta}\,\delta_3^\mu\right), \quad \bar{m}^\mu = \frac{1}{r}\left(\delta_2^\mu - \frac{i}{\sin\theta}\,\delta_3^\mu\right). \qquad (11.14)$$

It has been shown by Newman and Penrose /174/ and — independently of them and in a different form — by Kaigorodov /74/ that the metric $g_{\mu\nu}$ can be represented as the combination

$$g_{\mu\nu} = l_\mu n_\nu + n_\mu l_\nu - m_\mu \bar{m}_\nu - \bar{m}_\mu m_\nu,$$

with

$$l_\mu l^\mu = n_\mu n^\mu = \bar{m}_\mu m^\mu = 0.$$

The ten independent real components of the Riemann tensor in vacuum ($R_{\alpha\beta} = 0$) can be characterized uniquely by five complex scalars ("tetrad components of the Riemann tensor" **):

$$\Phi_0 = R_{\alpha\beta\gamma\delta}\, l^\alpha m^\beta l^\gamma m^\delta,$$
$$\Phi_1 = R_{\alpha\beta\gamma\delta}\, l^\alpha n^\beta l^\gamma m^\delta,$$
$$\Phi_2 = R_{\alpha\beta\gamma\delta}\, \bar{m}^\alpha n^\beta l^\gamma m^\delta, \qquad (11.15)$$
$$\Phi_3 = R_{\alpha\beta\gamma\delta}\, \bar{m}^\alpha n^\beta l^\gamma n^\delta,$$
$$\Phi_4 = R_{\alpha\beta\gamma\delta}\, \bar{m}^\alpha n^\beta \bar{m}^\gamma n^\delta.$$

Gravitational radiation is said to be emergent from a system or incident upon the system depending on whether the initial data (the information function in our case) are given on an isotropic hypersurface in the absolute future, or in the absolute past (in the linearized theory these solutions are called retarded or advanced potentials). Assuming that only emergent waves are present in the radiation (i. e., disregarding the scattering of the incident external radiation

---

* In the general case the existence of such vectors is not at all guaranteed. However, for gravitational fields induced by isolated distributions of sources such vectors always exist, given certain asymptotic (boundary) conditions.
** Such components can be defined for any tensor having all the algebraic properties of the Riemann tensor in a vacuum, e.g., for the Weyl tensor.

by the system*), and also specifying a definite class L of functions Φ_A $(A = 0, 1, 2, 3, 4)$ in formulas (11.15), we can show /175, 176/ that in an asymptotically flat space-time one of the scalars Φ_A, say $\Phi_{A'}$, admits of expansion of the form

$$\Phi_{A'} = \sum_{n=0}^{L} r^{-(5+n)} \Phi_{A'}^n + O\left(r^{-(5+L)}\right),$$

where the expansion coefficients $\Phi_{A'}^n$ are independent of r.

Let this scalar be Φ_0. According to Newman and Penrose /177/, it is sufficient to take it in C^2:

$$\Phi_0 = \Phi_0^0 r^{-5} + \Phi_0^1 r^{-6} + \Phi_0^2 r^{-7} + O\left(r^{-7}\right). \tag{11.16}$$

Then, making use of the Bianchi identities and of the identity

$$R_{\alpha\beta\gamma\cdot,\,\delta}^{\cdots\delta} = 0,$$

which follows from them in the case (2.2), we obtain the asymptotic expansions of the remaining Φ_A:

$$\Phi_1 = \Phi_1^0 r^{-4} + O\left(r^{-5}\right), \quad \Phi_2 = \Phi_2^0 r^{-3} + O\left(r^{-1}\right),$$
$$\Phi_3 = \Phi_3^0 r^{-2} + O\left(r^{-3}\right), \quad \Phi_4 = \Phi_4^0 r^{-1} + O\left(r^{-2}\right), \tag{11.17}$$

where Φ_1^0, Φ_2^0, Φ_3^0, Φ_4^0 are independent of r. For the Bondi metric the coefficients Φ_A^0 depend only on θ and u, and

$$\Phi_4^0 = C(u, \theta)_{,00}.$$

In the case of axial symmetry the coefficients Φ_A^0 of the expansions (11.16) − (11.17) can be expressed in terms of the associated Legendre functions /182, 183/:

$$\Phi_4^0 = \sum_{n=2}^{\infty} a_n(u)\, P_n^2(\cos\theta), \quad \Phi_3^0 = \sum_{n=1}^{\infty} b_n(u)\, P_n^1(\cos\theta),$$

$$\Phi_2^0 = \sum_{n=0}^{\infty} c_n(u)\, P_n^0(\cos\theta), \quad \Phi_1^0 = \sum_{n=1}^{\infty} e_n(u)\, P_n^1(\cos\theta), \tag{11.18}$$

$$\Phi_0^m = \sum_{n=2}^{\infty} h_n^m P_n^2(\cos\theta).$$

---

* The scattering of gravitational radiation incident upon a system of bodies has been discussed by Zerilli /178, 408/, Vishveshwara /179/, and Couch, Kinnersley and Torrence /180, 181/.

In this form the expansion coefficients are analogous to the retarded potentials of the wave equation of the special theory of relativity.

Indeed, in flat space-time the axially symmetric solution of the wave equation in polar coordinates is given by

$$\varphi^{(n)} = \psi^{(n)}(r, u) \, P_n(\cos \theta), \tag{11.19}$$

where the functions $\psi^{(n)}$ are defined as the solution of the equations

$$\psi^{(n)}_{,11} - 2\psi^{(n)}_{,01} + 2r^{-1}(\psi^{(n)}_{,1} - \psi^{(n)}_{,0}) - r^{-2} n(n+1)\psi^{(n)} = 0 \tag{11.20}$$

and describe 2^n-pole radiation. In turn, the solution of equations (11.20) has the form of a polynomial in r^{-1}:

$$\psi^n = \sum_k \underset{(k)}{L}(u) \, r^{-(k+1)},$$

the coefficients of the polynomial satisfying the recurrence relation

$$2(k+1)\frac{d}{du} \underset{(k+1)}{\overset{(n)}{L}} = (n-k)(n-k+1)\underset{(k)}{\overset{(n)}{L}}.$$

In view of this analogy, we can regard the quantities Φ_A characterizing the Riemann tensor as being a solution of a generally covariant wave equation of the Zel'manov type (7.4).

This analogy allows us to define the multipole moments of an axially symmetric system of sources in the following way:

$$\text{monopole (mass)} \quad M = -\frac{1}{4}\int_0^\pi (\Phi_2^0 + \bar{\Phi}_2^0) \, P_0^0(\cos \theta) \sin \theta \, d\theta, \tag{11.21}$$

$$\text{dipole moment} \quad D = -\frac{1}{2}\int_0^\pi \Phi_1^0 P_1^1(\cos \theta) \sin \theta \, d\theta, \tag{11.22}$$

$$\text{Quadrupole moment} \quad Q = -\frac{1}{2}\int_0^\pi \Phi_0^0 P_2^0(\cos \theta) \sin \theta \, d\theta,$$

and so forth.

For the Bondi metric (11.3) we obtain from (11.21)

$$M = M_B + \frac{1}{4}\int_0^\pi (C\bar{C})_{,0} \sin \theta \, d\theta, \tag{11.23}$$

where M_B denotes the Bondi mass of the system, given by formula (11.12). Analogously, the law of conservation of the Bondi mass (11.13) becomes

$$\frac{dM_B}{du} = -\frac{1}{2}\int C_{,0}\bar{C}_{,0}\sin\theta\,d\theta + \frac{1}{4}\int (C\bar{C})_{,00}\sin\theta\,d\theta. \tag{11.24}$$

Definition (11.21) should be regarded as more general than Bondi's definition (11.12), as it is not linked to the choice of a particular system of coordinates. According to the interpretation given by Newman, the quantity M can be treated as the total mass including the energy of radiation, whereas the quantity M_B is the mass of the system in a stationary state ("Weyl" mass).

3. Gravitational radiation of arbitrary isolated systems. The Sachs metric

We saw that the tetrad components of the Riemann tensor for the Bondi metric break down into three groups, the dominant terms at large distances being of order r^{-1} in the first group, of order r^{-2} in the second group and of order r^{-3} in the third group. Thus it has proved possible to express the Riemann tensor as the sum of three terms, proportional to the first, second and third inverse powers, respectively, of the affine parameter r:

$$R_{\alpha\beta\gamma\delta} = r^{-1}\cdot N_{\alpha\beta\gamma\delta} + r^{-2}\cdot III_{\alpha\beta\gamma\delta} + I_{\alpha\beta\gamma\delta}\cdot O(r^{-3}). \tag{11.25}$$

It was found that $N_{\alpha\beta\gamma\delta}$, $III_{\alpha\beta\gamma\delta}$ and $I_{\alpha\beta\gamma\delta}$ are tensors having the same algebraic properties as Rieman tensors belonging to types N, III and I, respectively. An analogous decomposition was established by Robinson and Trautman for their solution of the equations of gravitation, which describes spherical gravitational waves:

$$R_{\alpha\beta\gamma\delta} = r^{-1}N_{\alpha\beta\gamma\delta} + r^{-2}III_{\alpha\beta\gamma\delta} + r^{-3}D_{\alpha\beta\gamma\delta}; \tag{11.26}$$

here $D_{\alpha\beta\gamma\delta}$ is a tensor having the same algebraic structure as a type D Riemann tensor. It should be mentioned that the physical meaningfulness of these results is further substantiated by the fact that for electromagnetic radiation (as Goldberg and Sachs have shown /184/) we have a decomposition of the field tensor $F_{\mu\nu}$ which is clearly interpretable in terms of near zone (induction zone) and far zone (wave zone). In other words, the general physical analogy between the theory of electromagnetic radiation and the Bondi-Sachs approach described above indicates that it is legitimate to interpret the Bondi-Sachs results in terms of a wave zone of radiation (terms of types N and III) and an induction zone (terms of types I and D).

Indeed, the dominant terms at large distances from the emitting system belong to type N (wave zone), whereas at small distances from the sources they are terms of type I or D, which describe the properties of a stationary field (of the Weyl type for the Bondi metric and of the Schwarzschild type for the Robinson-Trautman metric). Here the term $N_{\alpha\beta\gamma\delta}$ for the Bondi metric is proportional to $C_{,00}$, characterizing the relationship between the information function $C_{,0}$ and the asymptotic behavior of the radiation field.

Sachs /185/ put forward an extension of (11.25) to the case of the gravitational radiation of arbitrary isolated systems.

It is easily shown that the coordinate lines φ in the Bondi coordinate system are trajectories of the Killing vector field /58/ normal to a certain three-dimensional hypersurface. Assuming that the metric tensor $g_{\mu\nu}$ can depend not only on u, r, θ but also on the coordinate φ, let us construct a more general coordinate system suitable for an arbitrary system of sources with no spatial symmetry whatsoever.

Let $u\,(x^\alpha)$ be a scalar field defining the isotropic three-dimensional hypersurface (2.15), i.e., satisfying the eikonal equation (2.22):

$$g^{\alpha\beta}u_{,\alpha}u_{,\beta} = 0.$$

Further, let there be a congruence of isotropic geodesic lines with direction vector $l_\alpha = u_{,\alpha}$, orthogonal to the hypersurface $u = \mathrm{const.}$ We also introduce θ and φ — two scalar functions satisfying the equations

$$\theta_{,\alpha}l^\alpha = \varphi_{,\alpha}l^\alpha = 0. \tag{11.27}$$

Let us further define the scalar r

$$r^4 = (K \sin\theta)^{-1}, \tag{11.28}$$

where

$$K \equiv (g^{\alpha\beta}\theta_{,\alpha}\theta_{,\beta})(g^{\mu\nu}\varphi_{,\mu}\varphi_{,\nu}) - (g^{\alpha\beta}\theta_{,\alpha}\theta_{,\beta})^2 > 0.$$

The condition that $K \neq 0$ is a consequence of equations (11.27); the requirement that $K > 0$ is sufficient in order for the scalar r to be real and positive.

It can be shown /185/ that an asymptotically flat space-time V_4 will satisfy all of the requirements mentioned if and only if its metric is representable in Bondi coordinates as

$$ds^2 = Br^{-1} \exp{(2\beta)}\, du^2 + 2 \exp{(2\beta)}\, du\, dr - $$
$$- r^2 H_{ab}\, (dx^a - A^a du)\, (dx^b - A^b\, du) \qquad (11.29)$$
$$(a, b = 2, 3),$$

where the two-dimensional quadratic form $h_{ab}\, dx^a dx^b$ is given by

$$2h_{ab}\, dx^a\, dx^b = [\exp{(2\gamma)} + \exp{(2\delta)}]\, d\theta^2 +$$
$$+ 4 \operatorname{sh}{(\gamma - \delta)} \sin{\theta}\, d\theta d\varphi +$$
$$+ [\exp{(-2\gamma)} + \exp{(-2\delta)}] \sin^2{\theta}\, d\varphi^2,$$

and the six functions V, $U^a\ (a = 2,\ 3)$, β, γ, δ depend on all four coordinates u, r, θ and φ.

Having required that the coordinate lines $\varphi\, (u,\ r,\ \theta = \text{const})$ be trajectories of a certain normal Killing vector field, we obtain as a special case the axially symmetric Bondi metric defined by the conditions

$$\gamma = \delta, \quad u^3 = 0, \quad \partial g_{\alpha\beta}/\partial\varphi = 0. \qquad (11.30)$$

4. Geodesic rays. The peeling theorem

One of the assumptions under which the Sachs metric (11.29) was obtained is the existence in V_4 of a congruence of isotropic geodesics (known as g e o d e s i c   r a y s). We will therefore consider the types of gravitational fields that admit of geodesic rays.

As we noted in Chapter 8, every empty space-time V_4 admits of at least one and at most four isotropic vector fields l^a (Debever vectors) satisfying the algebraic relation (3.29) − (3.32), in which the Weyl tensor is replaced − in our case − by the Riemann tensor $R_{\alpha\beta\gamma\delta}$.

Debever vectors are not as a rule the direction vectors of congruences of isotropic geodesics. However, as Sachs shows /110/, all algebraically special empty spaces V_4, i.e., Petrov type D, II, N and III spaces, admit of a geodesic isotropic vector field l^a,

$$l^\alpha l^\beta_{;\alpha} = 0, \tag{11.31}$$

satisfying the condition (3.31) and hence necessarily the condition (3.32). The corresponding congruence of geodesic rays has zero shear (Goldberg-Sachs theorem, see /184, 195/):

$$2\sigma^2 \equiv l_{(\alpha;\beta)}l^{\alpha;\beta} - \frac{1}{2}(l^\alpha_{;\alpha})^2 = 0. \tag{11.32}$$

If there exists a solution of the eikonal equation (2.22), then condition (11.32) means that there is no distortion of the shape of the shadow cast upon a screen by an opaque object oriented orthogonally to the rays. ˙ Depending on whether the expansion of the congruence

$$\varepsilon = \frac{1}{2} l^\alpha_{;\alpha} \tag{11.33}$$

equals zero or does not equal zero, the wave front will correspond to plane or spherical gravitational waves. *

This suggests that algebraically special fields correspond to gravitational waves far from the source system while algebraically general fields represent a gravitational field near the sources, "perturbing" the gravitational wave front. To substantiate this conclusion mathematically, let us examine the asymptotic behavior of the Riemann tensor of an asymptotically flat space-time described by a Sachs metric.

Assuming that the functions that enter into the Sachs metric (11.29) are infinitely differentiable with respect to r (which, as we will see, is not generally obligatory) and expanding them in Taylor series in powers of r^{-1}, we can show by direct calculation with the field equations (2.2) that all the Φ_A in (11.15) are nonzero and that their expansions begin with terms of varying orders, namely from r^{-1} to r^{-5}. Taking the general Newman formulas (11.16) — (11.17)

---

* If the space-time admits of an isotropic geodesic congruence with nonzero shear, the corresponding field of gravitational radiation is interpreted as a field of cylindrical waves. Examples of axially symmetric gravitational fields of this type with an infinite linear distribution of sources are the Einstein-Rosen solution /187/, and also the Jordan-Ehlers /188/ and Kompaneets /189/ solutions that develop it. Unlike the plane and spherical wave fields considered earlier, they belong to the algebraically general type I and, like gravitational fields of isolated sources (Bondi and Sachs), admit of peeling into terms of type N, II and I (see the works of Stachel /188/ and Marder /190—192/). Researches by Weber and Wheeler /193/ and Krishna Rao /194—196/ have been specially devoted to the wave properties of nonstationary axially symmetric gravitational fields.

for the asymptotic form of Φ_A into account, we arrive at the following peeling of the Riemann tensor (Sachs' "peeling
theorem" /110/:

$$R = {}_0N r^{-1} + {}_0III r^{-2} + {}_0II r^{-3} + {}_0I r^{-4} + I' r^{-5} + \ldots \qquad (11.34)$$

Here, ${}_0N$, ${}_0III$, ... denote tensors with the algebraic structure of
the Riemann tensors of types N, III, etc., respectively (indices
have been dropped for conciseness), and the index 0 on the left
means that these tensors are covariantly constant along the corresponding geodesic rays. In the fourth and fifth terms, I' and ${}_0I$ are
distinguished by the fact that the tensor I' has no geodesic rays
while ${}_0I$ has geodesic rays. Further, the sum of the terms up to a
certain given order inclusive is a tensor of the same algebraic
type as its last term. The coefficient ${}_0N$ is proportional to $\mathcal{C}_{,00}$,
where $\mathcal{C}_{,0}$ is a function which goes over into the Bondi information
function under the conditions (11.30). In particular, for $\mathcal{C}_{,0}=0$ for
the Bondi metric ${}_0N = {}_0III = {}_0II = 0$, and we arrive at the stationary
axially symmetric Weyl metric (11.10).

On the basis of the peeling theorem, the gravitational fields of
isolated sources can be given the following algebraic interpretation.
A field set up by a material system in the empty space surrounding
it belongs to the first Petrov type (I or D). If a system emits,
then at distances significantly greater than the dimensions of the
system itself and the wavelength of its emission (i.e., in the wave
zone) the gravitational field will be approximately of type N. In
other words, from the standpoint of an observer lying at a large
distance (in a fixed direction) from the emitting system, terms of
type N will predominate in the Riemann tensor; for an observer
whose distance from the system is small compared with the dimensions of the system itself and with the wavelength of its emission
(near zone), terms of type I or D will predominate in the Riemann
tensor depending on the nature of the wave front. Lastly, at
distances great by comparison with the dimensions of the source
system but small compared with the wavelength of its emission
(transitional zone), the gravitational field is described by a Riemann tensor of type II or III depending on the nature of the source
distribution.

As shown by Sachs /148, 185/ and Persides /197/, given certain
special assumptions (possibility of expansion of the metric in
infinite series in r^{-1}, Euclidean asymptotic form at infinity), the
Riemann tensor peeling (11.34) is feasible for arbitrary gravitational fields in empty space possessing geodesic rays. This
possibility is guaranteed by conditions (11.16) − (11.17) obtained

above which give the asymptotic form of the tetrad components of the Riemann tensor. For cases where the space-time does not admit of a congruence of geodesic rays, Lehman /198/ and Goldberg /199/ formulated and proved the following weaker statement: in these cases one of the isotropic Debever vector fields is asymptotically geodesic, i. e.,

$$l_{\alpha;\beta} l^\beta = O(r^{-n}) \qquad (n \geqslant 2). \tag{11.35}$$

If we assume that the peeling (11.34) still holds for this case, it follows that the vector l^α no longer remains the direction vector for the geodesic ray in spaces corresponding to tensors N, III, etc., of the expansion. However, there should then exist a congruence of isotropic geodesics with tangent vector l'^α which are asymptotes of the trajectories of the vector l^α. One might then expect that the congruence l'^α represents geodesic rays only in a space-time corresponding to the first four terms of the peeling (11.34):

$$l'_{[\rho} R_{\alpha]\beta\gamma[\delta} l'_{\sigma]} l'^\beta l'^\gamma = O(r^{-5}), \tag{11.36}$$

i. e., that it is asymptotically a Debever vector.

Lastly, if the vector field l'^α satisfies condition (11.36) and moreover is a gradient field ($l_\alpha' = \varphi_{,\alpha}$), then, as Newman and Penrose demonstrate /174/, the peeling (11.34) always holds.

5. General algebraic structure of the Riemann tensor

It is obvious that the Sachs peeling formula (11.34) is not generally covariant since the parameter r serves as distance coordinate along the geodesic. However, the algebraic classification of canonical types of Riemann tensors makes it possible to formulate the peeling of a Riemann tensor of algebraically general structure in a generally covariant manner.

To do this we use the Newman-Penrose formalism. In an isotropic complex tetrad (l^μ, n^μ, m^μ, $\bar{m}^\mu$) whose vectors satisfy the relations

$$
\begin{aligned}
l_\alpha l^\alpha = n_\alpha n^\alpha = m_\alpha m^\alpha = l_\alpha m^\alpha = n_\alpha m^\alpha = 0, \\
l_\alpha n^\alpha = m_\alpha \bar{m}^\alpha = 1,
\end{aligned}
\tag{11.37}
$$

we define three simple bi-vectors

$$V_{\alpha\beta} = 2l_{[\alpha}\bar{m}_{\beta]}, \quad U_{\alpha\beta} = 2n_{[\alpha}m_{\beta]},$$
$$M_{\alpha\beta} = 2l_{[\alpha}n_{\beta]} + 2\bar{m}_{[\alpha}m_{\beta]}. \tag{11.38}$$

Then, as shown by Kammerer /200/ and Szekeres /134/, to all possible algebraic types of the Riemann tensor in a vacuum corresponds the following general combination:

$$R_{\alpha\beta\gamma\delta} + i \,{}^*R_{\alpha\beta\gamma\delta} = C_1 V_{\alpha\beta} V_{\gamma\delta} + C_2 \,(V_{\alpha\beta} M_{\gamma\delta} +$$
$$+ M_{\alpha\beta} V_{\gamma\delta}) + C_3 \,(M_{\alpha\beta} M_{\gamma\delta} + U_{\alpha\beta} V_{\gamma\delta} + V_{\alpha\beta} U_{\gamma\delta}) +$$
$$+ C_4 \,(U_{\alpha\beta} M_{\gamma\delta} + M_{\alpha\beta} U_{\gamma\delta}) + C_5 U_{\alpha\beta} U_{\gamma\delta}, \tag{11.39}$$

where $C_1, \ldots, C_5$ are arbitrary scalars.

Using the canonical form of the matrix $\| R_{ab} \|$ of the Riemann tensor in the bi-vector space R_6, one can show that there is, to each type of gravitational field (Ch. 3), an expansion of the Riemann tensor in the bi-vectors (11.38) corresponding to some particular case of expression (11.39), where some of the scalars $C_1, \ldots, C_5$ (not more than four) vanish. The problem of expressing the Riemann tensor in terms of bi-vectors for the case of empty spaces (and the Weyl tensor in the general case) was solved for all types of gravitational fields by Debever /81/. Comparing Debever's results with expression (11.39), we arrive at the following conclusions. Let a given gravitational field be algebraically special. Then $C_4 = C_5 = 0$, i.e., the expansion (11.39), generally speaking, comprises only the first three terms; in this case the vector field l^{α} defines geodesic rays. Further, let $C_3 = 0$; the Riemann tensor then belongs to type III. For the case $C_2 = C_3 = C_4 = C_5 = 0$ the gravitational field is of type N with the vector l^{α} as Debever vector. Lastly, the condition $C_3 \neq 0$ characterizes fields of type II and D.

Comparing expression (11.39) with the Sachs peeling formula (11.34), we see that each of the first five terms of the asymptotic expansion of the Riemann tensor in r^{-1} has the algebraic structure of the corresponding term in expression (11.39). It is therefore of interest to study the asymptotic behavior of the coefficients $C_1, \ldots, C_5$ in (11.39). To do this we choose a canonical parameter r on the geodesic ray with tangent vector l^{α}. If we assume that the condition $r \to \infty$ always corresponds to the asymptotic value of the Riemann tensor, then in the general case there is no need to assume that the space-time is asymptotically flat. Moreover, instead of the rigorous Sachs condition regarding the infinite differentiability of the metric with respect to the parameter r, we confine ourselves to the assumption that the components of the Riemann tensor, as also those of the vectors $l^{\alpha}, n^{\alpha}, m^{\alpha}, \bar{m}^{\alpha}$, are functions of the coordinates of class C^6 (which corresponds to our aim of investigating the asymptotic behavior of the first five terms of the expansion in r^{-1}).

We insert expression (11.39) in the Bianchi identities and proceed to regard the latter as equations for the functions $C_1, \ldots, C_5$. Studying the main (by order of smallness) terms of the solution of these equations, we find that for $r \to \infty$ the coefficients C_N in (11.39), $N = 1, 2, 3, 4, 5$, tend to zero as $1/r^N$, respectively.

Thus the Sachs peeling theorem can be proved under far more general assumptions. A rigorous proof of this kind was first given by Kammerer /200/; as he assumed C^5-smoothness, his proof covers only the first four terms in (11.39). This corresponds to the fact that geodesic rays exist only for the first four terms in (11.39). Kammerer's result can be extended to the fifth term using, say, considerations relating to asymptotically geodesic congruences.

6. Asymptotic symmetries. Bondi-Metzner group

From the peeling theorem we have seen that at large distances from the source system even the properties of asymptotically plane gravitational wave fields are algebraically complex. The nontrivial character of the asymptotic forms of Bondi and Sachs fields of gravitational radiation is particularly striking when one studies their asymptotic symmetries.

Indeed one might have expected from physical considerations that on the asymptotic hypersurface $r \to \infty$ there would act a group of motions of the metric of the same order as the order of maximum mobility of the space V_4 of the corresponding type, i. e., of Petrov type N. However, due to the fact that at large distances the radiation field of an insular system is described only approximately by the structure of the type N Riemann tensor, it turns out that there is no group of motions that conserves the asymptotic form of the field and the boundary conditions as well. However, there exists a group of coordinate transformations satisfying these requirements; for axially symmetric isolated source distributions it is known as the Bondi-Metzner group /171/. This group contains the Lorentz group as subgroup (but not a normal one) and includes, moreover, the infinite-dimensional group of "supertranslations."

The fact that the information function $C_{,0}$ has very simple transformation properties with respect to the Bondi-Metzner group plays a very important part in the physical interpretation of this group. It makes it possible to express the conserved integral quantities in terms of the group invariants. An extension of the Bondi-Metzner group to the case of arbitrary isolated systems was put forward by Sachs /148/.

7. Asymptotic properties of the Einstein-Maxwell fields

The Bondi-Sachs method has also been extended to the case of gravitational radiation by isolated systems in nonempty space-time (Kozarzewski /201/, Hawking /202/, Stachel /203/). In particular, Kozarzewski /201/ shows that the asymptotic behavior of a gravitational field induced by arbitrary isolated systems of electrically charged bodies is also determined by the Sachs peeling formula. This result seems natural since geodesic rays are the trajectories of propagation of gravitational and electromagnetic radiation alike.

The analogy between the gravitational and electromagnetic fields is also clearly discernible in their asymptotic behavior. Thus starting from the integral form of the Maxwell equations Goldberg and Kerr /152/ established that the electromagnetic field of a bounded distribution of charges and currents admits of the following asymptotic expansion:

$$F_{\mu\nu} = r^{-1}N^F_{\mu\nu} + r^{-2}\,\text{III}^F_{\mu\nu} + r^{-3}J_{\mu\nu}. \tag{11.40}$$

Here r is an affine parameter which varies along the isotropic gradient directions l^α, i.e., along the electromagnetic rays; all the components $J_{\mu\nu} = J_{[\mu\nu]}$ are functions bounded above and the antisymmetric tensors $N^F_{\mu\nu}$ and $\text{III}^F_{\mu\nu}$ satisfy the relations

$$N^F_{\mu\nu}l^\nu = 0, \quad \text{III}^F_{\mu\nu}l^\nu = al_\mu \; (a \text{ is a scalar}), \tag{11.41}$$

in complete analogy with the algebraic relations characteristic for the Riemann tensors of types N or III, respectively.

It follows from formula (11.41) that in a coordinate system in which the parameter r characterizes the distance from the system of sources, the field $F_{\mu\nu}$ becomes isotropic at a distance from the system, i.e., satisfies the relations

$$l_{[\lambda}F_{\beta\gamma]} = 0, \quad l^\alpha F_{\alpha\beta} = 0. \tag{11.42}$$

However, as Chevreton /149/ shows, conditions (11.42) are

necessary but not sufficient for plane electromagnetic waves in Minkowski space-time; in order for the electromagnetic field $F_{\mu\nu}$ to fit the case of plane waves, it is necessary and sufficient that the following be satisfied in addition to (11.42):

$$l_{[\lambda}F_{\beta\gamma],\sigma} = 0, \quad l^{\alpha}F_{\alpha\beta,\sigma} = 0. \tag{11.43}$$

Consider conditions (11.42) — (11.43) in the general case of a curved space-time. As Mariot /260, 261/ shows, the trajectories of the vector field l^{α} satisfying relations (11.42) form a congruence of isotropic geodesics (11.31). Differentiating the relations (11.42) covariantly and recalling (11.43), we obtain

$$F_{[\beta\gamma}l_{\lambda];\sigma} = 0, \quad F_{\alpha\beta}l^{\alpha}_{;\sigma} = 0, \tag{11.44}$$

whence it follows /149/ that the tensor $l_{\lambda;\sigma}$ can be expressed as the product of two vectors:

$$l_{\lambda;\sigma} = A_{\sigma}l_{\lambda}, \tag{11.45}$$

where A_{σ} is a vector orthogonal to the vector l_{λ}. It follows automatically from formulas (11.45) that for the congruence of geodesics defined by the vector l^{α}, the rotation ω, the dilation ε and the shear σ tend to zero. This means that at infinite distances from a system of arbitrary charged sources the electomagnetic and gravitational fields are fields of plane waves with common congruence of geodesic rays.

Chapter 12

GRAVITATIONAL WAVES AND CHRONOMETRIC INVARIANTS

1. Chronometric invariants

The preceding chapters were devoted mainly to the study of gravitational fields from the standpoint of generally covariant criteria for the existence of gravitational waves. A gravitational field which satisfies the generally covariant wave criterion will have a wave character irrespective of the choice of coordinate system. But it would be interesting to drop the requirement of general covariance and formulate a criterion for g r a v i t a t i o n a l - i n e r t i a l w a v e s covariant only with respect to transformations of the three-dimensional coordinate frames in which a chosen reference body is at rest. Further, such a criterion would have to be invariant under transformations that conserve the coordinate lines of time x^0 since these are world lines of the reference body. In other words, this criterion reflects the observer's choice of a frame of reference and its fulfillment may therefore be regarded as a sign of the reality of the waves for the given choice of reference body; indeed such waves can generally be eliminated by passage to a different reference body, due to the dependence of the inertial properties on the state of motion of the observers.

Let us then consider the transformations given by

$$\tilde{x}^0 = \tilde{x}^0 (x^0, x^1, x^2, x^3), \qquad (12.1)$$

$$\tilde{x}^i = \tilde{x}^i (x^1, x^2, x^3), \qquad (12.2)$$

which have the property that $\frac{\partial \tilde{x}^i}{\partial x^0} = 0$. The transformations (12.1) — (12.2), where x^0 is the timelike coordinate, are obviously the most general transformations between coordinate systems at rest relative to a given reference body.

In formulating the criterion we will confine ourselves to invariance under the transformations (12.1), i.e., chronometric invariance, and to covariance with respect to the transformations (12.2), i.e., spatial covariance. Thus for a specified reference body, freedom of coordinate transformations is restricted by the chronometric invariance (12.1) and the spatial covariance (12.2). Transformations (12.1) — (12.2) constituted the base on which Zel'manov constructed his formalism of chronometric invariants /204 — 206/.

Chronometric invariants, i.e., three-dimensional physical quantities invariant under the transformations (12.1), can be regarded as observables in the general theory of relativity, i.e., quantities directly linked to physical measurements. The chronometrically invariant approach to gravitational-inertial waves is thus all the more interesting as the waves so defined can be treated as a subject of immediate physical measurement.

Following Zel'manov /204, 205/, we introduce chronometrically invariant operators of differentiation, designating them by means of stars to distinguish them from the usual ones:

$$ {}^*\partial = \frac{1}{\sqrt{g_{00}}}\,\partial_0, \qquad {}^*\partial_i = \partial_i - \frac{g_{0i}}{g_{00}}\,\partial_0. \tag{12.3} $$

We also introduce the chronometrically invariant spatial metric tensor

$$ b_{ik} = -\,g_{ik} + \frac{g_{0i}\,g_{0k}}{g_{00}}, \quad b^{ik} = -\,g^{ik}, \quad b = \det\|b_{ik}\|. \tag{12.4} $$

For the chronometrically invariant gravitational-inertial force vector F_i and tensor A_{ik} of absolute rotation of the frame of reference Σ relative to the locally co-moving geodesic system Σ_0, we have the expressions /206/

$$ F^j = \frac{b^{ij}}{W}\,({}^*\partial_i W - {}^*\partial V_i), \tag{12.5} $$

$$ A_{ik} = {}^*\partial_{[i}\,V_{k]} + F_{[i}\,V_{k]}, \tag{12.6} $$

where W and V_i are the scalar and vector potentials of the gravitational-inertial field, respectively:

$$ W = (1 - \sqrt{g_{00}}), \qquad V_i = -\,g_{0i}/\sqrt{g_{00}}. $$

The chronometrically invariant tensor D_{ik} of deformation velocities of the three-dimensional space of reference of the system Σ relative to the locally co-moving system Σ_0 is given by the expressions /205/

$$D_{ik} = \frac{1}{2} {}^*\partial b_{ik}, \quad D^{ik} = -\frac{1}{2} {}^*\partial b^{ik}, \quad D = {}^*\partial \ln \sqrt{b}. \tag{12.7}$$

Here $D = D_i^i$ is the rate of relative volumetric expansion of an element of space.

We also define the chronometrically invariant analogs of the Christoffel symbols and the operation of chronometrically invariant three-dimensional covariant differentiation /205/

$$\Delta_{ij}^l = \frac{1}{2} b^{kl} ({}^*\partial_i b_{jk} + {}^*\partial_j b_{ik} - {}^*\partial_k b_{ij}), \tag{12.8}$$

$${}^*\nabla_i Q_j^{\cdots k} = {}^*\partial_i Q_j^{\cdots k} - \Delta_{ij}^l Q_l^{\cdots k} + \dots + \Delta_{il}^k Q_j^{\cdots l}, \tag{12.9}$$

with

$${}^*\nabla_i b_{jk} = 0, \quad {}^*\nabla_i b_j^k = 0, \quad {}^*\nabla_i b^{jk} = 0.$$

Within the formalism of chronometric invariants, in addition to the dynamic quantity F_i, kinematic quantity A_{ik} and static quantity D_{ik}, it is also possible to introduce a fourth geometric characteristic of the co-moving three-dimensional space, namely the spatial curvature tensor K_{lkij}:

$$K_{kilj} = \frac{1}{2} (H_{ki[lj]} + H_{[ki]lj}), \tag{12.10}$$

where

$$H_{kil}^{\cdots j} = {}^*\partial_k \Delta_{il}^j - {}^*\partial_i \Delta_{kl}^j + \Delta_{il}^m \Delta_{km}^j - \Delta_{kl}^m \Delta_{im}^j, \tag{12.11}$$

and

$$K_{lkij} = -K_{klij} = -K_{lkji} = K_{ijlk}. \tag{12.12}$$

As Zel'manov shows, the twenty independent components of the four-dimensional Riemann tensor $R_{\mu\alpha\beta\nu}$ can be collected in three chronometrically invariant tensors expressed in terms of F_i, A_{ik}, D_{ik} and K_{iklj}. Thus we introduce the following three-dimensional tensors /91/:

$$X^{ij} = -\frac{R_{0\cdot0\cdot}^{\cdot i \cdot j}}{g_{00}}, \quad Y^{ijk} = -\frac{R_{0\cdots}^{\cdot ijk}}{\sqrt{g_{00}}}, \quad Z^{iklj} = R^{iklj}. \tag{12.13}$$

It is easy to show that the tensors X^{ij}, Y^{ijk} and Z^{iklj} are chrono-metric invariants. Indeed, let $Q_{00\cdots0}^{ik\cdots p}$ be the components of a world (four-dimensional) tensor of rank n in which all the upper indices are nonzero while all the lower indices (m in number) are zero. Then, performing the transformation (12.1), it is seen that the quantities

$$T^{ik\cdots p} = \frac{Q_{00\cdots0}^{ik\cdots p}}{(g_{00})^{m/2}} \tag{12.14}$$

constitute a chronometrically invariant three-dimensional tensor of rank $n - m$. Note incidentally that formula (12.14) can serve as an algorithm for the construction of chronometric invariants of the form $Q_{00\cdots0}^{ik\cdots p}$ out of world tensors. It is obvious from the definitions (12.13) that the tensors X^{ij}, Y^{ijk} and Z^{iklj} were constructed according to this precise rule, and they therefore satisfy the condition of chronometric invariance.

Expressing the components of the world tensor $R_{\alpha\beta\gamma\delta}$ in terms of the chronometrically invariant quantities (12.5) − (12.7), (12.10), we obtain the Zel'manov formulas defining the relation between the tensors (12.13) and these quantities:

$$X_{ij} = {}^{\bullet}\partial D_{ij} - (D_i^l + A_{i\cdot}^{\cdot l})(D_{jl} + A_{jl}) + {}^{\bullet}\nabla_{(i}F_{j)} - \frac{1}{2}F_iF_j, \tag{12.15}$$

$$Y_{ijk} = {}^{\bullet}\nabla_j(A_{ik} + D_{ik}) - {}^{\bullet}\nabla_i(A_{jk} + D_{jk}) - 2A_{ij}F_k, \tag{12.16}$$

$$Z_{iklj} = 2(D_{i[k}D_{l]j} - A_{i[k}A_{l]j} + A_{ij}A_{kl}) - K_{iklj}. \tag{12.17}$$

Here

$$X_k^k = \frac{R_{00}}{g_{00}}, \quad Y_{\cdots l}^{il\cdot} = \frac{R_0^i}{\sqrt{g_{00}}}, \quad Z_{\cdots i}^{ijl\cdot} + X^{ij} = -R^{ij}, \tag{12.18}$$

$$X_{ij} = X_{ji}, \quad Y_{ijk} = -Y_{jik}, \quad Y_{(ijk)} = 0, \tag{12.19}$$

and the tensor Z_{klij} has the symmetry and antisymmetry properties (12.12) of the tensor K_{klij}. We see that the twenty independent components of the Riemann tensor $R_{\alpha\beta\gamma\delta}$ can be expressed in terms of the six independent components of the tensor X_{ij}, eight of the tensor Y_{ijk} and six of the tensor Z_{klij}.

2. Chronometrically invariant definition of gravitational-inertial waves

Thus the Riemann world tensor $R_{\alpha\beta\gamma\delta}$ breaks down into three chronometrically invariant three-dimensional tensors (12.13), expressible in turn in terms of the gravitational-inertial physical characteristics of the three-dimensional space co-moving with the chosen reference body, (12.5) — (12.7) and (12.10). We will relate the definition of gravitational-inertial waves to the four gravitational-inertial characteristics (12.5) — (12.7) and (12.10), and also to the quantities (12.13) which are expressed in terms of these according to formulas (12.15) — (12.17).

A chronometrically invariant definition of the d'Alembert operator in the general theory of relativity, realizing Zel'manov's idea, has been formulated in /94/.

The chronometrically invariant criterion for the existence of gravitational-inertial waves is that the following three-dimensional chronometric invariants — the vectors F_i, the tensors D_{ik}, A_{ik}, K_{klij} and the scalars composed of these, as well as the tensors $X_{ij}, Y_{ijk}, Z_{klij}$ expressed in terms of these — satisfy equations of the form

$$^{\bullet}\Box P = Q. \tag{12.20}$$

The following notation is introduced here:

$$^{\bullet}\Box = {}^{\bullet}\nabla^2 - \frac{1}{a^2} {}^{\bullet}\partial {}^{\bullet}\partial, \quad {}^{\bullet}\nabla^2 \equiv b^{ik} {}^{\bullet}\nabla_i {}^{\bullet}\nabla_k, \tag{12.21}$$

so that $^{\bullet}\Box$ is the chronometrically invariant spatially covariant d'Alembert wave operator and a is a scalar function of the coordinates. It is assumed that Q does not explicitly contain second derivatives of the sought function P. The latter will be called wave function according to tradition, in the sense of equation (12.20). The role of the wave function P will be played by various chronometrically invariant quantities of a three-dimensional-tensor nature. Investigating the chronometrically invariant wave criterion reduces to analyzing whether it is fulfilled for various chronometrically invariant characteristics of the frame of reference and gravitational field with respect to this frame. Accordingly it is necessary to distinguish between gravitational-inertial waves of force F_i, deformation D_{ik} and curvature K_{klij}.

In /94/ this criterion was used to analyze a number of known solutions of the Einstein equations in a vacuum. It was shown that it is met for all known solutions of Petrov type N (solutions of Peres /160/, Takeno /153, 163/, Petrov /65/ et al.) but not for the "cylindrical wave" solutions of Einstein-Rosen /187/ and Kompaneets /189/, which are not of type N. Note that the latter two solutions (Petrov type I) fail to satisfy any of the generally covariant criteria for gravitational waves considered in the preceding chapters (criteria of Lichnerowicz, Bel, Pirani, Zel'manov, et al.).

Let us look at wave equations of the form (12.20) for gravitational fields corresponding to certain exact solutions of Einstein's equations in a vacuum (2.2).

The Peres solution (9.30) — (9.31) belongs to Petrov type N. In order to simplify the calculations we impose the additional condition* $f_{,1} = f_{,2} = 0$ upon f as a result of which the only field equation (9.31) is identically satisfied.

Using formulas (12.3), we have the following for an arbitrary function P of argument $(x^0 + x^3)$:

$$^*\partial P = \frac{1}{\sqrt{1-2f}} P_{,3}, \quad ^*P_{,3} = \frac{1}{1-2f} P_{,3},$$

$$^*\partial^*\partial P = \frac{1}{(1-2f)^2} [P_{,00}(1-2f) + f_{,3}P_{,3}],$$

$$^*\partial_3^*\partial_3 P = \frac{1}{(1-2f)^3} [P_{,33}(1-2f) + 2f_{,3}P_{,3}].$$

From the above, expressing $P_{,00}$ in terms of $^*\partial^*\partial P$ and $P_{,33}$ in terms of $^*\partial_3^*\partial_3 P$, and noting that

$$^*\nabla^2 P \equiv b^{ik}(^*\partial_i^*\partial_k P - \Delta_{ik}^{j\,*}\partial_j P),$$

we reduce the ordinary wave equation for the function $P(x^0 + x^3)$

$$P_{,33} - P_{,00} = 0$$

to the required form in the given frame of reference

---

* In actual fact this condition means that we are confining ourselves to a flat space-time, since the nonzero components of the Riemann tensor for the metric (9.30) are given by

$$R_{3113} = R_{3110} = R_{0110} = R_{0110} = f_{,11}, \quad R_{3223} = R_{3220} = R_{0220} = f_{,22},$$
$$R_{3123} = R_{3120} = R_{0123} = R_{0120} = f_{,12}.$$

Thus our case will fit inertial waves only. The more general case of gravitational-inertial waves in a space-time with $R_{\alpha\beta\gamma\delta} \neq 0$ will be considered later for different exact solutions of the Einstein equations.

$$(*\nabla^2 - *\partial*\partial)\, P = 0. \tag{12.22}$$

Since the three-dimensional scalars

$$F_i F^i = \frac{(f_{,3})^2}{(1-2f)^3}, \quad D = \frac{f_{,3}}{(1-2f)^{3/2}}$$

for this metric likewise depend on the argument $x^0 + x^3$ only
($A_{ik} = 0$ for $f_{,1} = f_{,2} = 0$), it follows that they satisfy equation (12.22),
i. e., that they are solutions of the chronometrically invariant equation
(12.20) for $Q = 0$, $a = 1$.

Let us now obtain the wave equations for the gravitational-
inertial force vector F^i and the deformation velocity tensor D_{ik} in
the given reference system. The field of the vector F_i is given by

$$F_1 = 0. \quad F_2 = 0, \quad F = -\frac{f_{,3}}{(1-2f)^2};$$

computing the quantity $*\Box F_i$, we obtain the form of the right-hand
side of equation (12.20) provided that it does not contain
derivatives higher than the first order in F_i. If such derivatives
are present on the right, it obviously follows that the equation is
not a wave equation; this is the situation, for example, for the
Einstein-Rosen and Kompaneets metrics.

The results of calculations for the Peres metric lead to the
following chronometrically invariant spatially covariant equations:

$$\overset{.}{\Box}\, F^i = -\, 3F^i\, (^*\nabla_j F^j + \tfrac{1}{3}\, F_j F^j), \tag{12.23}$$

$$\overset{.}{\Box}\, D_{ij} = -\, 2D_{ij}\, (3^*\partial D + 2D_{kl} D^{kl}). \tag{12.24}$$

Equations (12.23) $-$ (12.24) are obviously chronometrically invariant equations for a wavelike gravitational-inertial field, the
nonlinearities on the right representing the sources of the gravitational-inertial perturbations.

The Takeno solution (10.5) also belongs to Petrov type N. Upon
calculating the tensor of the angular velocity of absolute rotation (12.6)
for the metric (10.5), we find that it vanishes: $A_{ik} = 0$. But, as
Zel'manov shows /206/, this is necessary and sufficient to make
all g_{0i} vanish in this region by the transformation (12.1). Therefore, assuming from now on that $S = 0$ in the metric (10.5), we find
that the scalars

$$F_i F^i = -\frac{P_{,3}}{4P^2},$$

$$D = -\frac{1}{2mP^{1/2}}(PM_{,3} + MP_{,3})$$

satisfy the chronometrically invariant wave equation

$$^{\bullet}\Box G = \frac{1}{2M} b^{ik} {}^{\bullet}\nabla_i G^{\bullet}\nabla_k M,$$

where G is any of the chronometrically invariant scalars $F^i F_i$ and D_i^i.

For the gravitational-inertial force vector the wave equation becomes

$$^{\bullet}\Box F^i = F^i(-2F_j F^j + 3{}^{\bullet}\partial D + 2D_{jl}D^{jl} - D^2) +$$

$$+ \frac{1}{2M} b^{ik} {}^{\bullet}\nabla_k M (2F_j F^j - {}^{\bullet}\partial D - D_{jl}D^{jl}),$$

from which it follows, in particular, that the sources of wave perturbations of the gravitational-inertial field depend on the deformation of the frame of reference.

The Petrov solution (9.15) was examined in a different coordinate system by Bondi, Pirani and Robinson /143/; Synge /172/ interpreted it in the language of "body gravitational waves." We will write as follows:

$$ds^2 = dx^{0\,2} - dx^{1\,2} + \alpha\, dx^{2\,2} + 2\beta\, dx^2\, dx^3 + \gamma\, dx^{3\,2}, \qquad (12.25)$$

where α, β, γ are functions of the argument $x^0 + x^1$ related by a single differential equation /65/. For this solution, in the frame of reference (12.25), $F^i = 0$, $A_{ik} = 0$, and the scalar D is given by

$$D = \frac{1}{2} {}^{\bullet}\partial \ln(\alpha\gamma - \beta^2)$$

and satisfies a scalar wave equation of the type (12.20) for $a = 1$:

$$^{\bullet}\Box D = D\,(b^{ik} {}^{\bullet}\nabla_i D^{\bullet}\nabla_k D)^{1/2}.$$

We turn now to solutions of Petrov type T_1. It appears that the wave criterion under consideration — unlike other generally covariant criteria — can be satisfied by certain type T_1 metrics as well. Thus the metrics

$$ds^2 = -\alpha^{-1} dx^{0\,2} + \alpha\, dx^{1\,2} + \gamma\, dx^{2\,2} + \gamma\, \mathrm{sh}^2\, x^2\, dx^{3\,2},$$

$$ds^2 = -\alpha^{-1} dx^{0\,2} + \alpha\, dx^{1\,2} + \gamma\, dx^{2\,2} + \gamma\, \mathrm{ch}^2\, x^2\, dx^{3\,2}$$

where α and γ are functions of the argument $x^0 + x^1$ ($\alpha < 0$, $\gamma < 0$) satisfying a certain system of differential equations /94/, define gravitational fields of type D /207/. The three-dimensional space of the frame of reference is holonomic ($A_{ik} = 0$), and the chronometrically invariant scalars D and $F_i F^i$ satisfy the wave equation (12.20) for $a = \alpha$:

$$^*\nabla^2 G - \frac{1}{\alpha^2}\, ^*\partial^*\partial G = b^{ik}\, ^*\nabla_i G^* \nabla_k \ln \frac{\gamma}{\alpha}.$$

A solution which merits special discussion is that of Einstein-Rosen /187/, which belongs to type I:

$$ds^2 = e^{2(\gamma-\alpha)}(dx^{0\,2} - dx^{1\,2}) - x^{1\,2} e^{-2\alpha}\, dx^{2\,2} - e^{2\alpha}\, dx^{3\,2}, \tag{12.26}$$

where γ and α are functions of x^1 and x^0 satisfying the differential equations

$$\alpha_{,11} + \frac{1}{x^1}\alpha_{,1} - \alpha_{,00} = 0, \tag{12.27}$$

$$\gamma_{,1} = x^1\,[(\alpha_{,1})^2 + (\alpha_{,2})^2], \quad \gamma_0 = 2x^1\alpha_{,1}\alpha_{,0}. \tag{12.28}$$

It can be shown /94/ that although the "cylindrical waves" equation (12.27) admits of chronometrically invariant formulation (12.20) for $a = 1$,

$$^*\Box\,\alpha = b^{ik}\, ^*\nabla_i\alpha^*\nabla_k(\alpha - \gamma) + \,^*\partial\alpha^*\partial\gamma - (^*\partial\alpha)^2,$$

neither it not an analogous equation of the type (12.20) with a different right-hand side and different a will be satisfied by the chronometrically invariant scalars D and $F_i F^i$($A_{ik} = 0$), or by any of their scalar functions.

An analogous result holds for the Kompaneets metric /189/, which generalizes the Einstein-Rosen metric:

$$ds^2 = \alpha\, dx^{0\,2} - \alpha\, dx^{1\,2} - \gamma\, dx^{2\,2} - 2\beta\, dx^2 dx^3 - \delta\, dx^{3\,2}, \tag{12.29}$$

where $\alpha, \beta, \gamma, \delta$ are functions of x^1 and x^0. From the field equations one can arrive at two equations for "interacting cylindrical waves":

$$[x^1(PQ-1)^{-1/2}P_{,1}]_{,1} - x^1[(PQ-1)^{-1/2}P_{,0}]_{,0} = 0, \tag{12.30}$$

$$[x^1(PQ-1)^{-1/2}Q_{,1}]_{,1} - x^1[(PQ-1)^{-1/2}Q_{,0}]_{,0} = 0, \tag{12.31}$$

where the following notation is used:

$$P = \gamma(\gamma\delta - x^{1\,2})^{-1/2}, \quad Q = \delta(\gamma\delta - x^{1\,2})^{-1/2}.$$

As in the case of the Einstein-Rosen metric, the system of equations (12.30) — (12.31) admits of chronometrically invariant spatially-covariant formulation (12.20) for $a = 1$:

$$^\bullet\Box\gamma = \frac{1}{8\alpha\beta^2\lambda^2}[(\beta^2 - \lambda)\pi + \omega\gamma^2], \tag{12.32}$$

$$^\bullet\Box\delta = \frac{1}{8\alpha\beta^2\lambda^2}[(\beta^2 - \lambda)\omega + \pi\delta^2], \tag{12.33}$$

where $\lambda = \gamma\delta - \beta^2$, and π and ω are certain functions of $\alpha, \beta, \gamma, \delta$ and their first derivatives. However, equations of the (12.20) type are likewise not satisfied by D, F_iF^i or by their scalar functions.

To close this section we will discuss the question of the general relationship between the chronometrically invariant criterion (12.20) and the generally covariant Zel'manov criterion (Ch. 7) examined in /165/. Writing down the system of 20 equations

$$g^{\rho\sigma}R_{\alpha\beta\gamma\delta;\rho\sigma} = 0$$

in chronometrically invariant spatially covariant form, we arrive, after fairly extensive calculations, at the following three systems of equations:

$$(^\bullet\nabla^2 - {}^\bullet\partial\,{}^\bullet\partial)\,X^{ij} = \underset{(1)}{A^{ij}} \text{ (six equations)}, \tag{12.34}$$

$$(^\bullet\nabla^2 - {}^\bullet\partial\,{}^\bullet\partial)\,Y^{ijk} = \underset{(2)}{A^{ijk}} \text{ (eight equations)}, \tag{12.35}$$

$$(^\bullet\nabla^2 - {}^\bullet\partial\,{}^\bullet\partial)\,Z^{klij} = \underset{(3)}{A^{klij}} \text{ (six equations)}, \tag{12.36}$$

where the right-hand sides $\underset{(1)}{A^{ij}}, \underset{(2)}{A^{ijk}}, \underset{(3)}{A^{klij}}$ are chronometrically invariant spatial tensors of the second, third and fourth rank, respectively, and contain no derivatives higher than the first order in the "wave functions" X^{ij}, Y^{ijk}, Z^{klij}. These equations are given in expanded form in Appendix II.

Thus any space-time V_4 satisfying the Zel'manov generally covariant criterion of gravitational waves will also satisfy the chronometrically invariant criterion of gravitational-inertial waves.

The role of the wave functions in the corresponding wave equations of the type (12.20) is filled by the chronometrically invariant tensors (12.13), i.e., by the quantities X^{ij}, Y^{ijk}, Z^{klij}, which represent the Riemann tensor in the given frame of reference.

3. Physical conditions of existence of gravitational-inertial waves

Since equations (12.20) are not generally covariant, the waves described by these equations are closely related to the physical characteristics of the chosen frame of reference and more specifically to the chronometrically invariant quantities F_i, A_{ik} and D_{ik} (12.5) — (12.7). Let us investigate what part these physical quantities play in wave equations of the type (12.20) and how they influence the existence of gravitational-inertial waves. It is clear, for instance, that the choice of a frame of reference based on the form of the quantities F^i, A_{ik} and D_{ik} may lead to restrictions under which the tensors X^{ij}, Y^{ijk} and Z^{klij} become stationary, i.e., time-independent. Then the chronometrically invariant d'Alembertian (12.21) in equations (12.20) degenerates into a Laplacian, testifying to the absence of physical gravitational-inertial waves in the given frame of reference.

Moreover, in the chosen frame of reference the three-dimensional Laplacian $^{\bullet}\nabla^2$ entering the expression for $^{\bullet}\square$ (12.21) may make the "wave function" vanish. This situation may be realized, for example, whenever the functions P in (12.20) are homogeneous: $^{\bullet}\nabla_i P = 0$.

Thus both of the above situations (stationarity and homogeneity of the wave function) can be regarded as sufficient (but not generally speaking necessary) conditions for the absence of gravitational-inertial waves in the specified frame of reference.

By expressing the identities (7.8) in chronometrically invariant notation, one can easily show /208/ that in the Einstein spaces (3.7) the chronometrically invariant representatives of the Riemann tensor X^{ij}, Y^{ijk}, Z^{iklj} always satisfy the wave equation (12.20) for $a = 1$ and a definite choice of the right-hand side of Q. Thus the question of the existence of gravitational-inertial waves for the quantities X^{ij}, Y^{ijk}, Z^{iklj} in Einstein spaces reduces merely to investigation of the nontriviality (in the above sense) of the left-hand sides of these wave equations.

In /208/ a study was made — not just for Einstein spaces but in the general case as well — of the sufficient conditions under which a frame of reference does not admit of gravitational-inertial

waves, i. e., the left-hand side of equation (12.20) necessarily
becomes degenerate. A complete classification of frames of reference not admitting of gravitational-inertial waves (either due to
stationarity of the wave function of due to its homogeneity) is given
in this work for all chronometrically invariant quantities playing
the part of wave functions.

Let us quote the results of this study for the case of an arbitrary
gravitational field in a medium with the energy-momentum tensor
$T_{\alpha\beta}$. We introduce, in accordance with Zel'manov /205/, the
concepts of chronometrically invariant density, pressure and stress
tensor of the medium:

$$\rho = T_{00}/g_{00}, \quad J^i = T^i_0/\sqrt{g_{00}}, \quad U^{ij} = T^{ij}. \tag{12.37}$$

Let the part of wave functions be played by the chronometrically
invariant representatives $X^{ij}, Y^{ijk}, Z^{iklj}$ of the Riemann world tensor.
We will investigate the wave equation (12.20) for these functions in
frames of reference such that:

a) all chronometrically invariant mechanical characteristics
of the frame of reference (12.5) — (12.7) tend to zero,

b) one of these is nonzero,

c) two of these are nonzero, and

d) all three chronometrically invariant mechanical characteristics of the frame of reference are nonzero: $F^i \neq 0$, $A_{ik} \neq 0$,
$D_{ik} \neq 0$, and we will determine which frames of reference fail to
admit of gravitational-inertial waves, due to the homogeneity or
stationarity of the wave functions.

Let the following homogeneity conditions be fulfilled:*

$$^*\nabla_j F_i = 0, \quad ^*\nabla_j A_{ik} = 0, \quad ^*\nabla_j D_{ik} = 0, \quad ^*\nabla_j K_{ik} = 0,$$
$$^*\partial_i \rho = 0, \quad ^*\nabla_j U_{ik} = 0, \quad ^*\nabla_j J^i = 0. \tag{12.38}$$

One can show that in this case all the wave functions are homogeneous, i. e.,

$$^*\Box P = - \, ^*\partial^* \partial P$$

for any of the tensors (12.13). Thus when the homogeneity conditions (12.38) are fulfilled, there are no gravitational-inertial
waves.

---

* The conditions (12.38), first pointed out by Zel'manov, differ from the homogeneity conditions
which he gives in /205/ in that in (12.38) the equations $\dfrac{^*\partial p}{\partial x^i} = 0$, $^*\nabla_j \beta_{ik} = 0$ have been
replaced by the equation $^*\nabla_j U_{ik} = 0$, and the equation $^*\nabla_j q_i = 0$ by the equation $^*\nabla_j J_i = 0$.

Assuming next that the space is inhomogeneous, let us investigate another sufficient condition for the absence of gravitational-inertial waves, namely, stationarity of the wave functions. We begin with case (a), where

$$F^i = 0, \ A_{ik} = 0, \quad D_{ik} = 0, \tag{12.39}$$

i. e., the chosen frame of reference falls freely, does not rotate and is not deformed. * The quantities (12.13) then become

$$X^{ij} = 0, \quad Y^{ijk} = 0, \quad Z^{iklj} = - K^{iklj}. \tag{12.40}$$

It appears that the third condition in (12.39) leads to stationarity of the three-dimensional curvature tensor K^{iklj}, and consequently there are no gravitational-inertial waves in this frame of reference.

Conditions (12.39), which define the frame of reference, make it possible to recover uniquely the general form of the space-time metric V_4. Indeed, joint fulfillment of the first and second conditions of (12.39) means that in the given frame of reference it is possible to parametrize the time lines x^0 so as to have simultaneously /205/

$$g_{00} = 1, \quad g_{0i} = 0. \tag{12.41}$$

The third condition (12.39) will then guarantee stationarity of the three-dimensional metric tensor (12.4). According to Cotton's result (see /65/, p. 389), the three-dimensional metric b_{ik} may be transformed in this case to a diagonal form. Thus in order for there to exist a frame of reference satisfying conditions (12.39), it is necessary and sufficient that the given V_4 be a reducible space of the special type

$$ds^2 = dx^{0\,2} + g_{11}dx^{1\,2} + g_{22}dx^{2\,2} + g_{33}dx^{3\,2},$$
$$g_{ii} = g_{ii}(x^1, x^2, x^3). \tag{12.42}$$

It can be proved that the Einstein space (3.7) with metric of the type (12.42) is always flat (see /65/, p. 390).

Consider now the case when the second of conditions (12.39) is not fulfilled:

$$F^i = 0, \quad A_{ik} \neq 0, \quad D_{ik} = 0, \tag{12.43}$$

---

* Here, and henceforth when speaking of the free fall, rotation and deformation of a frame of reference, we will be referring to the corresponding motions of the three-dimensional space of the given frame of reference with respect to the locally co-moving geodesic system.

i. e., the frame of reference rotates while falling freely and without being deformed. The first condition in (12.43) permits us to choose a parametrization of the time lines x^0 such that the following conditions be fulfilled /205/:

$$g_{00} = 1, \quad {}^*\partial g_{0i} = 0.$$

One can show that in a frame of reference with the properties (12.43), all g_{ik} are also stationary. From this it follows that the metric $g_{\alpha\beta}$ of the space-time V_4 is stationary and therefore that the quantities (12.13) are stationary too. Thus a frame of reference of the type (12.43) will not admit of gravitational-inertial waves. The well-known Gödel metric /209/ is an example which fits this case.

Next, consider the case where the first condition in (12.39) is violated:

$$F^i \neq 0, \quad A_{ik} = 0, \quad D_{ik} = 0, \tag{12.44}$$

i. e., the frame of reference accelerates without rotating or becoming deformed. The space-time metric can then be reduced to the form

$$ds^2 = g_{00}(x^0, x^1, x^2, x^3) dx^{0\,2} + g_{11}dx^{1\,2} + g_{22}dx^{2\,2} + g_{33}dx^{3\,2},$$
$$g_{ii} = g_{ii}(x^1, x^2, x^3). \tag{12.45}$$

The quantities (12.13) in this frame of reference assume the form

$$X^{ij} = \frac{1}{2}({}^*\nabla^i F^j + {}^*\nabla^j F^i) - F^i F^j, \tag{12.46}$$
$$Y^{ijk} = 0, \tag{12.47}$$
$$Z^{iklj} = -K^{iklj} \tag{12.48}$$

Due to the third condition of (12.44) Z^{iklj} is stationary and thus the problem reduces to investigating the wave properties of X^{ij}.

Using the chronometrically invariant form of the field equations, we can write X^{ij} as

$$X^{ij} = (K^{ij} + \Lambda b^{ij}) + \frac{\lambda}{2}(\rho b^{ij} + 2U^{ij} - Ub^{ij}), \tag{12.49}$$

where Λ is the cosmological constant.

From this it follows that waves of X^{ij} are impossible in a vacuum owing to the stationarity of this "wave function," even though as a rule the four-dimensional metric $g_{\alpha\beta}$ is then nonstationary.

In the general case $(T_{\alpha\beta} \neq 0)$ it follows from the field equations and from the conservation laws that the mass density ρ is independent of time in the frame of reference under consideration. But the stress tensor U^{ij} is generally nonstationary. Thus the non-stationarity of X^{ij} is due in this case to the nonstationarity of the stress tensor U^{ij}, and the question of the absence of waves in a medium needs to be analyzed in detail for every choice of $T_{\alpha\beta}$ in the field equations.

Let us first require that the given frame of reference be co-moving with the medium. In this case the stress tensor may be expressed as

$$U^{ij} = p b^{ij} - \beta^{ij} = p_{(0)} b^{ij} - \alpha^{ij}, \tag{12.50}$$

where β^{ij} is the first viscosity, which develops in anisotropic deformation, α^{ij} is the second viscosity, which develops in isotropic deformation, p is the true pressure, and $p_{(0)}$ is the equilibrium pressure, determined from the equation of state. Since the viscosity of the medium is not felt in the co-moving frame of reference in the absence of deformation, it follows that $U^{ij} = p b^{ij}$, and, therefore, that $p = p_{(0)}$.

If the medium is baroclinic, i.e., if $p_0 = p_0(\rho, \tau)$, where τ is the absolute temperature, then

$$^{\bullet}\partial X^{ij} = -\frac{\lambda}{2} \frac{\partial p}{\partial \tau} \, ^{\bullet}\partial \tau \, b^{ij}, \tag{12.51}$$

and thus the X^{ij} are generally nonstationary. In the case of a barotropic medium, for which $p_{(0)} = p_{(0)}(\rho)$, the frame of reference under consideration does not admit of gravitational-inertial waves in view of the stationarity of the stress tensor. We will show that in a barotropic medium the four-dimensional metric tensor $g_{\alpha\beta}$ is also stationary.

Under the above assumptions the equations for the relativistic conservations laws become

$$^{\bullet}\partial \rho = 0, \tag{12.52}$$

$$\frac{1}{\rho + p} \partial_i p = - \partial_i \ln \sqrt{g_{00}}. \tag{12.53}$$

Here equation (12.53) is the chronometrically invariant analog of the condition of equilibrium in hydrodynamics extended to the case of the gravitational field /210/. Equations (12.52) − (12.53) together lead to the following expression for g_{00}:

$$g_{00} = \exp 2\,[T\,(x^0) + R\,(x^i)], \qquad (12.54)$$

where R and T are arbitrary functions of their arguments. With the help of the coordinate transformation

$$d\tilde{x}^0 = [\exp T\,(x^0)]\,dx^0, \quad d\tilde{x}^i \equiv dx^i \qquad (12.55)$$

the metric can be reduced to the stationary form

$$ds^2 = \exp\,[2\tilde{R}\,(\tilde{x}^i)]\,d\tilde{x}^{0\,2} + \tilde{g}_{11}\,d\tilde{x}^{1\,2} + \tilde{g}_{22}\,d\tilde{x}^{2\,2} + \tilde{g}_{33}\,d\tilde{x}^{3\,2},$$
$$\tilde{g}_{ii} = \tilde{g}_{ii}\,(\tilde{x}^1, \tilde{x}^2, \tilde{x}^3). \qquad (12.56)$$

(An example of such a frame is that in which the Schwarzschild metric is usually written). The main conclusion to emerge from the case under consideration is that if the medium is barotropic, then the frame of reference co-moving with it will not admit of the existence of gravitational-inertial waves.

In discussing the case of an arbitrary energy-momentum tensor our only assumption was that the frame of reference is co-moving with the medium. However, certain variants of the energy-momentum tensor for which this assumption does not hold are of interest. The first such example is the energy-momentum tensor of an ideal fluid:

$$T_{\alpha\beta} = (\rho + p)\,u_\alpha u_\beta - p g_{\alpha\beta}.$$

It follows from the field equations that the corresponding frame of reference is co-moving with the mass, i.e., $J^i = 0$. From the chronometrically invariant formulation of the field equations one can show that the frame of reference must also be co-moving with the medium in this case. This means that in an ideal fluid, as in the previous instance, gravitational-inertial waves cannot exist if the medium is barotropic.

Consider another example — the energy-momentum tensor of dissipative systems:*

$$T_{\alpha\beta} = (\rho + p)\,u_\alpha u_\beta + p g_{\alpha\beta} + \tau_{\alpha\beta}. \qquad (12.57)$$

In the frame of reference corresponding to the notation of (12.57) viscosity does not develop in view of the third condition of (12.44),

---

* The following considerations are valid assuming that the dissipative processes (viscosity and thermal conduction) are not too strong /210/.

and since the frame of reference is co-moving with the mass there is no flux of heat. In this frame of reference, therefore, $T_{\alpha\beta}$ for a dissipative medium reduces to the $T_{\alpha\beta}$ for an ideal fluid discussed above.

The third example is that of the energy-momentum tensor of the electromagnetic field (2.30). Let

$$^{\bullet}F^{\alpha\beta} = \frac{1}{2}\eta^{\alpha\beta\mu\nu}F_{\mu\nu}$$

be the tensor dual to the Maxwell tensor. We set

$$\frac{F^{\cdot i}_{0\cdot}}{\sqrt{g_{00}}} \equiv d^i, \qquad \frac{^{*}F^{\cdot i}_{0\cdot}}{\sqrt{g_{00}}} \equiv h^i, \tag{12.58}$$

where d^i and h^i are the chronometrically invariant stress vectors of the electric and magnetic fields, respectively. One can show /211/ that these vectors are related to the chronometrically invariant representatives of the energy-momentum tensor of the electromagnetic field by the following relations:

$$\rho = \frac{1}{2}(b^2 + d^2), \quad h^2 = b_{mn}h^m h^n, \quad d^2 = b_{mn}d^m d^n, \tag{12.59}$$

$$J^i = \eta^{imn}d_m h_n, \tag{12.60}$$

$$U^{ij} = \rho b^{ij} - (h^i h^j + d^i d^j). \tag{12.61}$$

In order for the electromagnetic field $F_{\mu\nu}$ to be isotropic, i.e., in order for it to satisfy the relations

$$F_{\mu\nu}F^{\mu\nu} = 0, \quad F_{\mu\nu}{}^{*}F^{\mu\nu} = 0,$$

or, in chronometrically invariant form,

$$b = d, \quad b^m d_m = 0,$$

it is necessary and sufficient that the condition

$$J = \rho \quad (J^2 = b^{ik}J_i J_k) \tag{12.62}$$

be satisfied /211/. It follows from (12.62) that a frame of reference co-moving with the "mass," in which $J^i = 0$, cannot be realized in an isotropic electromagnetic field; from now on, therefore, we will consider the electromagnetic field to be anisotropic.

The tensor X^{ik} for the electromagnetic field becomes

$$X^{ik} = (K^{ik} + \Lambda b^{ik}) + \lambda U^{ik}, \qquad (12.63)$$

whence it follows that

$$*\partial X^{ik} = -\lambda * \partial (h^i h^k + d^i d^k). \qquad (12.64)$$

Let us determine for which anisotropic electromagnetic fields the tensor X^{ik} is stationary. In chronometrically invariant form the Maxwell equations are given by

$$\varepsilon^{imn} (*\nabla_m - F_m) (h_n \sqrt{b}) = *\partial (d^i \sqrt{b}),$$
$$\varepsilon^{imn} (*\nabla_m - F_m) (d_n \sqrt{b}) = -*\partial (h^i \sqrt{b}),$$
$$*\nabla_m d^m = 2h^m \Omega_m, \qquad (12.65)$$
$$*\nabla_m h^m = 2d^m \Omega_m.$$

From the condition that $J^i = 0$ follows the collinearity of the vectors h_i and d_i:

$$d^i = \chi h^i. \qquad (12.66)$$

Setting $*\partial d^i = *\partial h^i = 0$ and taking (12.66) into account, we obtain, from equations (12.65),

$$*\partial_m \chi h_n = *\partial_n \chi h_m; \qquad (12.67)$$

then

$$h_n = \sigma(x^i) *\partial_n \chi, \qquad d_n = \chi(x^i) \sigma(x^j) *\partial_n \chi. \qquad (12.68)$$

But every vector l_i proportional to the gradient satisfies an equation of the form

$$l_{[i} *\nabla_j l_{k]} = 0. \qquad (12.69)$$

Thus in an anisotropic electromagnetic field gravitational-inertial waves X^{ik} are not present if the chronometrically invariant stress vectors of the electric and magnetic fields satisfy condition (12.69).

Lastly, let us consider the case where the third condition of (12.39) is not satisfied, i.e., where the frame of reference falls freely and does not rotate but undergoes deformation; such a system is termed semigeodesic (synchronous):

$$F^i = 0, \quad A_{ik} = 0, \quad D_{ih} \neq 0. \tag{12.70}$$

According to (12.15) — (12.17), in this frame of reference the three-dimensional tensors (12.13) become

$$X^{ij} = -DD^{ij} + D_k^i D^{jk} + (K^{ij} + \Lambda b^{ij}) +$$
$$+ \frac{\lambda}{2}(\rho b^{ij} + 2U^{ij} - Ub^{ij}), \tag{12.71}$$

$$Y^{ijk} = {}^*\nabla^j D^{ik} - {}^*\nabla^i D^{jk}, \tag{12.72}$$

$$Z^{iklj} = D^{ik}D^{lj} - D^{il}D^{kj} - K^{iklj} \tag{12.73}$$

and are generally nonstationary.

Let us turn now to case (c), in which two of the conditions (12.39) are not met. Let the frame of reference accelerate and rotate without becoming deformed:

$$F^i \neq 0, \quad A_{ik} \neq 0, \quad D_{ih} = 0. \tag{12.74}$$

The tensors (12.13) then become

$$X^{ij} = 3A_{\cdot j}^{i\cdot}A^{kj} + (K^{ij} + \Lambda b^{ij}) + \frac{\lambda}{2}(\rho b^{ij} + 2U^{ij} - Ub^{ij}), \tag{12.75}$$

$$Y^{ijk} = {}^*\nabla^j A^{ik} - {}^*\nabla^i A^{jk} + 2A^{ji}F^k, \tag{12.76}$$

$$Z^{iklj} = A^{ik}A^{lj} - A^{il}A^{kj} + 2A^{ij}A^{kl} - K^{iklj}. \tag{12.77}$$

Making use of the identity

$$ {}^*\partial A_{ik} + {}^*\partial_{[i}F_{k]} = 0 \tag{12.78}$$

and recalling that in an undeformed frame of reference ${}^*\partial A_{ih} = {}^*\partial A^{ik}$, we conclude, from (12.75), that the nonstationarity of X^{ik} is due to the rotational character of the field F^i and to the nonstationarity of the chronometrically invariant representatives of the energy-momentum tensor. Similarly, from (12.76) and (12.77) it is clear that the nonstationarity of Y^{ijk} is due to the rotational character and nonstationarity of the field F^i, and that the nonstationarity of Z^{iklj} is due entirely to the rotational character of the field F^i. Thus for the case of rotational fields (${}^*\nabla_{[k}F_{i]} \neq 0$) a frame of reference of the type (12.74) does not preclude the existence of gravitational-inertial waves of all three chronometrically invariant representatives of the Riemann tensor.

On the other hand, if the field F^i is irrotational, ${}^*\nabla_{[k}F_{i]} = 0$, then it follows from (12.76) that Z^{iklj} is stationary. The tensor Y^{ijk} is generally nonstationary in this case, since

$$^{\bullet}\partial Y^{ijk} = 2A^{ji\,\bullet}\partial F^k \neq 0. \tag{12.79}$$

The tensor X^{ik} is nonstationary only for $T_{\alpha\beta} \neq 0$. In the latter case the equations for the conservation laws in the frame of reference (12.74) lead to the conditions $J^i \neq 0$, $^{\bullet}\partial\rho \neq 0$ — unlike case (12.39).

The condition that $J^i \neq 0$ means that the given frame of reference can exist not only in an anisotropic, but also in an isotropic electromagnetic field . Let it be co-moving with the medium. Then $U^{ik} = pb^{ik}$ in formula (12.50) and

$$^{\bullet}\partial X^{ij} = \frac{\lambda}{2}\,(^{\bullet}\partial\rho - {}^{\bullet}\partial p)\,b^{ij}. \tag{12.80}$$

In this case the function X^{ij} will be nonstationary in a baroclinic as well as in a barotropic medium, unlike the third case considered. The special case where the barotropic medium is characterized by the equation of state $p = \rho$ (medium of superhigh density, e. g., near a singularity) constitutes an exception; here $^{\bullet}\partial X^{ij}$ vanishes. Thus a frame of reference characterized by acceleration and nonstationary rotation does not preclude the existence of gravitational-inertial waves X^{ij}, Y^{ijk}, Z^{iklj}. A frame of reference characterized by acceleration and stationary rotation does not admit of the existence of waves X^{ij} (in vacuum or in a medium described by the equation $p = \rho$), nor does it admit of the existence of waves Z^{iklj}.

For a frame of reference satisfying the demands (12.44) we find that in the case under consideration the functions X^{ij}, Y^{ijk}, Z^{iklj} have precisely the same form (12.71) $-$ (12.73) as in a semigeodesic frame of reference and are, as a rule, nonstationary.

In the case where

$$F_i = 0, \quad A_{ik} \neq 0, \quad D_{ik} \neq 0,$$

the functions X^{ij}, Y^{ijk}, Z^{iklj} are given by

$$X^{ik} = -3A^i_{\cdot j}A^{kj} - DD^{ik} - D^i_j D^{kj} + (K^{ik} + \Lambda b^{ik}) + {} \\ + \frac{\lambda}{2}\,(\rho b^{ik} + 2U^{ik} - Ub^{ik}), \tag{12.81}$$

$$Y^{ijk} = {}^{\bullet}\nabla^j(D^{ik} + A^{ik}) - {}^{\bullet}\nabla^i(D^{jk} + A^{jk}), \tag{12.82}$$

$$Z^{iklj} = D^{ik}D^{lj} - D^{il}D^{kj} - K^{iklj} + A^{ik}A^{lj} - A^{il}A^{kj} + 2A^{ij}A^{kl}. \tag{12.83}$$

Since $F_i = 0$, it follows from the relation

$$^{\bullet}\partial A_{ik} = -\frac{1}{2}\,(D^{im}b^{kn} + b^{im}D^{kn})\,A_{mn} \tag{12.84}$$

that the nonstationarity of the "wave functions" is due entirely
to the deformation of the frame of reference. Unlike A^{ik}, the tensor
A_{ik} is stationary in this case.

Lastly, looking at the case where none of the three characteristics of the frame of reference vanishes,

$$F_i \neq 0, \ A_{ik} \neq 0, \ D_{ik} \neq 0,$$

we see that all three "wave functions" (12.15) — (12.17) are generally
speaking nonstationary.

We have been investigating the conditions sufficient for the
absence of gravitational-inertial waves characterizable by chronometrically invariant "representatives" of the Riemann tensor, i.e.,
homogeneity and stationarity of the quantities (12.13). We note
that the homogeneity of all of these simultaneously is caused by
the homogeneity of space.

Besides the waves X^{ij}, Y^{ijk} and Z^{iklj} studied here, it is also interesting to analyze gravitational-inertial waves for which it is the
chronometrically invariant characteristics of the frame of reference
itself that serve as wave functions: waves of deformation D_{ik},
waves of rotation A_{ik}, waves of gravitational-inertial force F_i,
and waves of curvature K_{iklj}. The results of this analysis are as
follows /208/:

Waves of rotation A_{ik} are present for $F_i = 0$ and for any
D_{ik} and absent for $F_i \neq 0$ if $D_{ik} \neq 0$ or (for $D_{ik} = 0$) $^*\nabla_{[k}F_{i]} \neq 0$
(rotational gravitational-inertial field).

Waves of acceleration (force) F_i are generally
present (i.e., the field F_i is not stationary) for any A_{ik} and D_{ik}.

Waves of deformation D_{ik} are present only if $^*\nabla_j D_{ik} \neq 0$
(inhomogeneity of the deformation) and for $^*\partial^*\partial b_{ik} \neq 0$, irrespective
of the properties of A_{ik} and F_i.

Waves of curvature K_{ijkl} are present in any deformed
frame of reference ($D_{ik} \neq 0$)

This exhausts the list of gravitational-inertial waves in arbitrary frames of reference. Further research might profitably
concern the effect of gravitational-inertial waves on concrete
physical systems. In particular, research on the effect of
gravitational-inertial waves on systems of test bodies, as mentioned by a number of authors /95, 212 — 214/, could bring to light
possible ways of detecting gravitational waves in the laboratory.
The chronometrically invariant approach could play an important
role here as a means of describing the observables — physical
quantities, measured by laboratory means. Accordingly it will be
useful to discuss the problem of the experimental detection of
gravitational waves.

Chapter 13

THE PROBLEM OF GRAVITATIONAL WAVES
AND PHYSICAL EXPERIMENT

1. Geodesic deviation of test particles

The expression of the field functions in the language of observable quantities accessible to physical measurement is bound to be
important in any attempt to compare the results of the theory of
gravitational radiation with the experimental data. Such
observables have already been considered in Chapter 11, namely
the invariant geometric objects characterizing the Riemann tensor
as a field function within the framework of a tetrad formalism.
In another variant, the chronometrically invariant approach of
Chapter 12, we introduced the chronometrically invariant "components" of the Riemann tensor. We will now consider the problem
of the physical basis for the experimental detection of gravitational
radiation.

The most convenient way of observing the quantities which
characterize gravitational waves is to record the motion of test
particles. Let there be given a set of test particles moving along
geodesic lines $x^\alpha(s)$, where s is the arc length along the geodesic.
Let $x^\alpha(s, v)$ be a one-parameter family of such curves, a change in
the parameter v corresponding to passage from one geodesic to
another. We introduce the two vectors

$$u^\alpha(s, v) = \frac{\partial x^\alpha}{\partial s}, \qquad \eta^\alpha(s, v) = \left(\frac{\partial x^\alpha}{\partial v}\right) dv,$$

of which the first is the tangent to the geodesic and the second is the
infinitesimal displacement for one particle relative to another,
which is orthogonal to the tangent. Let $\frac{D}{ds}$ be the covariant differential of displacement along the geodesic, divided by the element ds.

The quantity

$$\frac{D^2\eta^\alpha}{ds^2}$$

is called the g e o d e s i c d e v i a t i o n and is interpreted physically
as the measure of the relative acceleration of two infinitely close
particles moving along adjacent geodesics. The role of this
quantity in the theory of gravitation is obvious from the well-known
e q u a t i o n o f g e o d e s i c d e v i a t i o n:

$$\frac{D^2\eta^\alpha}{ds^2} + R^\alpha_{\beta\gamma\delta}u^\beta u^\delta \eta^\gamma = 0 \qquad (13.1)$$

(see, for instance, /60, 172/).

Equation (13.1) shows that the relative acceleration of two near-
by particles moving without being influenced by external (nongravitational) forces is completely determined by the physical components
of the curvature tensor. Consequently if we perturb the components
of the Riemann tensor we modify the relative acceleration of the two
particles. Conversely, by observing the relative acceleration of
the particles we can measure the perturbations of the Riemann
tensor due to incoming gravitational radiation.

Let us suppose that the test particles are connected by a spring.
The gravitational waves can then be recorded from the oscillations
of the spring. The characteristic frequency of the system may coincide with one of the spectral harmonics of the gravitational waves;
it will then be possible to observe even the weakest gravitational
waves from the resonance.

Now let the vector η^α connect not two adjacent test particles
but rather two infinitely close points of a piezoelectric crystal.
The deformation produced in the crystal by a gravitational wave
incident upon it will induce an electric field inside it. The integral
of this field strength is a potential difference the measurement of
which gives the physical components of the curvature tensor induced
by the gravitational radiation /95/. If the integral of equation
(13.1) is treated as the Fourier transform of $R^\alpha_{\beta\gamma\delta}$ to η^α, then
measuring the geodesic deviation reduces to measuring a single
Fourier component (namely the resonance component) of the entire
spectrum of gravitational radiation. It is therefore of interest to
determine which frequencies are possible in the gravitational
radiation produced by various sources.

2. Possible sources of gravitational waves

In view of the difficulties encountered in generating gravitational waves in the laboratory it has proved advisable in experiments to look for gravitational waves of cosmic origin. The problem then arises of arriving at some sort of theoretical evaluation of the possible energy-mass loss due to gravitational emission for different sources. Estimates of this kind have been obtained for binary stars (Cooperstock /33/, Forward and Berman /215/), for collapsed stars (Zel'dovich-Novikov /34/), quasars (Cooperstock /32/), pulsars (Weber /31/, Shklovskii /216/), neutron stars describing nonspherical pulsations (Thorne /30/), and also the metagalaxy as a whole (Wheeler /36/). Let us briefly review the available results.

The first cosmic objects to be considered as a possible source of gravitational radiation were the binary stars /15/. The presence of a quadrupole moment in these systems provides grounds for believing that they lose energy, and thus the parameters of the stellar orbits are changing. These changes can be recorded by astronomical observations. Using the Landau-Lifshits energy pseudotensor to evaluate the energy of quadrupole gravitational radiation of a binary system in the linear approximation, one can show that the energy loss E by a system of two bodies of mass m_1 and m_2 travelling along circular orbits around a common center of inertia at a distance r one from the other, is given by

$$-\frac{dE}{dt} = \frac{32k}{5} \left(\frac{m_1 m_2}{m_1 + m_2} \right)^2 r^4 \omega^6,$$

where k is the Newtonian gravitational constant and ω is the circular frequency of revolution. From here the rate at which the bodies converge due to radiative energy loss is easily determined:

$$v = \dot{r} = -\frac{64k^3 m_1 m_2 (m_1 + m_2)}{5r^3}$$

Subsequently a formula was also obtained for the mean flux of energy emitted by a pair of bodies of mass m_1 and m_2 revolving along elliptical orbits of semimajor axis a and eccentricity ε:

$$\frac{1}{T} \int_0^T \frac{dE}{dt} \, dt = \frac{32}{5} \frac{k^4 m_1^2 m_2^2 (m_1 + m_2)}{a^5} \left(1 + \frac{73}{24} \varepsilon^2 + \frac{37}{96} \varepsilon^4 \right),$$

where T is the period of revolution. Expressions were also obtained /217/ for the energy loss of binary systems and their gravitational radiation spectrum in the case of hyperbolic motion, free fall and other types of motion.

As in the case of the problem of energy, research has been carried out into the problem of the loss of gravitational momentum by binary stars due to their gravitational emission (Cooperstock /33/). Within the limits of the linearized theory of gravitation it was shown that binary stars may lose gravitational momentum (defined via the energy-momentum pseudotensor) with an intensity of the same order as energy. A formula was obtained expressing explicitly the functional dependence of the total momentum flux on the difference in phase of the components of the binary system.

According to computations by Forward and Berman /215/, for binary neutron stars the theoretical maximum emission rate is $P \sim 6 \cdot 10^{48}$ watt, and it does not depend on the sum of the masses of the pair components.

Other than binary stars cosmic sources of gravitational radiation may consist of cosmic bodies (planets, asteroids and so forth) falling on collapsed stars. It is easy to compute (in the linear approximation) that if such a source lies at distance of ~ 500 Mpc from the Earth, then for, say, $m = m_\odot$ and $M = 10^2 \, m_\odot$ (M being the mass of the collapsed star and m the mass of the body falling on it in a straight line or along a spiral), near the Earth the flux of power emitted may amount to 0.7 erg/cm^2 sec /34/. However, it is not known how frequent such processes are in the metagalaxy. Basing themselves on rigorous solutions of the field equations, Forward and Berman /215/ propose to refine the estimate obtained by Zel'dovich and Novikov /34/ for the gravitational power emitted by collapsed stars from the linearized theory of gravitation.

Thorne concludes /30/ that neutron stars which pulsate in nonspherical manner can give rise to considerably stronger gravitational emission (compared with binary stars). In contradistinction with the approach usually employed to the problem of the gravitational radiation of binary stars, in which the stars are represented as material points and the calculations are carried out in the linear approximation, in Thorne's work use is made of concrete models of neutron stars, the calculations being carried out by an approximation method in which the Schwarzschild solution is the point of departure.

On the average the period of pulsation T of a neutron star lies within the range $10^{-4} - 10^{-3}$ sec. If we assume that the pulsation energy is entirely converted into the energy of gravitational radiation,

then given certain logical assumptions regarding oscillation amplitude, a neutron star may, according to Thorne, emit energy of the
order of 10^{51} erg in one period of pulsation. These estimates
agree as to order of magnitude with similar ones by Wheeler /238/,
although the latter are valid only in the linear approximation.

Thorne and his colleagues have carried out a general study of
the nonradial pulsations of stellar models in the Einstein theory
of gravitation /218 — 222/. We will briefly describe their method.
Let the unperturbed line element

$$(ds^2)_0 = e^\nu dt^2 - e^\lambda dr^2 - r^2 (d\theta^2 + \sin^2 \theta \, d\varphi^2) \qquad (13.2)$$

describe a spherically symmetric equilibrium configuration

$$\nu = \nu (r), \quad \lambda = \lambda (r).$$

The gravitational field of a perturbed configuration (a pulsating
and, generally, revolving star) will then be given by the line
element

$$ds^2 = (ds^2)_0 + h_{\alpha\beta} \, dx^\alpha \, dx^\beta,$$

where $h_{\alpha\beta}$ is the perturbation of the metric tensor relative to
the stationary metric (13.2). The displacement ξ of an element
of ideal fluid from the equilibrium position, deviations of
density and pressure from equilibrium values inside the fluid ($\delta\rho$
and δp, respectively) as well as perturbations $h_{\alpha\beta}$ of the metric,
are expanded in spherical harmonics /218/. The perturbed metric
is written as follows:

$$ds^2 = e^\nu (1 + H_0 Y^l_m) \, dt^2 + 2H_1 Y^l_m \, dt \, dr - e^\lambda (1 - H_0 Y^l_m) \, dr^2 -$$
$$- r^2 (1 - K Y^l_m)(d\theta^2 + \sin^2\theta \, d\varphi^2), \qquad (13.3)$$

where the functions $H_0(t, r), H_1(t, r), H_2(t, r)$ and K characterize
perturbations of the metric, and $Y^l_m (\theta, \varphi)$ is an ordinary spherical
harmonic:

$$Y^l_m (\theta, \varphi) = \left[\frac{2l + 1}{4\pi} \frac{(l - m)!}{(l + m)!} \right]^{1/2} P^m_l (\cos \theta) \, e^{im\phi}.$$

Inserting the metric (13.3) in Einstein's equations and retaining
only terms linear in the perturbations $h_{\alpha\beta}$, we can solve these
equations by numerical integration. Machine calculations for
specially selected models of neutron stars /221, 222/ have made it

possible to determine the frequency spectrum of their gravitational radiation, pulsation periods ($\sim 10^{-3}$ sec), pulse powers ($\sim 10^{52}$ erg per sec) and the decay times of perturbations due to emission (~ 1 sec).

Cooperstock /32/ investigated the transfer of energy by gravitational radiation from quasi-stellar sources (quasars). He uses the Fowler model /223/, according to which a quasar consists of a core formed by two collapsed stars and an outer quasi-stable shell; the transfer of energy by gravitational radiation from the rotating core to the shell leads to "polar explosion," giving rise to an intensive movement of stellar material in the direction of the axis of rotation of the core. If the shell describes radial oscillations, then the power of resonance gravitational radiation of the core calculated with the Landau-Lifshits pseudotensor will exhibit an angular dependence of the form $\sim \sin^2 \theta$ (the angle θ gives the direction of radiation relative to the core's axis of rotation). Thus radiation is absent in the direction of the rotational axis and reaches a maximum in the equatorial plane. In cases where the shell is also rotating, the power emitted will also depend on the coincidence or noncoincidence of the directions of rotation of the core and the shell.

Estimates have been made of the intensity of gravitational radiation of cosmological origin. Since gravitons are absorbed only very weakly by matter, once interstellar gravitational radiation had appeared (e. g., in the primordial "explosion" of the Universe) it might have persisted to the present day, its total intensity in the metagalaxy depending on the rate of expansion. According to Wheeler's calculations /224/, the present rate of expansion of the metagalaxy gives an energy density of gravitational radiation for the metagalaxy of $10^{-29} - 10^{-28}$ g/cm^3, i. e., a power flux of 10^3 erg/cm^2 sec, with a period of $T \sim 10^6$ years.

The intensity of the gravitational bremsstrahlung of the Sun due to chaotic thermal (nonrelativistic) atomic collisions — a quantity not previously investigated — has been computed by Carmeli /35/. His computation is based on application of the classical method of Fourier integrals to the Landau-Lifschits expression for the intensity of gravitational radiation in the weak-field approximation. Carmeli obtained a sensational result according to which the power of the Sun's gravitational bremsstrahlung is of the order of $P \sim 6 \cdot 10^{15}$ erg/sec, four orders higher than the power of gravitational radiation due to the total quadrupole moment of the planets of the solar system. Carmeli also obtained the frequency spectrum of gravitational bremsstrahlung of arbitrary systems of interacting particles.

In addition to gravitational bremsstrahlung, mention must also be made of the possibility of gravitational emission by the Sun due to nuclear explosions as well as to the thermal motions of atoms generating a relative quadrupole moment. However, it is very difficult to determine the scale of nuclear explosions on the Sun (Braginskii and Rudenko give a few estimates of their power /158/).

Today among the strongest sources of cosmic gravitational radiation are believed to be p u l s a r s , including one possible model, that of neutron stars pulsating with a period of $10^{-4} - 10^{-3}$ sec. If we assume that the energy of pulsation is entirely converted into energy of gravitational radiation, then — as we noted earlier — within a single pulsation period a neutron star may emit energy of the order of 10^{51} erg or about 0.1% of the rest mass of the star itself /30/.* This result was used by Weber /31/ to evaluate the order of magnitude of the Riemann tensor components

$$X^{ij} \sim R_{0 \cdot 0 \cdot}^{\cdot i \cdot j},$$

generated by the gravitational radiation of pulsars. It was found that for a pulsar mass of $M = 10^{33}$ g, the lower bound of values of $R_{0 \cdot 0 \cdot}^{\cdot i \cdot j}$ is of the order of

$$R_{0 \cdot 0 \cdot}^{\cdot i \cdot j} \geqslant 5 \cdot 10^{-42} \text{ cm}^{-2}.$$

3.   Devices for the laboratory detection of gravitational waves

The gravitational radiation field has been recorded experimentally with the aid of the quadrupole harmonic mass-detector, the first example of which was built in 1964 at the University of Maryland by Weber, Zipoy and Forward /212/. The sensitive element of the instrument is an aluminum cylinder weighing 1.5 tons, suspended in a cylindrical vacuum chamber on a metal filament. Where it touches the filament the cylinder is sheathed in a piezoelectric quartz envelope connected to a sensitive voltmeter in the radio receiver system. After certain improvements introduced by Sinsky /226/, the sensitivity of the mass detector

---

* For other pulsar models the power emitted may be considerably less. Thus for pulsar NP 0532 in the Crab Nebula, within the framework of the model of a rotating neutron star whose rotational axis is inclined to the axis of symmetry of its magnetic field, the gravitational power emitted was estimated to be of the order of $8 \times 10^{32} - 8 \times 10^{33}$ erg/sec /225/.

was such as to enable measurement of relative displacements of
the cylinder ends (e. g., expansions and contractions due to
incident gravitational radiation) of the order of 10^{-16} cm. An
experiment for detecting gravitational radiation using two groups
of n identical, closely placed parallel cylinders was subsequently suggested by Braginskii. If the oscillations in these groups
are excited in phase, the gravitational radiant power will then be
roughly four times greater than from a single group.

In a further refinement of his device, Weber developed a
system which works on the principle of coincidence of signals of
identical frequency from two detectors /227/. It consists of two
mass detectors with a relaxation time of 30 sec timed to the
frequency $\omega = 10^4$ rad/sec and placed at a distance of 2 km from
each other. During 1967 this system recorded coincidences
(accurate to $\Delta t = 0.20$ sec) of signals with a mean periodicity
of one per month. In Weber's opinion it is extremely unlikely
that the recorded coincidences were purely random. Weber
assumes that the signals he detected were due to cosmic
gravitational radiation. He demonstrated that to detect gravitational radiation from pulsars using this device for a measurement time
of the order of one month, it is sufficient to record effective displacements $\delta \sim 3 \cdot 10^{-10}$ cm. The level of modern experimental
technology may thus be high enough to allow detection of cosmic
gravitational radiation.

Increasing the separation of the detectors, one increases the
sensitivity of the device. Accordingly Weber later employed six
detectors /228/, one in the Argonne National Laboratory and the
rest in the laboratory of the University of Maryland. The distance
between these laboratories amounts to 1,000 km. The detectors
were adjusted to the expected gravitational radiation frequency of
collapsed supernovas in our Galaxy — 1,660 Hz. The signal coincidences recorded by this instrument during a period of several
months nearly preclude the possibility of attributing them to random
coincidences. Weber interprets these results as proof of the
existence of powerful gravitational radiation in the Galaxy.

Weber later performed a second series of experiments /229/
which confirmed his original results. A special feature of these
experiments was maximum insulation of the apparatus from
external influences of electromagnetic and seismic nature.

The possibility of the existence of gravitational radiation in the
Galaxy in the frequency band around 1,660 Hz impelled a number
of researchers to seek new sources of gravitational waves in the
Universe. According to calculations by Greenstein /230/, cosmic
gravitational radiation at 1,660 Hz may arise from close encounters

of stars in massive stellar clusters with a mean periodicity of once per week. Here the pulsed character of the radiation makes it likely that it is due to binary encounters of unstable relativistic objects — neutron or collapsed stars.

One would expect gravitational radiation to have an important influence on the evolution not just of individual stars or stellar clusters, but of the Galaxy as a whole. Thus the gravitational radiation flux of the Galaxy recorded by Weber does not preclude our attributing the observable expansion of the Galaxy to the loss of its mass ensuing from the emission of gravitational waves /231/. However, as many researches show /231 — 235/, this interpretation is far from indisputable, and leads to contradictions with other astrophysical observations. That the interpretation of Weber's experiments is not unique has been demonstrated in works by Braginskii, Zel'dovich and Rudenko /236, 237/.

Seismic methods which make it possible to use the Earth as detector may play an important role in the problem of the detection of gravitational waves. This possibility seems attractive in that the quadrupole moment of the Earth is many orders higher than laboratory detectors. The frequency of the Earth's eigenoscillations (of the order of 1 millihertz) makes it possible to record the resonant harmonics of gravitational radiation from pulsars. However, as Weber has shown /31/, this method is limited by the high noise temperature of the terrestrial core and thus would require measurement of effective displacements $\delta \sim 2 \cdot 10^{-17}$ cm, which lies at the very limit of possibility of modern measuring techniques.

A more effective approach may be to use individual seismically insulated inhomogeneities on the Earth's surface capable of absorbing gravitational radiation in the frequency band around 1 hz. In the linear approximation of Einstein's theory, the problem of the reaction of an elastic body to incident gravitational waves was investigated by Dyson /258, 259/. He found that the absorption of gravitational waves by an elastic body takes place exclusively due to inhomogeneities in its shear modulus, such absorption being absent in a homogeneous medium. According to estimates by Dyson, the intensity of seismic signals due to gravitational radiation from probably theoretical models of pulsars at 1 Hz frequency is five orders lower than the noise level. However, the possibility of seismic recording of gravitational radiation of pulsars cannot be regarded as definitively closed. In particular, De Sabbata /239/ has recently suggested using local inhomogeneities on the Moon's surface — "mascons" — to detect gravitational waves from pulsars at the same frequency (1 Hz; see also /240/).

Mironovskii /241/ suggested using a variant of the Weber mass detector to detect gravitational radiation from binary stars. The receiver is a friction-free torsion pendulum of period T_0. The formula expressing the gravitational power emitted by a system of two material points moving along circular orbits about a common center of gravity gives the following expression for the spectral density of gravitational radiation of binary stars:

$$\rho\,(T) = 2Nf\,(2T)\,\varphi\,(T).$$

Here N is the number of stars of a given type in the Galaxy and $T = 2\pi/\omega$ is the period of the gravitational wave ($T = \tau/2$, where τ is the period of revolution of the star's components about the common center of gravity; due to the equivalence of the components, the frequency of the gravitational radiation is doubled).

In recording the emission of binary stars (fairly widespread in the Galaxy), the most suitable stars belong to the *WUM* class, totalling $N \sim 10^8$ in the Galaxy. For stars in this class the function $\rho\,(T)$ has a sharp maximum for $T = 0^d.15$ (d standing for "day"). The gravitational radiation spectrum corresponds to periods of revolution of $0.1 - 0.5$.

The energy emitted by close pairs of binary stars of class *WUM* can be evaluated using the Landau-Lifshits pseudotensor. Knowing the function $\rho\,(T)$ and integrating numerically over periods with $N = 10^8$, Mironovskii obtained 10^{38} erg/sec for the total gravitational power emitted by this type in the Galaxy, which is only five orders less than the corresponding electromagnetic radiation. Within the Solar System the flux should then be about 10^{-7} erg/sec cm^2.

In order to explore the possibility of recording this radiation, Mironovskii studied the equation of motion of a torsion pendulum. If a pendulum in equilibrium is oriented along the x-axis of an orthogonal geodesic coordinate system, then the equation of geo-desic deviation for motion in the oscillation plane xy of a point of the pendulum lying at the distance l from the rotational axis is given by

$$\ddot{y} + \omega_0^2 y = -c^2 l \sum_i R_{2010}\,(\boldsymbol{r}_i\,\boldsymbol{n}_i)\sin\,(2\Omega_i t + \varphi_i). \qquad (13.4)$$

Here R_{2010} is the Riemann tensor component corresponding to the radiation field of the i-th star, Ω_i is its angular velocity of revolution, and $\boldsymbol{r}_i$ and $\boldsymbol{n}_i$ are vectors characterizing the position of the star and the orientation of its orbit in space, respectively.

Solving equation (13.4) and averaging over the distribution of the stars in space, orientations of the orbits and receiving device and distributions of phases and frequencies, we obtain /241/:

$$(\bar{y}^2)^{1/2} \approx 10^{-19} l T_0^{-1/2} \sqrt{f(2T_0)t} \ [\text{cm}],$$ (13.5)

where $f(\tau)$ is the probability density for distribution of WUM stars over periods of revolution, T_0 is the period of eigenoscillations of the pendulum and t is the observation time.

Formula (13.5) gives the mean deviation $\bar{y}$ of the pendulum from the x-axis and is independent of the choice of energy pseudotensor. Mironovskii gives the following estimate for two WUM stars near us:

$$(\bar{y}^2)^{1/2} = 6 \cdot 10^{-16} \text{ cm}.$$

As we know from the works of Weber and Braginskii, it is now possible in practice to measure periodic mechanical displacements up to an order to 10^{-16} cm. One may therefore hope to see Mironovskii's suggestion realized experimentally.

Besides the principle of deviation of geodesics for test particles, used in experiments with the quadrupole mass detector, researchers have recently turned to another principle by means of which the interaction of the electromagnetic and gravitational fields can be exploited for the experimental detection of gravitational waves.

As we remarked in previous chapters, there exist a number of rigorous solutions of the gravitational field equations describing the propagation of gravitational and electromagnetic waves along the same trajectories. The existence of such gravitational fields follows from the general solution of the Cauchy problem for Einstein's equations, according to which the characteristic hypersurfaces of the equations of gravitation and electromagnetism (wave-front surfaces), and their bicharacteristics (trajectories of wave propagation) as well, coincide. As a result a field of electromagnetic radiation can induce gravitational waves. It is natural to expect that the converse effect — stimulation of dynamic electromagnetic fields by gravitational waves — is also present (e.g., as a result of the action of gravitational radiation on the field of a system of charged bodies).

This effect was studied by Heintzman /242/, who examined the motion of test particles in a gravitational plane wave in the weak-field approximation. As the velocity of an uncharged test particle is not altered by interaction with a passing gravitational wave, it follows that a system of electrically neutral test particles cannot absorb gravitational radiant energy. Hence the idea suggests itself of using a system of charged particles and recording the gravitational radiation according to the variations of the electromagnetic energy of the detector system. Heintzman

computed the amount of gravitational wave energy absorbed not only
for the case of weak fields in the linear approximation, but also for
two exact solutions of the field equations: the metrics of Einstein-
Rosen cylindrical waves and Bondi plane waves. He found that in
all three cases the electromagnetic energy of the system of
charged test particles is altered by the absorption of energy of
gravitational waves: in the first and third case (plane waves in the
linear approximation and Bondi plane waves) the amounts of
absorbed energy are finite, while in the second case (Einstein-Rosen
cylindrical waves) the detector can receive an unlimited amount of
gravitational wave energy. These results are sufficient grounds
for using a system of charged test particles as laboratory detector
of gravitational waves.

A slightly different method of detection was considered by
Vodyanitskii and Dimanshtein /465/. They obtained a solution
of the Einstein-Maxwell system of equations for the weak field in
the form of a plane monochromatic wave. The following formula
was put forward for the power of the gravitational signal (received
by an electrical antenna with amplifier):

$$P \approx \frac{1}{4\pi} S \frac{(E_{(0)2})^2 (\Omega + \omega)^2 (h_{(0)}^{22})^2}{16\omega^2} ;$$

here S is the effective surface of the antenna, Ω and ω are the
frequencies of the gravitational and electromagnetic waves,
respectively, propagating in opposite directions along the Ox axis,
and $E_{(0)2}$ and $h_{(0)}^{22}$ are the amplitudes of the corresponding electromagnetic and gravitational field components.

A method for the experimental detection of gravitational waves
using dynamical electromagnetic fields has also been considered.
It is based on observation of the fluctuations produced by gravitational waves in electromagnetic radiation.

A theory of perturbations (fluctuations) of the electromagnetic
field due to the gravitational field was constructed in the linear
approximation by Cooperstock /243/. He solved the equations for
perturbations of the electromagnetic and gravitational fields in the
case where a plane-polarized monochromatic electromagnetic
wave of high frequency propagates between two ideally conducting
parallel walls, interacting with a gravitational plane wave of low
frequency. The fluctuations of the field were computed for two
mutual orientations of the direction of wave propagation: where the
directions coincided ("longitudinal orientation"), and where they
were mutually orthogonal ("transverse orientation"). Since it may
be that macroscopic systems generate low-frequency gravitational

radiation, Cooperstock suggested that this radiation might be detected by observing fluctuations in the intensity of electromagnetic radiation of celestial bodies.

This problem was subjected to detailed investigation by Winterberg /244/. He demonstrated that in the linear approximation the problem of the intensity fluctuations of a light signal in a medium with statistically distributed gravitational waves is equivalent to the problem of intensity fluctuations of a light signal in a medium with statistical distribution of inhomogeneities. On the average this effect is described by the formula

$$\left(\frac{\Delta I}{I_0}\right)^2 = \frac{32\sqrt{\pi}}{3}\left(\frac{\Delta n}{n_0}\right)^2\left(\frac{x}{l}\right)^3, \tag{13.6}$$

where I_0 is the signal intensity averaged over time, ΔI the deviation from the mean value I_0, n_0 the mean value of the refractive index of the medium, Δn the deviation from n_0, x the distance between the source and the observer, and l the characteristic dimension of inhomogeneities in density. Defining the effective value $n(\theta, \varphi)$ of the refractive index of otherwise empty space filled with gravitational waves by means of the relation

$$dl/dt = 1/n(\theta, \varphi),$$

one can obtain the effective Δn and n_0 for the case of plane waves in a linear approximation. Then averaging with use of formula (13.6) gives us the expression

$$\frac{\Delta I}{I_0} = 1.6|h|\left(\frac{x}{l}\right)^{3/2}. \tag{13.7}$$

Here l is the characteristic length of the gravitational wave, $h = \det \|h_{\mu\nu}\|$, $h_{\mu\nu}$ being a small correction to the pseudo-Euclidean metric.

The values of $|h|$ and l were estimated for three types of sources: binary stars, quasars and the entire Universe. (In the latter case, the author had in mind the relict gravitational radiation, under the assumption that at an early stage in the evolution of the Universe it was in thermodynamic equilibrium with the relict electromagnetic radiation at a temperature of 3°K). For binary stars the coefficient $k = 1.6 |h| l^{-3/2}$ in formula (13.7) is found to be $k = 5.9 \cdot 10^{-40}$, which for a distance $x = 10^{23}$ cm yields fluctuations of radiation intensity of the order of $5.9 \cdot 10^{-5}$, i.e., values which can be recorded by sensitive scintillation counters outside the Earth's atmosphere.   The possible gravitational emission of quasars was estimated to be $k \approx 2.3 \cdot 10^{-40}$, which for $x = 10^{27}$ cm yields values easily measured even under terrestrial conditions: $\Delta I/I_0 \approx 7.3$.   Lastly, for gravitational waves of cosmological origin fluctuations amount to ~ 0.5 for a star 10^2 light years away.   However, the latter value is practically impossible to observe since in observations of this kind the stellar diameter would have to exceed the length of the gravitational wave.

Nontheless from the standpoint of principle Winterberg's method has not been given sufficient theoretical grounding.   As Zipoy and Bertotti point out /245/, extrapolation of the formula (13.6) given by Scheffler /246/ for electromagnetism to the case of gravitational fluctuations is not admissible in the case of a strong gravitational field.   Stellar scintillation estimates may therefore refer to purely coordinate effects, i.e., nonphysical and thus unobservable effects.

We also note that the methods described above for direct measurement of gravitational radiation intensity with quadrupole mass detectors entirely disregard the possible quantum effects of the interaction of gravitational waves with the crystal detector.   These effects have been investigated by some authors /247 — 254/.   Their researches tend to confirm that it is possible to detect and generate gravitational waves by the techniques of quantum electronics.

The plans for a resonant receiver of gravitational waves using the interaction of gravitational waves with the atomic structure of matter have been worked out in principle by Lavrent'ev /252/, and also by Kopvillem and Nagibarov /249, 250/.   Energy is first stored in the receiver of directed gravitational radiation by optical stimulation, and the gravitational ray serves to create optimum conditions for release of this energy in a definite direction in the form of a coherent electromagnetic ray.

Kopvillem and Nagibarov /248, 255, 256/ also investigated the possibility of generating directed gravitational radiation in the laboratory by exciting coherent periodic oscillations of mass quadrupoles in the electron shell of atoms with the help of lasers. The general idea of these works consists of creating a special, so-called "superemissive" state of matter, the stimulation of which by sequences of brief, powerful pulses might be used to generate gravitational rays.   A superemissive state of matter can be induced by coherent fluxes not only of photons but also of other elementary particles (electrons, neutrons, protons and so forth).

4. Relationship between the theoretical and experimental aspects of the problem of gravitational waves

The foregoing methods for experimental detection of gravitational waves, as we saw, are not free of flaws as far as theoretical grounding is concerned. Thus in Weber's calculations the equation of geodesic deviation is not related to physical observables, while the very concept of observables in the general theory of relativity is still far from unambiguous. Hence the necessity for choosing a certain preferred frame of reference, and this choice is never unique.

Others among the methods considered are based on the linearized theory of gravitation, whose flaws we discussed earlier; on this argument rests, in particular, the critique of Winterberg's method given by Zipoy and Bertotti /245/.

Let us note a few basic traits of the relationship between the theory of gravitational waves and experimental physics.

The design of any experiment is necessarily based on definite premises without which interpretation of the experimental data would be impossible. Thus the process of measurement (comparing length with a standard) which underlies experiments is based on a definite specification of a method for identifying objects of one type. From this point of view the principle of relativity which underlies the physical theory precedes experiment (see /257/). The theoretical formulation of the concept of gravitational waves may therefore be regarded as the basic premise for the interpretation of experimental results.

In this respect a significant drawback of the conception of gravitational waves considered earlier is their internal incompleteness, resulting in multiplicity and inconsistency of the criteria. The latter is evidence that the level of the theoretical concepts themselves is not high enough in this field.

Thus with regard to the best known of these criteria — the Lichnerowicz criterion — the very formulation contains arbitrary elements and inconsistencies with the initial premises. According to the basic premise, a gravitational wave is characterized by discontinuities in derivatives of the type $g_{ij,00}$ on the characteristic hypersurface in that coordinate system in which this hypersurface is expressed by equation (2.15). Yet one can point to gravitational fields satisfying the Lichnerowicz criterion for which the metric components $g_{\alpha\beta}$ are smooth functions of the coordinates, their derivatives nowhere exhibiting Hadamard discontinuities. An example is the Petrov metric

$$ds^2 = 2dx^0dx^1 - \mathrm{sh}^2 x^0 \, dx^{2^2} - \sin^2 x^0 \, dx^{3^2},$$

for which

$$\partial_\alpha \varphi = \delta_1^\beta g_{\alpha\beta} = g_{1\alpha},$$

i. e., $\varphi = x^0 + \text{const}$. It is obvious that on the "wave front" surface ($x^0 = \text{const}$) the curvature tensor components

$$R_{0202} = -\operatorname{sh}^2 x^0, \qquad R_{0303} = -\sin^2 x^0$$

cannot have Hadamard discontinuities.

Other covariant criteria for gravitational waves based on the concept of Hadamard discontinuity in the Riemann tensor components — discussed in previous chapters — suffer from the same flaw.

In conclusion we can state that, from the theoretical as well as from the experimental point of view, the problem of gravitational waves is still very far from solved. But it remains one of the most pressing and fundamentally important problems not just of gravitation theory, but of modern physics as a whole, a problem to which researchers are devoting ever more attention. It is therefore reasonable to expect that it will find an elegant solution and assume its proper place in the rigorous picture of Einstein's theory of gravitation.

Appendix I

We will prove certain theorems used in the text. Let $R_{\alpha\beta\gamma\delta}$ be the Riemann tensor of a space V_4, antisymmetric in each of the index pairs $\alpha\beta$ and $\gamma\delta$. We introduce the two tensors conjugate to it:

$$*R_{\alpha\beta\gamma\delta} = \frac{1}{2}\,\eta_{\alpha\beta\rho\sigma}\,R^{\rho\sigma\cdot\cdot}_{\cdot\cdot\gamma\delta}, \quad R^{*}_{\alpha\beta\gamma\delta} = \frac{1}{2}\,\eta_{\gamma\delta\rho\sigma}\,R^{\rho\sigma\cdot\cdot}_{\cdot\cdot\alpha\beta}. \tag{I.1}$$

It follows in an obvious manner from the definition (I.1) that

$$*R_{\alpha\beta\gamma\delta} = R^{*}_{\gamma\delta\alpha\beta}. \tag{I.2}$$

Theorem 1. The following relations hold in Einstein spaces:

$$*R_{\alpha\beta\gamma\delta} = *R_{\gamma\delta\alpha\beta}. \tag{I.3}$$

Proof. Due to (I.2) condition (I.3) is equivalent to

$$*R_{\alpha\beta\gamma\delta} = R^{*}_{\alpha\beta\gamma\delta}. \tag{I.4}$$

Thus to prove the theorem it is sufficient to prove (I.4). In order to do so we will make use of the relations (/172/)

$$\eta^{\sigma\mu\nu\lambda}\,\eta_{\sigma\alpha\beta\gamma} = -\,\delta^{\mu\nu\lambda}_{\alpha\beta\gamma}, \tag{I.5}$$

$$\eta^{\sigma\rho\mu\nu}\,\eta_{\sigma\rho\alpha\beta} = -\,2\delta^{\mu\nu}_{\alpha\beta}, \tag{I.6}$$

$$\eta^{\sigma\rho\epsilon\mu}\,\eta_{\sigma\rho\epsilon\alpha} = -\,6\delta^{\mu}_{\alpha}, \tag{I.7}$$

where the tensor $\delta^{\mu\nu\alpha\cdots}_{\lambda\beta\gamma\cdots}$ is a generalized Kronecker symbol obeying the following rules: if $\mu,\ \nu,\ \alpha,\ldots$ are all different and $\lambda,\ \beta,\ \gamma,\ldots$ are obtained from them by a certain permutation, then it is equal to ± 1 depending on whether the permutation $\delta^{\mu\nu\alpha\cdots}_{\lambda\beta\gamma\cdots}$ is even or odd; in the remaining cases it is zero. Multiplying both sides of

$$*R_{\rho\sigma\nu\lambda} = \frac{1}{2}\,\eta_{\rho\sigma\alpha\beta}\,R^{\alpha\beta\cdot\cdot}_{\cdot\cdot\nu\lambda}$$

by $-\dfrac{1}{2}\,\eta^{\mu\epsilon\rho\sigma}$, we obtain, owing to relations (I.6)

$$-\frac{1}{2}\,\eta^{\mu\epsilon\rho\sigma}{}^{*}R_{\rho\sigma\nu\lambda} = \frac{1}{2}\,\delta^{\mu\epsilon}_{\alpha\beta}R^{\alpha\beta\cdot\cdot}_{\cdot\cdot\nu\lambda} = R^{\mu\epsilon\cdot\cdot}_{\cdot\cdot\nu\lambda}.$$

Contracting in the indices ϵ and ν, we obtain from this

$$R^{\mu}_{\lambda} = -\frac{1}{2}\,\eta^{\mu\nu\rho\sigma}{}^{*}R_{\rho\sigma\nu\lambda}. \tag{I.8}$$

Multiplying (I.8) by $\eta_{\mu\alpha\beta\gamma}$, replacing λ by δ and using (I.5), we have

$$\eta_{\mu\alpha\beta\gamma}R^{\mu}_{\delta} = \frac{1}{2}\,\delta^{\nu\rho\sigma}_{\alpha\beta\gamma}{}^{*}R_{\rho\sigma\nu\delta} =$$

$$= \frac{1}{2}\,({}^{*}R_{\alpha\beta\gamma\delta} + {}^{*}R_{\beta\gamma\alpha\delta} + {}^{*}R_{\gamma\alpha\beta\delta} - {}^{*}R_{\beta\alpha\gamma\delta} - {}^{*}R_{\alpha\gamma\beta\delta} - {}^{*}R_{\gamma\beta\alpha\delta}) = 3{}^{*}R_{[\alpha\beta\gamma]\delta}.$$

Consequently, in the Einstein spaces (3.7)

$$3{}^{*}R_{[\alpha\beta\gamma]\delta} = \varkappa\eta_{\mu\alpha\beta\gamma}\delta^{\mu}_{\delta} = \varkappa\eta_{\delta\alpha\beta\gamma}. \tag{I.9}$$

Rewriting (I.9) as

$$3{}^{*}R_{[\beta\alpha\delta]\gamma} = \varkappa\eta_{\delta\alpha\beta\gamma}$$

and adding, we obtain

$$2{}^{*}R_{\alpha\beta\gamma\delta} = {}^{*}R_{\alpha\gamma\beta\delta} + {}^{*}R_{\beta\delta\alpha\gamma} + {}^{*}R_{\alpha\delta\gamma\beta} + {}^{*}R_{\gamma\beta\alpha\delta} + 2\varkappa\eta_{\delta\alpha\beta\gamma}. \tag{I.10}$$

We interchange the indices α and γ, as well as β and δ, in (I.10):

$$2{}^{*}R_{\gamma\delta\alpha\beta} = {}^{*}R_{\gamma\alpha\delta\beta} + {}^{*}R_{\delta\beta\gamma\alpha} + {}^{*}R_{\gamma\beta\alpha\delta} + {}^{*}R_{\alpha\delta\gamma\beta} + 2\varkappa\eta_{\delta\alpha\beta\gamma}. \tag{I.11}$$

Comparing (I.10) and (I.11), we see that relations (1.4) hold, which proves the theorem.

In conformity with this theorem, it is customary to set the following in Einstein spaces:

$$^{*}R_{\alpha\beta\gamma\delta} = R^{*}_{\alpha\beta\gamma\delta} = \overset{*}{R}{}^{*}_{\alpha\beta\gamma\delta}. \tag{I.12}$$

Lemma. In spaces V_4 the equations

$$l^{\alpha}{}^{*}R_{\alpha\beta\gamma\delta} = 0 \tag{I.13}$$

are equivalent to equations

$$l_\lambda R_{\alpha\beta\gamma\delta} + l_\alpha R_{\beta\lambda\gamma\delta} + l_\beta R_{\lambda\alpha\gamma\delta} = 0. \tag{I.14}$$

P r o o f . Let there exist a vector l^α in V_4 satisfying equations (I.13). Multiplying equations (I.13) by $\eta_{\mu\alpha\beta\nu}$, we have, owing to relations (I.5),

$$\eta_{\mu\alpha\beta\gamma} {}^* R^{\mu\nu\cdots}_{\lambda\tau} l_\nu = \frac{1}{2} \eta_{\mu\alpha\beta\gamma} \eta^{\mu\nu\rho\sigma} R_{\rho\sigma\lambda\tau} \, l_\nu = -\frac{1}{2} \delta^{\nu\rho\sigma}_{\alpha\beta\gamma} l_\nu R_{\rho\sigma\lambda\tau} =$$
$$= -(l_\alpha R_{\beta\gamma\lambda\tau} + l_\beta R_{\gamma\alpha\lambda\tau} + l_\gamma R_{\alpha\beta\lambda\tau}) = 0, \tag{I.15}$$

i.e., l^α satisfies equations (I.14) as well.

Conversely, let there exist a vector l^α satisfying equations (I.14); we will show that it also satisfies equations (I.13). Performing the calculations of (I.15) in reverse order, we obtain relations equivalent to the initial condition:

$$\eta_{\mu\alpha\beta\gamma} {}^* R^{\mu\nu\cdots}_{\cdot\cdot\lambda\tau} l_\nu = 0.$$

Let us multiply these equations by $\eta^{\varepsilon\alpha\beta\gamma}$. Owing to the identities (I.7) we obtain the following result:

$$\delta^\varepsilon_\mu l_\nu {}^* R^{\mu\nu\cdots}_{\cdot\cdot\lambda\tau} = 0,$$

whence

$$l_\nu {}^* R^{\varepsilon\nu\cdots}_{\cdot\cdot\lambda\tau} = 0,$$

i.e., l^α satisfies condition (I.13), which proves the lemma.

Note that in the formulation of the lemma it is essential that l^α be contracted with one of the first two indices of $R_{\alpha\beta\gamma\delta}$, in view of the inequivalence of the pairs $\alpha\beta$ and $\gamma\delta$, which follows from definition (I.1). In the case of Einstein spaces, on the other hand, owing to Theorem 1 the index pairs are equivalent and the conditions $l^\alpha {}^* R_{\alpha\beta\gamma\delta} = 0$ and $l^\alpha {}^* R_{\gamma\delta\alpha\beta} = 0$ become equivalent.

T h e o r e m 2 . In the Einstein spaces $*T_i$ (3.7) the equations

$$l^\alpha R_{\alpha\beta\gamma\delta} = 0 \tag{I.16}$$

are equivalent to the equations

$$l_\lambda R_{\alpha\beta\gamma\delta} + l_\alpha R_{\beta\lambda\gamma\delta} + l_\beta R_{\lambda\alpha\gamma\delta} = 0. \tag{I.17}$$

P r o o f . Let there exist a vector l^α in $*T_i$ satisfying equations (I.16); we will show that it satisfies equations (I.17) as well. Multiplying the initial equations $l^\delta R^{\rho\sigma\cdots}_{\cdot\cdot\gamma\delta} = 0$ by $\frac{1}{2} \eta_{\mu\nu\rho\sigma}$, we obtain

$$l^\delta {}^* R_{\mu\nu\gamma\delta} = 0. \tag{I.18}$$

Owing to Theorem 1 the tensor $*R_{\mu\nu\gamma\delta}$ is symmetric with respect to the index pairs $\mu\nu$ and $\gamma\delta$, and it follows from (I.19) that

$$l^\delta *R_{\gamma\delta\mu\nu} = 0. \tag{I.19}$$

But, according to the lemma, condition (I.19) is equivalent to condition (I.17), which proves the first half of Theorem 2.

Conversely, let a certain vector l^α in $*T_i$ satisfy equations (I.17). According to the lemma, it satisfies equations (I.13); but, owing to Theorem 1, these equations are equivalent to the following:

$$l^\alpha R^*_{\alpha\beta\gamma\delta} = 0,$$

i.e.,

$$\eta_{\gamma\delta\cdot\cdot}^{\cdot\cdot\rho\sigma} R_{\rho\sigma\alpha\beta} l^\alpha = 0. \tag{I.20}$$

Multiplying (I.20) by $\eta^{\gamma\delta\cdot\cdot}_{\cdot\cdot\varepsilon\tau}$ and using the identity (I.6), we obtain

$$\delta^{\rho\sigma}_{\varepsilon\tau} R_{\rho\sigma\alpha\beta} l^\alpha = 2R_{\varepsilon\tau\alpha\beta} l^\alpha = 0,$$

i.e., the vector l^α also satisfies equations (I.16). Thus Theorem 2 is proved.

Theorem 3. The following identity holds in the Einstein spaces (3.7):

$$g^{\rho\sigma} R_{\alpha\beta\gamma\delta;\rho\sigma} + R^{\cdots\rho}_{\alpha\beta\sigma\cdot} R^{\cdots\sigma}_{\gamma\delta\rho\cdot} + 2(R^{\cdots\rho}_{\delta\sigma\alpha\cdot} R^{\cdots\sigma}_{\beta\rho\gamma\cdot} - R^{\cdots\rho}_{\delta\sigma\beta\cdot} R^{\cdots\sigma}_{\alpha\rho\gamma\cdot} + \varkappa R_{\alpha\beta\gamma\delta}) = 0. \tag{I.21}$$

Proof: Differentiating covariantly the Bianchi identies

$$R_{\alpha\beta\gamma\delta;\rho} + R_{\alpha\beta\delta\rho;\gamma} + R_{\alpha\beta\rho\gamma;\delta} = 0 \tag{I.22}$$

and multiplying the result by the tensor $g^{\rho\sigma}$, we obtain

$$g^{\rho\sigma} R_{\alpha\beta\gamma\delta;\rho\sigma} + R^{\cdots\sigma}_{\alpha\beta\delta\cdot;\gamma\sigma} - R^{\cdots\sigma}_{\alpha\beta\gamma\cdot;\delta\sigma} = 0. \tag{I.23}$$

Next, applying the Ricci differential identities (see /9/) to the Riemann tensor

$$2R_{\alpha\beta\gamma\delta,[\rho\sigma]} = R_{\lambda\alpha\gamma\delta} R^{\cdots\lambda}_{\rho\sigma\alpha\cdot} + R_{\alpha\lambda\gamma\delta} R^{\cdots\lambda}_{\rho\sigma\beta\cdot} + R_{\alpha\beta\lambda\delta} R^{\cdots\lambda}_{\rho\sigma\gamma\cdot} + R_{\alpha\beta\gamma\lambda} R^{\cdots\lambda}_{\rho\sigma\delta\cdot}, \tag{I.24}$$

we express the second and third terms in (I.23) in terms of $R^{\cdots\sigma}_{\alpha\beta\delta\cdot;\sigma\gamma}$ and $R^{\cdots\sigma}_{\alpha\beta\gamma\cdot;\sigma\delta}$, respectively, as well as terms quadratic in the Riemann tensor (and not containing derivatives of $R_{\alpha\beta\gamma\delta}$). Allowing further for the identity

$$R^{\cdots\sigma}_{\alpha\beta\gamma\cdot;\sigma} = 2R_{\gamma[\alpha;\beta]}, \tag{I.25}$$

which follows from the Bianchi identities (I.22), we see that in the Einstein spaces (3.7)

$$R^{\cdots\sigma}_{\alpha\beta\gamma\cdot;\sigma} = 0. \tag{I.26}$$

Using relations (I.26), we cancel terms of the form $\quad$ and $R^{\cdots\sigma}_{\alpha\beta\gamma\cdot;\sigma\delta}$ in the equalities obtained and arrive at relations (I.21). Theorem 3 has been proved.

Appendix II

We will give the wave equations (12.34) − (12.36) in expanded form for the chronometrically invariant components X^{ij}, Y^{ijk} and Z^{ijkl} of the Riemann tensor. To this end let us use the Zel'manov generally covariant definition of gravitational waves:

$$g^{\alpha\rho}R_{\alpha\beta\gamma\delta;\alpha\rho} = 0. \tag{II.1}$$

The system of twenty equations (II.1) is obviously equivalent to the following three systems of equations, the first consisting of six equations, the second of eight and the third of six again:

$$g^{\sigma\rho}R^{\cdots ij\cdot}_{00\cdot\cdot;\sigma\rho} = R^{\cdots ij;0\cdot}_{00}{}_0 + R^{\cdots ij;n\cdot}_{00}{}_n = 0, \tag{II.2}$$

$$g^{\sigma\rho}R^{\cdot ijk\cdot}_{0\cdot\cdot\cdot;\sigma\rho} = R^{\cdot ijk;0\cdot}_{0}{}_0 + R^{\cdot ijk;n\cdot}_{0}{}_n = 0, \tag{II.3}$$

$$g^{\sigma\rho}R^{kijl}_{\cdots\cdots;\sigma\rho} = R^{kijl;0\cdot}{}_0 + R^{kijl;n\cdot}{}_n = 0. \tag{II.4}$$

We will write each of the three systems in chronometrically invariant form. To do this we will use definitions (12.13) as well as the formulas for chronometrically invariant and spatially-covariant differentiation (see Ch.11).

Describing equations (II.2) term by term and expressing each term in terms of the corresponding chronometric invariants, we obtain the following equations:

$$(^*\nabla^n_n - {}^*\partial{}^*\partial)\, X^{ij} + 2\,(^*\nabla_n - F_n)\, [Y^{\cdot(ij)}_m\,(D^{nm} + A^{nm})] -$$
$$- [F^{n*}\nabla_n X^{ij} + D^*\partial X^{ij} + (D^i_n + A^{\cdot i}_{n\cdot})^*\partial X^{nj} + (D^j_n + A^{\cdot j}_{n\cdot})^*\partial X^{ni}] +$$
$$+ (^*\partial + D)\, [2F^n Y^{\cdot(ij)}_{n\cdot\cdot} - X^{ni}\,(D^j_n + A^{\cdot j}_{n\cdot}) - X^{nj}\,(D^i_n + A^{\cdot i}_{n\cdot})] +$$
$$+ 2\,(D^{nm} + A^{nm})^*\nabla_n Y^{\cdot(ij)}_{m\cdot\cdot} + 2F_n\,[^*\partial Y^{n(ij)} - Y^{m(ij)}\,(D^n_m + A^{n\cdot}_{\cdot m})] +$$
$$+ 2F_n\,[(D^i_m + A^{\cdot i}_{m\cdot})\,(Y^{\cdot jm}_{n\cdot\cdot} + Y^{\cdot mj}_{n\cdot\cdot}) + (D^j_m + A^{\cdot j}_{m\cdot})\,(Y^{\cdot mi}_{n\cdot\cdot} + Y^{\cdot im}_{n\cdot\cdot})] -$$
$$- 2D^m_n\,[X^{ni}\,(D^j_m + A^{\cdot j}_{m\cdot}) + X^{nj}\,(D^i_m + A^{\cdot i}_{m\cdot})] -$$
$$- 2X^{nm}\,(D^i_n + A^{\cdot i}_{n\cdot})\,(D^j_m + A^{\cdot j}_{m\cdot}) + 2X^{ij}\,(D_{kl}D^{kl} + A_{kl}A^{kl} - F_l F^l) +$$
$$+ 2F_n^{\ (i}X^{j)n} + 2Z^{\cdot\cdot(ij)}_{nm\cdot\cdot}\,[F^n F^m - (D^{ln} + A^{ln})\,(D^m_l + A^{\cdot m}_{l\cdot})] = 0. \tag{II.5}$$

Here, F^i, D_{ij}, A_{ij} are the vector of gravitational-inertial force, the deformation velocity tensor and the tensor of angular velocity of rotation of the three-dimensional space of the given reference system Σ with respect to a locally co-moving geodesic system Σ_0 /205/ (these quantities were introduced in Chapter 12). Despite the unwieldy aspect of these equations, each of the terms that enter into them has a fairly clear physical interpretation. The first term evidently represents the result of the action of the wave operator (12.21) on a chronometrically invariant wave function. Let us look at the physical meaning of other chronometrically invariant operators in equations (II.5). Thus the relativistic operator

$$*\nabla_i - F_i,$$

contracted with a certain chronometrically invariant three-dimensional vector t_i, expresses the "physical divergence" of the vector t^i, the difference between it and the mathematical divergence $*\nabla_i t^i$ being due to the fact that at different points of the boundary of an element of three-dimensional volume, the value $d\tau$ of the chronometrically invariant time interval

$$d\tau = \frac{g_{0\alpha} dx^\alpha}{\sqrt{g_{00}}}$$

varies for the same value of dt. The relativistic operator of "physical differentiation" with respect to the time $*\partial + D$ differs from the mathematical (chronometrically invariant) operator of differentiation with respect of the time $*\partial$ in that it allows for deformation with time of the spatial coordinate network in which the function to be differentiated is specified.

Analogously, expressing equations (II.3) in chronometrically invariant form, we obtain the wave equations for the chronometrically invariant tensor Y^{ijk}:

$$(b^{mn}*\nabla_m*\nabla_n - *\partial*\partial)\,Y^{ijk} + (*\partial + D)\,[Y^{mik}\,(D^j_m + A^{\cdot j}_{m\cdot}) -$$
$$- Y^{ijm}\,(D^k_m + A^{\cdot k}_{m\cdot}) - Y^{mjk}\,(D^i_m + A^{\cdot i}_{m\cdot}) + (2F^{[i}X^{j]k} - F^n Z^{\cdot ijk}_{n\cdots})] -$$
$$- (*\nabla_n - F_n)\,[X^{ik}\,(D^{nj} + A^{nj}) - X^{jk}\,(D^{ni} + A^{ni}) +$$
$$+ Z^{\cdot ijk}_{m\cdots}\,(D^{nm} + A^{nm})] + [(A^{\cdot n}_{m\cdot} - D^n_m)(*\nabla_n - F_n)\,Z^{mijk} +$$
$$+ (D^{ni} + A^{ni})*\nabla_n X^{jk} - (D^{nj} + A^{nj})*\nabla_n X^{ik}] - [F^{n*}\nabla_n Y^{jk} +$$
$$+ D*\partial Y^{ijk} + (D^i_n + A^{\cdot i}_{n\cdot})*\,\partial Y^{njk} - (D^j_n + A^{\cdot j}_{n\cdot})*\partial Y^{nik} +$$
$$+ (D^k_n + A^{\cdot k}_{n\cdot})*\partial Y^{ijn} + (2F^{[j*}\partial X^{i]k} + F^{n*}\partial Z^{\cdot ijk}_{n\cdots})] +$$
$$+ F_n\{2F^{[i}Y^{j]nk} + F^k Y^{ijn} + (D^{ni} + A^{ni})\,X^{jk} - (D^{nj} + A^{nj})\,X^{ik} +$$
$$+ 2\,[2Y^{nk[i}F^{j]} + Z^{nmik}\,(D^j_m + A^{\cdot j}_{m\cdot}) - Z^{mnjk}\,(D^i_m + A^{\cdot i}_{m\cdot}) +$$
$$+ Z^{mijn}\,(D^k_m + A^{\cdot k}_{m\cdot})]\} + 2\,\{2F^{[i}X^{j]}\,(D^k_n + A^{\cdot k}_{n\cdot}) +$$
$$+ X^{nk}\,[F^i\,(D^j_n + A^{\cdot j}_{n\cdot}) - F^j\,(D^i_n + A^{\cdot i}_{n\cdot})]\} +$$

$$+ 2 \{D_{mn} \left[Y^{mkj}(D^{ni} + A^{ni}) - Y^{mki}(D^{nj} + A^{nj}) - Y^{ijm}(D^{nk} + A^{nk})\right] +$$

$$+ 2A_{mn} \left[Y^{m(ik)}(D^{nj} + A^{nj}) - Y^{m(jk)}(D^{ni} + A^{ni})\right] +$$

$$+ Y^{mnk}(D_n^i + A_n^{\cdot i})(D_m^j + A_m^{\cdot j}) + (D_n^k + A_n^{\cdot k})\left[Y^{min}(D_m^j + A_m^{\cdot j}) -\right.$$

$$\left. - Y^{mjn}(D_m^i + A_m^{\cdot i})\right]\} +$$

$$+ Y^{ijk}(D_{nm}D^{nm} + A_{nm}A^{nm} - F_n F^n) = 0. \tag{II.6}$$

Lastly, equations (II.4) yield the following system of chronometrically invariant wave equations for the tensor Z^{kijl}:

$$(b^{mn} {}^*\nabla_m {}^*\nabla_n - {}^*\partial {}^*\partial) Z^{kijl} + ({}^*\partial + D) \left[2Y^{ij[k}F^{l]} + 2Y^{kl[i}F^{j]} +\right.$$

$$+ (D_n^l + A_n^{\cdot l}) Z^{ni\ k} - (D_n^k + A_n^{\cdot k}) Z^{ni\ l} + (D_n^j + A_n^{\cdot j}) Z^{knil} -$$

$$\left. - (D_n^i + A_n^{\cdot i}) Z^{knjl}\right] -$$

$$- ({}^*\nabla_n - F_n) \left[(D^{nk} + A^{nk}) Y^{ijl} + (D^{ni} + A^{ni}) Y^{klj} -\right.$$

$$- (D^{nl} + A^{nl}) Y^{ijk} - (D^{nj} + A^{nj}) Y^{kli}] +$$

$$+ (D^{nl} + A^{nl}) {}^*\nabla_n Y^{ijk} - (D^{nk} + A^{nk}) {}^*\nabla_n Y^{i\ l} +$$

$$+ (D^{nj} + A^{nj}) {}^*\nabla_n Y^{kli} - (D^{ni} + A^{ni}) {}^*\nabla_n Y^{klj} -$$

$$- \left[F^n {}^*\nabla_n Z^{kijl} + D {}^*\partial Z^{ki\ l} + F^k {}^*\partial Y^{ijl} -\right.$$

$$- F^l {}^*\partial Y^{ijk} + F^i {}^*\partial Y^{klj} - F^j {}^*\partial Y^{kli} +$$

$$+ (D_n^k + A_n^{\cdot k}) {}^*\partial Z^{ni\ l} - (D_n^l + A_n^{\cdot l}) {}^*\partial Z^{nijk} + (D_n^i + A_n^{\cdot i}) {}^*\partial Z^{knjl} -$$

$$\left. - (D_n^j + A_n^{\cdot j}) {}^*\partial Z^{knil}\right] +$$

$$+ 4 \left[F^i F^{[k} X^{l]j} + F^j F^{[l} X^{k]i}\right] + F_n \left[Y^{ijk}(D^{nl} + A^{nl}) -\right.$$

$$- Y^{ijl}(D^{nk} + A^{nk}) +$$

$$+ Y^{kli}(D^{nj} + A^{nj}) - Y^{klj}(D^{ni} + A^{ni}) +$$

$$+ 2(Z^{nij[k}F^{l]} - Z^{nkl[i}F^{j]})] +$$

$$+ 2 \{(D^{ni} + A^{ni}) \left[X^{kj}(D_n^l + A_n^{\cdot l}) - X^{lj}(D_n^k + A_n^{\cdot k})\right] +$$

$$+ (D^{nj} + A^n) \left[X^{kj}(D_n^k + A_n^{\cdot k}) - X^{ki}(D_n^l + A_n^{\cdot l})\right]\} +$$

$$+ 2 \left[(D_n^i + A_n^{\cdot i})(2Y^{nj[k}F^{l]} + F^j Y^{kln}) +\right.$$

$$+ (D_n^j + A_n^{\cdot j})(2Y^{ni[l}F^{k]} - F^i Y^{kln}) +$$

$$+ (D_n^k + A_n^{\cdot k})(2Y^{nl[i}F^{j]} + F^l Y^{i\ n}) +$$

$$+ (D_n^l + A_n^{\cdot l})(2Y^{nk[j}F^{i]} - F^k Y^{ijn})] +$$

$$+ 2 \{A_m^{\cdot n} \left[Z^{mijk}(D_n^l + A_n^{\cdot l}) - Z^{mijl}(D_n^k + A_n^{\cdot k}) + Z^{kmil}(D_n^j + A_n^{\cdot j}) -\right.$$

$$- Z^{kmjl}(D_n^i + A_n^{\cdot i})] + (D_n^k + A_n^{\cdot k}) \left[Z^{mijn}(D_m^l + A_m^{\cdot l}) +\right.$$

$$+ Z^{nmil} (D_m^j + A_{m.}^{\cdot j})] - (D_n^j + A_{n.}^{\cdot j}) [Z^{kmnl} (D_m^i + A_{m.}^{\cdot i}) +$$

$$+ Z^{mnik} (D_m^l + A_{m.}^{\cdot l})] + (D_m^i + A_{m.}^{\cdot i}) [Z^{nmjk} (D_n^l + A_{n.}^{\cdot l}) -$$

$$- Z^{nmjl} (D_n^k + A_{n.}^{\cdot k})]\} = 0. \tag{II.7}$$

The physical interpretation of equations (II.6) and (II.7) is analogous to the above. Equations (II.5) − (II.7) constitute the complete system of chronometrically invariant equations describing gravitational-inertial waves in the specific frame of reference. Since these equations are none other than the generally covariant equations (II.1) written down in an arbitrary (fixed) frame of reference, it follows that they are satisfied for any empty space-time of Petrov type N (in the given frame of reference). Thus equations (II.5) − (II.7) can serve as chronometrically invariant characteristic of type N gravitational fields in a vacuum.

BIBLIOGRAPHY

The reference list was compiled as follows: Numbers 1 through 262 are given in the order in which they were cited in the main text of the book. From number 263 on, works are grouped together in accordance with the seven research themes described in the Introduction. Works 263 – 283 belong to the first group, 284 – 316 to the second group, 317 – 336 to the third group, 337 – 389 to the fourth group, 390 – 414 to the fifth group, 415 – 421 to the sixth group and 422 – 458 and 465 to the seventh group. Works 459 – 464 are of the review type or are devoted to the question of the velocity of gravitational waves.

1. Einstein, A.– Sitz. Ber. Preuss. Akad. Wiss. 1:688. 1916.
2. Einstein, A.– Sitz. Ber. Preuss. Akad. Wiss. 1:154. 1918.
3. Hilbert, D.– Gött. Nachr. 1917.
4. Hilbert, D.– Math. Ann. 92:22. 1918.
5. Sobolev, S.L. Uravneniya matematicheskoi fiziki (Equations of Mathematical Physics). Gostekhizdat. 1954.
6. Bonnor, W.B. Perspectives in Geometry and Relativity, Indiana University Press, p.28. 1966.
7. Einstein, A., L. Infeld, and B. Hoffmann.– Ann. Math. 39:65. 1938.
8. Infeld, L. and J. Plebański. Motion and Relativity. Oxford. Pergamon Press. 1960.
9. Fock, V.A. Teoriya prostranstva, vremeni i tyagoteniya (The Theory of Space, Time and Gravitation). Fizmatgiz. English Translation: New York, Pergamon Press. 1959.
10. Gupta, S.– Proc. Phys. Soc. A65:161. 1952.
11. Bonnor, W. Atti del convegno sulla relatività generale: problemi dell'energia e ondre gravitazionali, p.119. Firenze. 1964 – 1965.
12. Bonnor, W.– Ann. Inst. Henri Poincaré 15:146. 1957.
13. Havas, P. and J.N. Goldberg.– Phys. Rev. 128:398. 1962.
14. Havas, P.– Journ. Math. Phys. 5:373. 1964.
15. Eddington, A.S. The Mathematical Theory of Relativity. Cambridge University Press. 1957.
16. Landau, L.D. and E.M. Lifshits. Teoriya polya (Field Theory). "Nauka." 1967.
17. Bonnor, W.– Trans. Roy. Phil. Soc., London A251:233. 1959.
18. Bonnor, W. and M.A. Rotenberg.– Proc. Roy. Soc. A289:47. 1966.
19. Rosen, N. and H. Shamir.– Revs. Mod. Phys. 29:429. 1957.
20. Bondi, H. Proc. of the Internat. School "Enrico Fermi", p. 202. New York – London. Acad. Press. 1962.
21. Rotenberg, M.A.– Proc. Phys. Soc., ser.2, 1:280. 1968.
22. Campbell, W.B.– Phys. Rev. D2:2123. 1970.
23. Eddington, A.S.– Proc. Roy. Soc. A102:268. 1923.
24. Cooperstock, F.I.– Phys. Rev. 165:1424. 1968.
25. Rotenberg, M.A.– Proc. Roy. Soc. A1:97. 1968.
26. Cooperstock, F.I. and D.J. Booth.– Nuov. Cim. 62B:163. 1969.
27. Hunter, A.J. and M.A. Rotenberg.– Journ. Phys. Soc. Am. (Gen. Phys.), ser.2, 2:34. 1969.
28. Rotenberg, M.A. Ph.D.Thesis, University of London. 1964.
29. Rotenberg, M.A.– Comm. Math. Phys. 5:23. 1967.

30. Thorne, K.S.— Phys. Rev. Lett. 21:320. 1968.
31. Weber, J.— Phys. Rev. Lett. 21:395. 1968.
32. Cooperstock, F.I.— Phys. Rev. 163:1368. 1967.
33. Cooperstock, F.I.— Phys. Rev. 165:1424. 1968.
34. Zel'dovich, Ya.B. and I.D.Novikov.— DAN SSSR 155:1033. 1964.
35. Carmeli, M. — Phys. Rev. 158:1243. 1967.
36. Wheeler, J.A. Gravitation, the Neutrino and Geometry. Bologna. Tipografia Compositori. 1960.
37. Isaacson, R.A.— Phys. Rev. 166:1263. 1968.
38. Isaacson, R.A.— Phys. Rev. 166:1272. 1968.
39. Brill, D. and J.B.Hartle.— Phys. Rev. 135, B271. 1964
40. Shulikovskii, V.I. Klassicheskaya differentsial'naya geometriya (Classical Differential Geometry). Fizmatgiz. 1963.
41. Yano, K. The Theory of Lie Derivatives and Its Applications. North-Holland Publishing Co. New York. 1957.
42. de Rahm, G. Variétés differentiables. Paris. Hermann. 1960.
43. Lichnerowicz, A. Edited by C. and B. de Witt. Relativity, Groups and Topology, p.827. New York. Gordon & Breach. 1964.
44. Isaacson, R.A. and J.Winicour.— Phys. Rev. 168:1451. 1968.
45. Madore, J.— Ann. Inst. Henri Poincaré 12:285. 1970.
46. Madore, J.— Ann. Inst. Henri Poincaré 12:365. 1970.
47. de Donder, T. La gravifique einsteinienne. Paris. 1921.
48. Lanczos, K.— Phys. Zs. 23:537. 1923.
49. Petrovskii, I.G. Lektsii ob uravneniyakh s chastnymi proizvodnymi (Lectures on Partial Differential Equations). Gostekhizdat. 1961.
50. Courant, R. Partial Differential Equations.— In: Methods of Mathematical Physics (with D.Hilbert), Vol.2. 1962.
51. Hadamard, J. Leçons sur la propagation des ondes et les équations de l'hydrodynamique. Paris. Hermann. 1903.
52. Lichnerowicz, A. Théories relativistes de la gravitation et de l'électromagnétisme. Paris. Masson. 1955.
53. Bers, L., F.John, and M.Schechter. Partial Differential Equations. New York, Interscience. 1964.
54. Lichnerowicz, A. Applications of Nonlinear Partial Differential Equations in Mathematical Physics.— Proc. of Symposia in Appl. Maths., Vol.XVII:189. Providence. 1965.
55. Trautman, A.— Compt. Rend. Acad. Sci. Colon. 246:1500. 1958.
56. Bel, L.— Compt. Rend. Acad. Sci. Colon. 245:2482. 1957.
57. Petrov, A.Z. Novye metody v obshchei teorii otnositel'nosti (New Methods in the General Theory of Relativity). "Nauka." 1966.
58. Eisenhart, L.P. Riemannian Geometry. Princeton, Princeton University Press. 1949.
59. Finzi, B.— Atti della Acad. Naz. Lincei 6:18. 1949.
60. Mitskevich, N.V. Fizicheskie polya v obshchei teorii otnositel'nosti (Physical Fields in General Relativity Theory). "Nauka." 1969.
61. Konopleva, N.P. and G.A.Sokolik. Prostranstvo i vremya v sovremennoi fizike (Space and Time in Modern Physics), p.82. "Naukova dumka." 1968.
62. Lichnerowicz, A.— Ann. Mat. pura ed appl. 50:1. 1960.
63. Tolman, R.C. Relativity, Thermodynamics and Cosmology. Oxford, Clarendon Press. 1950.
64. Petrov, A.Z.— Uchenye Zapiski Kazanskogo Universiteta, 114:8. 1954.
65. Petrov, A.Z. Prostranstva Einshteina (Einstein Spaces). Fizmatgiz. 1961.
66. Debever, R.— Compt. Rend. Acad. Sci. Colon. 249:1324. 1959.
67. Penrose, R.— Ann. of Phys. 10:171. 1960.

68. Bel, L. Colloques internationaux du Centre national de la recherche scientifique, p.119. Paris. 1962.

69. Pirani, F.A.E. Physik. Bl. **17**:114. 1961.

70. Pirani, F.A.E. Recent Developments in General Relativity, p.89. Oxford — New York. Pergamon Press. 1962.

71. Pirani, F.A.E. Edited by L.Witten. Gravitation: An Introduction to Current Research, p.199. New York. Wiley. 1962.

72. Wyman, M. and R.Trollope.— Journ. Math. Phys. **7**:1836. 1966.

73. Trollope, R.— Journ. Math. Phys. **8**:938. 1967.

74. Kaigorodov, V.R. Gravitatsiya i teoriya otnositel'nosti (Gravitation and the Theory of Relativity), No.3, p.161. Izdatel'stvo Kazanskogo Universiteta. 1967.

75. Bel, L.— Compt. Rend. Acad. Sci. Colon. **246**:3015. 1958.

76. Bel, L.— Compt. Rend. Acad. Sci. Colon. **247**:1094. 1958.

77. Bel, L.— Compt. Rend. Acad. Sci. Colon. **247**:2096. 1958.

78. Bel, L.— Compt. Rend. Acad. Sci. Colon. **248**:1297. 1959.

79. Bel, L.— Compt. Rend. Acad. Sci. Colon. **248**:2561. 1959.

80. Bel, L.— Cahiers Phys. **16**:59. 1962.

81. Debever, R.— Bull. Soc. Math. Belgique **10**:112. 1958.

82. Matte, A.— Canad. Journ. Math. **5**:1. 1953.

83. Synge, J.— Proc. Roy. Irish Acad. **A58**:4. 1957.

84. Le-Thanh-Phong.— Compt. Rend. Sci. Colon. **250**:987. 1960.

85. Geheniau, J. and R.Debever.— Bull. Acad. Roy. Belgique **42**:114. 1956.

86. Norden, A.P. and V.V.Vishnevskii.— Izvestiya Vuzov, Seriya "Matematika", **2**:9. 1959.

87. Lichnerowicz, A.— Compt. Rend. Acad. Sci. Colon. **246**:893. 1958.

88. Lichnerowicz, A.— Compt. Rend. Acad. Sci. Colon. **248**:2728. 1959.

89. Lichnerowicz, A.— Cahiers Phys. **12**:287. 1958.

90. Lichnerowicz, A.— Colloques internationaux du CNRS, p.93. Paris. 1962.

91. Zakharov, V.D. Problemy teorii gravitatsii i elementarnykh chastits (Problems of the Theory of Gravitation and Elementary Particles), p.114. Atomizdat. 1966.

92. Konopleva, N.P. GR-5.— Tezisy dokladov 5-i Mezhdunarodnoi konferentsii po gravitatsii i teorii otnositel'nosti. Izdatel'stvo Tbilisskogo universiteta, p.27. 1968.

93. Konopleva, N.P. Problemy teorii gravitatsii i elementarnykh chastits (Problems of the Theory of Gravitation and Elementary Particles). No.3:103. Atomizdat. 1970.

94. Zakharov, V.D.— Soobshchenie GAISh. No.131:42. 1964.

95. Weber, J. General Relativity and Gravitational Waves. New York, Interscience. 1961.

96. Roy, S. and L.Radhakrishna.— Proc. Roy. Soc. **A275**:245. 1963.

97. Petrov, A.Z. Prostranstva, opredelyaemye polyami tyagoteniya (Spaces Defined by Gravitational Fields). Doctor Thesis.— MGU. 1957.

98. Zakharov, V.D. Problemy teorii gravitatsii i elementarnykh chastits (Problems of the Theory of Gravitation and Elementary Particles), No.3:128. Atomizdat. 1971.

99. Savel'eva, N.A. Obshchekovariantnye gravitatsionnye volny i garmonicheskie koordinaty (Generally Covariant Gravitational Waves and Harmonic Coordinates). Thesis.— MGU. 1968.

100. Zakharov, V.D.— Vestnik MGU, Seriya Fiziki i Astronomii, No.2:3. 1966.

101. Zakharov, V.D. DAN SSSR **161**:563. 1965.

102. Takeno, H.— Tensor **12**:197. 1962.

103. Zakharov, V.D.—Vestnik MGU, Seriya Fiziki i Astronomii, No.2:59. 1965.

104. Nordtvedt, K. and H.Pagels.— Ann. of Phys. **17**:426. 1962.

105. Zakharov, V.D.— DAN SSSR **166**:324. 1966.

106. Kruchkovich, G.I.— UMN 9:1. 1954.
107. Zakharov, V.D. Sovremennye problemy gravitatsii.— Sbornik trudov 2-i Sovetskoi
        gravitatsionnoi konferentsii. Izdatel'stvo Tbilisskogo universiteta, p.259. 1967.
108. Peres, A.— Phys. Rev. 118:1105. 1960.
109. Debever, R.— Compt. Rend. Acad. Sci. Colon. 250:64. 1960.
110. Sachs, R.— Proc. Roy. Soc. A265:463. 1962.
111. Hély, J.— Compt. Rend. Acad. Sci. Colon. 251:1981. 1960.
112. Hély, J.— Compt. Rend. Acad. Sci. Colon. 252:3754. 1961.
113. Hély, J.— Compt. Rend. Acad. Sci. Colon. 257:2083. 1963.
114. Hély, J.— Compt. Rend. Acad. Sci. Colon. 262:1376. 1966.
115. Hély, J.— Compt. Rend. Acad. Sci. Colon. 263:38. 1966.
116. Hély, J.— Compt. Rend. Acad. Sci. Colon. 249:1867. 1959.
117. Hély, J.— Compt. Rend. Acad. Sci. Colon. 258:1415. 1964.
118. Zund, J.— Compt. Rend. Acad. Sci. Colon. 262:1081. 1966.
119. Zund, J. and J.Levine.— Compt. Rend. Acad. Sci. Colon. 264:1029. 1967.
120. Levine, J. and J.Zund.— Ann. mat. pura ed appl. 80:373. 1969.
121. Maldybaeva, E.Ya.— Izvestiya Vuzov, Seriya Fiziki, No.6:320. 1967.
122. Rashevskii, P.K. Geometricheskaya teoriya uravnenii s chastnymi proizvodnymi
        (Geometrical Theory of Partial Differential Equations). Gostekhizdat. 1947.
123. Maldybaeva, E. Ya. — DAN SSSR 172:320. 1967.
124. Konopleva, N.P. and G.A. Sokolik. Problemy teorii gravitatsii i elementarnykh
        chastits (Problems of the Theory of Gravitation and Elementary Particles). No.1:22.
        Atomizdat. 1966.
125. Lichnerowicz, A. Théorie globale des connections et des groupes d'holonomie. Roma,
        Edizioni cremonese. 1955.
126. Nikolaenko, V.M.— Izvestiya Vuzov, Seriya Fiziki, No.1:138. 1971.
127. Misra, R.M. and R.A.Singh.— Journ. Math. Phys. 7:1836. 1966.
128. Misra, R.M. and R.A.Singh.— Journ. Math. Phys. 8:1065. 1967.
129. Robinson, I. and A.Trautman.— Phys. Rev. Lett. 4:431. 1960.
130. Robinson, I. and A.Trautman.— Proc. Roy. Soc. A265:463. 1962.
131. Trautman, A.— UFN 89:3. 1966.
132. Ehlers, J.— Acad. Wiss. Mainz, Abh. Math. Naturwiss. No.11. 1961.
133. Shepley, L. and A.Taub.— Communications Math. Phys. 5:237. 1967.
134. Szekeres, P.— Journ. Math. Phys. 7:751. 1966.
135. Bartrum, P.C.— Journ. Math. Phys. 8:1464. 1967.
136. Pirani, F. and A.Schild.— Bull. Acad. Polon. Sci., cl.III, 9:543. 1961.
137. Kundt, W.— Zs. Phys. 163:77. 1961.
138. Foster, J. and E.T.Newman.— Journ. Math. Phys. 8:189. 1967.
139. Bartrum, P.C.— Journ. Math. Phys. 8:667. 1967.
140. Kerr, R.P. and A.Schild. Applications of Nonlinear Partial Differential Equations in
        Mathematical Physics.— Proc. of Symposia in Appl. Maths. 17:199. Providence. 1965.
141. Kerr, R.P. and A.Schild. Atti del convegno sulla relatività generale: problemi dell'
        energia e ondre gravitazionali, Firenze, p.222. 1965. Roma. 1965.
142. Mas, L.— Compt. Rend. Acad. Sci. Colon. A268:441. 1969.
143. Bondi, H., F.Pirani, and I.Robinson.— Proc. Roy. Soc. A251:519. 1959.
144. Penrose, R.— Revs. Mod. Phys. 37:215. 1965.
145. Kundt, W. Colloques internationaux du CNRS, p.155. Paris. 1962.
146. Ehlers, J. and W.Kundt. Edited by L.Witten. Gravitation: An Introduction to Current Research,
        p.49. New York — London. Wiley. 1962.

147. Jordan, P., J.Ehlers, and W.Kundt.— Abhandl. Dtsch. Akad. Wiss., Kl. Math. Natur-
     wiss., No.2:85. 1960.

148. Sachs, R. Edited by C. and B. de Witt. Relativity, Groups and Topology, p.152. New York.
     Gordon & Breach. 1964.

149. Chevreton, M.— Compt. Rend. Acad. Sci. Colon. 262:1227. 1966.

150. Newman, E.— Journ. Math. Phys. 2:324. 1961.

151. Goldberg, J.— Phys. Rev. 131:1367. 1963.

152. Goldberg, J. and R.Kerr.— Journ. Math. Phys. 5:172. 1964.

153. Takeno, H.— Tensor, 8:59. 1958.

154. Johari, V.B.— Progr. Theoret. Phys. 35:141. 1966.

155. Rosen, N. — Phys. Zs. Sowjetunion, 12:366. 1937.

156. Boardman, J. and P.G.Bergmann.— Phys. Rev. 115:1318. 1959.

157. Avez, A.— Compt. Rend. Acad. Sci. Colon. 252:3408. 1961.

158. Braginskii, V.B. and V.N.Rudenko. Gravitatsiya i teoriya otnositel'nosti (Gravitation
     and the Theory of Relativity), No.1:96. Izdatel'stvo Kazanskogo universiteta, 1963.

159. Dăngvu, H.— Compt. Rend. Acad. Sci. Colon. A268:297. 1969.

160. Peres, A.— Phys. Rev. Lett. 3:571. 1959.

161. Eisenhart, L.P.— Ann. of Math. 39:316. 1938.

162. Kruchkovich, G.I. and A.S. Solodovnikov.— Izvestiya Vuzov, Seriya matematiki,
     No.3 (10):147. 1959.

163. Takeno, H.— Tensor 6:15. 1956.

164. Vaidya, P. and J.Pandya.— Current Sci. 29:268. 1960.

165. Zakharov, V.D. Issledovanie polei tyagoteniya s tochki zreniya invariantnogo kriteriya
     gravitatsionnykh voln (Study of Gravitational Fields from the Standpoint of the Invariant
     Criterion for Gravitational Waves). Candidate Thesis.— MGU, 1966.

166. Kaigorodov, V.R. GR-5.— Tezisy dokladov 5-i Mezhdunarodnoi konferentsii po gravitatsii
     i teorii otnositel'nosti. Theses.   Izdatel'stvo Tbilisskogo universiteta, p.117. 1968.

167. Kaigorodov, V.R. and A.B.Pestov. Gravitatsiya i teoriya otnositel'nosti (Gravitation
     and the Theory of Relativity), No.6:46. Izdatel'stvo Kazanskogo universiteta, p.46.
     1969.

168. Takeno, H.— Sci. Rep. of Research Inst. Theoret. Phys. Hiroshima University, No.1:1. 1961.

169. Zakharov, V.D. Problemy gravitatsii (Problems of Gravitation).— Tezisy dokladov 2-i Sovets-
     koi gravitatsionnoi konferentsii, p.104. Izdatel'stvo Tbilisskogo universiteta. 1965.

170. Zakharov, V.D.— Tezisy dokladov VI Vsesoyuznoi konferentsii po teorii elementarnykh
     chastits, p.52. Izdatel'stvo Uzhgorodskogo universiteta. 1965.

171. Bondi, H., M. van der Burg, and A.Metzner.— Proc. Roy. Soc. A269:21. 1962.

172. Synge, J.L. Relativity: the General Theory. New York, Interscience. 1960.

173. Papapetrou, A.— Ann. Inst. Henri Poincaré, 14:79. 1971.

174. Newman, E.T. and R.Penrose.— Journ. Math. Phys. 3:566. 1962.

175. Newman, E.T. and R.Penrose.— Journ. Math. Phys. 4:998. 1962.

176. Penrose, R.— Proc. Roy. Soc. A284:159. 1965.

177. Newman, E.T. and R.Penrose.— Proc. Roy. Soc. A305:175. 1968.

178. Zerilli, F.J.— Phys. Rev. D2:2141. 1970.

179. Vishveshwara, C.V.— Nature 227: 937. 1970.

180. Couch, W.E., W.M.Kinnersley, and R.J.Torrence.— Phys. Lett. A31:576. 1970.

181. Couch, W.E. and R.J.Torrence.— Journ. Math. Phys. 11:2096. 1970.

182. Torrence, R.J. and A.J.Janis.— Journ. Math. Phys. 8:1355. 1967.

183. Newman, E.T. and R.Penrose.— Journ. Math. Phys. 7:863. 1966.

184. Goldberg, J. and R. Sachs.— Acta Phys. Polon. Suppl. 22:13. 1962.

185. Sachs, R.— Proc. Roy. Soc. 270:103. 1962.

186. Kundt, W. and A.Thompson.— Compt. Rend. Acad. Sci. Colon. 254:4257. 1962.

187. Einstein, A. and N.Rosen.— Compt. Rend. Acad. Sci. Colon. 223:43. 1937.
188. Stachel, J.— Journ. Math. Phys. 7:1321. 1966.
189. Kompaneets, A.S.— ZhETF 34:953. 1958.
190. Marder, L.— Proc. Roy. Soc. A244:524. 1958.
191. Marder, L.— Proc. Roy. Soc. A252: 45. 1959.
192. Marder, L.— Proc. Roy. Soc. A261:91. 1961.
193. Weber, J. and J.Wheeler.— Revs. Mod. Phys. 29:509. 1957.
194. Krishna Rao, J.— Current Sci. 32:350. 1963.
195. Krishna Rao, J.— Proc. Nat. Inst. India A30:439. 1964.
196. Krishna Rao, J.— Indian Journ. Pure and Appl. Math. 1:367. 1970.
197. Persides, S.— Proc. Roy. Soc. A320:349. 1970.
198. Lehman, E.— Compt. Rend. Acad. Sci. Colon. A264:488. 1967.
199. Goldberg, J.N.— Phys. Rev. 131:1367. 1963.
200. Kammerer, J.B.— Compt. Rend. Acad. Sci. Colon. 261:5003. 1965.
201. Kozarzewski, B.— Acta Phys. Polon. 27:775. 1965.
202. Hawking, S.W.— Journ. Math. Phys. 9:598. 1968.
203. Stachel, J.— Phys. Rev. 179:1251. 1969.
204. Zel'manov, A.L.— DAN SSSR 107:815. 1956.
205. Zel'manov, A.L.— Trudy shestogo soveshchaniya po voprosam kosmogonii, Vnegalakti-
     cheskaya astronomiya i kosmologiya, p.144. Izdatel'stvo AN SSSR. 1959.
206. Zel'manov, A.L. O deformatsii i krivizne soputstvuyushchego prostranstva (Deformation
     and Curvature of Co-Moving Spaces). Candidate Thesis, MGU. 1944.
207. Bondarenko, N.P.— Vestnik Kievskogo Universiteta, Seriya Astronomii, No.11:10. 1969.
208. Grigor'eva, L.B. and V.D. Zakharov. Gravitatsiya i teoriya otnositel'nosti (Gravitation
     and the Theory of Relativity), No.8. Izdatel'stvo Kazanskogo universiteta. 1972.
209. Gödel, K.— Revs. Mod. Phys. 21:447. 1949.
210. Landau, L.D. and E.M. Lifshits. Mekhanika sploshnykh sred (Mechanics of Continuous
     Media).— GITTL. 1953. Fluid Mechanics. Trans. by J.B.Sypesu and W.H.Reid.
     Reading, Mass., Addison-Wesley Pub. Co. 1959.
211. Pavlov, N.V. Issledovanie uravnenii deviatsii s tochki zreniya khronometricheski invari-
     antnykh velichin (Study of the Equations of Deviation from the Standpoint of the
     Chronometrically Invariant Quantities). Theses. MGU. 1968.
212. Weber, J. — In: Gravitation and Relativity, p.90. New York — Amsterdam. 1964.
213. Braginskii, V.B.— UFN 86:433. 1965.
214. Stanyukovich, K.P. and V.D. Zhakarov. Problemy teorii gravitatsii i elementarnykh
     chastits (Problems of the Theory of Gravitation and Elementary Particles), No.1:130.
     Atomizdat. 1966.
215. Forward, R.L. and D.Berman.— Phys. Rev. Lett. 18:1071. 1967.
216. Shklovskii, I.S.— Astrofizicheskii Zhurn. 46:114. 1969.
217. Ezawa, Z.F. and Y.Yamaguchi.— Journ. Phys. Soc. Japan 28:1083. 1970.
218. Thorne, K.S. and A.Campolattaro.— Astrophys. Journ. 149:591. 1967.
219. Thorne, K.S. GR-5.— Tezisy dokladov 5-i Mezhdunarodnoi konferentsii po gravitatsii i
     teorii otnositel'nosti, p.175. Theses. Izdatel'stvo Tbilisskogo universiteta. 1968.
220. Price, R. and K.S.Thorne.— Astrophys. Journ. 155:163. 1969.
221. Thorne, K.S.— Astrophys. Journ. 158:1. 1969.
222. Thorne, K.S.— Astrophys. Journ. 158:997. 1969.
223. Fowler, W.A.— Revs. Mod. Phys. 36:545. 1964.
224. Wheeler, J.A. Onzième conseil de l'institut international de physique, Solvay, p.112.
     Bruxelles. 1958.
225. Melosh, H.J.— Nature 224:781. 1969.
226. Sinsky, J. and J.Weber.— Phys. Rev. Lett. 18:795. 1967.

227. Weber, J.— Phys. Rev. Lett. **20**:1307. 1968.

228. Weber, J.— Phys. Rev. Lett. **22**:1320. 1969.

229. Weber, J.— Phys. Rev. Lett. **24**:276. 1970.

230. Greenstein, G.— Astrophys. Journ. **158**:145. 1969.

231. Sciama, D.W., G.B. Field, and M.J. Rees.— Phys. Rev. Lett. **23**:1514. 1969.

232. Kafka, P.— Mitteilungen der Astron. Gesellschaft, No.27:134. 1969.

233. Kafka, P.— Nature **226**:436. 1970.

234. Field, G.B., M.J. Rees, and D.W. Sciama.— Comments Astrophys. and Space Phys. **1**:187.
       1969.

235. Sciama, D.W. and G.B. Field.— Phys. Rev. **23**:1514. 1969.

236. Braginskii, V.B., Ya.B. Zel'dovich, and V.N. Rudenko.— Pis'ma ZhETF **10**:437. 1969.

237. Braginskii, V.B. and V.N. Rudenko.— UFN **100**:395. 1970.

238. Wheeler, J.A.— Ann. Rev. Astr. Astroph. **4**:393. 1966.

239. De Sabbata, V.— Memorie di Società Astronomico Italiano **41**:65. 1970.

240. Boccaletti, D., V. De Sabbata, C. Gualdi, and P. Fortini.— Nuov. Cim. **54**:134.
       1968.

241. Mironovskii, V.N.— ZhETF **49**:1650. 1965.

242. Heintzman, H.— Zs. Phys. **210**:380. 1968.

243. Cooperstock, F.— Ann. of Phys. **47**:173. 1968.

244. Winterberg, F.— Nuov. Cim. **B53**:264. 1968.

245. Zipoy, D. and B. Bertotti.— Nuov. Cim. **B56**:195. 1968.

246. Scheffler, H.— Astron. Nachr. **285**:156. 1960.

247. Nagibarov, V.R. and U.Kh. Kopvillem,— Pis'ma ZhETF **5**:445. 1967.

248. Kopvillem, U.Kh. and V.R. Nagibarov. Gravitatsiya i teoriya otnositel'nosti (Gravitation
       and the Theory of Relativity), No.4 — 5, p.60. Izdatel'stvo Kazanskogo universiteta.
       1968.

249. Kopvillem, U.Kh. and V.R. Nagibarov.— ZhETF **56**:113. 1969.

250. Nagibarov, V.R. and U.Kh. Kopvillem. Gravitatsiya i teoriya otnositel'nosti
       (Gravitation and the Theory of Relativity), No.6:60. Izdatel'stvo Kazanskogo
       universiteta. 1969.

251. Kopvillem, U.Kh. and V.I. Bashkov. Kvantovaya akustika (Quantum Acoustics).—
       Kazan' Izdatel'stvo AN SSSR (Collection of articles, in print).

252. Lavrent'ev, G.Ya.— ZhETF **39**:1316. 1969.

253. Lavrent'ev, G.Ya.— Pis'ma ZhETF **10**:495. 1969.

254. Halpern, L.E. and R. Desbrandes.— Ann. Inst. Henri Poincaré **A11**:309. 1969.

255. Kopvillem, U.Kh. and V.R. Nagibarov.— Pis'ma ZhETF **2**:529. 1965.

256. Nagibarov, V.R. and U.Kh. Kopvillem.— Izvestiya Vuzov, Seriya Fiziki, No.9:66. 1967.

257. Sokolik, G.A. and N.P. Konopleva.— In: Einshteinovskï sbornik, p.348. Nauka. 1967.

258. Dyson, F.J. Seismic Response of the Earth to a Gravitation Wave in the One-Hertz Band.—
       Inst. of Advanced Study, Princeton University, preprint. 1968.

259. Dyson, F.J.— Astrophys. Journ. **156**:529. 1969.

260. Mariot, L.— Compt. Rend. Acad. Sci. Colon. **238**:2055. 1954.

261. Mariot, L.— Compt. Rend. Acad. Sci. Colon. **239**:1189. 1954.

262. Pirani, F.— Phys. Rev. **105**:1089. 1957.

263. Pirani, F. Survey of Gravitational Radiation Theory.— King's College, preprint. 1960.

264. Lichnerowicz, A. Problèmes actuels en théorie de la relativité, p.1. Paris. Editions
       de la revue d'optique théorique et instrumentale. 1959.

265. Debever, R.— Compt. Rend. Acad. Sci. Colon. **249**:1744. 1959.

266. Debever, R.— Compt. Rend. Acad. Sci. Colon. **250**:64. 1960.

267. Debever, R. Atti del convegno sulla relatività generale: problemi dell'energia e onde
       gravitazionali, **1**:3. Firenze. 1964 — 1965.

268. D e b e v e r, R. and J.L e r o y .— Compt. Rend. Acad. Sci. Colon. 264:1121. 1967.

269. T r a u t m a n, A.— Bull. Acad. Polon. Sci., cl.III, 7, No.6. 1958.

270. T r a u t m a n, A. Lectures on the General Relativity.—King's College, preprint. 1958.

271. P e t r o v, A.Z. Geometriya i teoriya otnositel'nosti (Geometry and the Theory of Relativity). Izdatel'stvo Kazanskogo universiteta, p.3. 1958.

272. E h l e r s, J. and R.S a c h s .— Zs. Phys. 155:498. 1959.

273. S a c h s, R.— Zs. Phys. 157:462. 1960.

274. S a c h s, R. Recent Development in General Relativity, edited by L.Wittner, p.395. Oxford — New York. Wiley. 1962.

275. Z a k h a r o v, V.D. Problemy gravitatsii (Problems of Gravitation).— Tezisy dokladov 2-i Sovetskoi gravitatsionnoi konferentsii, p.28. Izdatel'stvo Tbilisskogo universiteta. 1965.

276. Z a k h a r o v, V.D. GR-5.— Tezisy dokladov 5-i Mezhdunarodnoi konferentsii po gravitatsii i teorii otnositel'nosti, p.20. Izdatel'stvo Tbilisskogo universiteta. 1968.

277. S t a r u s z k i e w i c z, A.— Bull. Acad. Polon. Sci., cl.III, 12:271. 1964.

278. P a r i z e t, J. Contribution à l'étude des ondes et des ondes de choc en relativité générale, Thèse du Doctorat.— Université de Paris. 1965.

279. M a l d y b a e v a, M.Ya. Sovremennye problemy gravitatsii (Modern Problems of Gravitation), p.50. Izdatel'stvo Tbilisskogo universiteta. 1967.

280. A i c h e l b u r g, P.C. Curvature Collineations for Gravitation pp-Waves.— International Centre for Theoretical Physics, Miramare — Trieste, preprint. 1969.

281. L u k a č e v i ć, I.— Matematički vesnik 6:365. 1969.

282. C o b u r n, N.— Colloques internationaux du Centre National de la Recherche Scientifique, Paris. 1967, p.131. 1969.

283. Y a d a v, B.P.— Progr. Theoret. Phys. 44:555. 1970.

284. I n f e l d, L.— Phys. Rev. 53:836. 1938.

285. I n f e l d, L. and A.E.S c h e i d e g g e r .— Canad. Journ. Math. 3:195. 1951.

286. I n f e l d, L.— Ann. of Phys. 6:341. 1959.

287. I n f e l d, L. and R.M i c h a l s k a - T r a u t m a n .— Ann. of Phys. 40:274. 1966.

288. R o s e n, N.— Phys. Rev. 110:291. 1958.

289. P e r e s, A. and N.R o s e n .— Phys. Rev. 115:1085. 1959.

290. P e r e s, A.— Nuv. Cim. 15:351. 1960.

291. A r n o w i t t, R., S.D e s e r, and C.M i s n e r ,— Proc. Roy. Soc. A251:519. 1959.

292. A r n o w i t t, R., S.D e s e r, and C.M i s n e r .— Ann. of Phys. 11:116. 1960.

293. A r n o w i t t, R., S.D e s e r, and C.M i s n e r .— Phys. Rev. 118: 1100. 1960.

294. G e i s s l e r, D., H.T r e d e r, and A.P a p a p e t r o u .— Ann. d. Phys. 2:344. 1959.

295. A r a k i, H.— Ann. of Phys. 7:456. 1959.

296. B r i l l, D.— Ann. of Phys. 7:466. 1959.

297. M ø l l e r, C. Max-Planck Festschrift, p.139. Berlin. Deutscher Verlag d. Wissenschaft. 1958.

298. M ø l l e r, C. Atti del convegno sulla relatività generale: problemi dell'energia e onde gravitazionali, Vol.II. Roma. 1964.

299. M ø l l e r, C. Proceedings of the Conference on the Theory of Gravitation, Warsaw, 1962, p.31. Paris — Warszawa. 1964.

300. G u t m a n, I.I. Tezisy i programma 1-i Sovetskoi gravitatsionnoi konferentsii, p.65. MGU. 1961.

301. G u t m a n, I.I. Gravitatsiya i teoriya otnositel'nosti (Gravitation and the Theory of Relativity), No.2:72. Izdatel'stvo Kazanskogo universiteta. 1965.

302. G u t m a n, I.I.— ZhETF 53:566. 1967.

303. B u d ' k o, L.I. Tezisy 2-i Sovetskoi gravitatsionnoi konferentsii, p.97. Izdatel'stvo Tbilisskogo universiteta. 1965.

304. S h i r o k o v, M.F. and L.I.B u d k o .— DAN SSSR 172:326. 1967.

305. Shirokov, M.F. and L.I. Budko. Sovremennye problemy gravitatsii (Modern Problems of Gravitation).— Trudy 2-i Sovetskoi gravitatsionnoi konferentsii, p.302. Izdatel'stvo Tbilisskogo universiteta. 1967.

306. Petrov, A.Z. Metodologicheskie problemy teorii izmerenii (Methodological Problems of Measurement Theory), p.57. Naukova dumka. Kiev. 1966.

307. Wu T'han Khiet.— Vestnik MGU, No.2:52. 1966.

308. Denisov, V.I.— Ukrainskii geometricheskii sbornik, No.4:22. Izdatel'stvo Kharkovskogo universiteta. 1967.

309. Signore-Poyet, M.— Compt. Rend. Acad. Sci. Colon. B264:829. 1967.

310. Signore, M.— Compt. Rend. Acad. Sci. Colon. A268:1161. 1969.

311. Signore, M.— Ann. Inst. Henri Poincaré 11:81. 1969.

312. Dozmorov, I.M.— Izvestiya Vuzov, Seriya Fiziki, No.7:130. 1969.

313. Dozmorov, I.M.— Izvestiya Vuzov, Seriya Fiziki, No.7:156. 1968.

314. Rodichev, V.I. and I.M. Dozmorov.— Izvestiya Vuzov, Seriya Fiziki, No.4:20. 1969.

315. Zakharov, V.N. GR-5.— Tezisy dokladov 5-i Mezhdunarodnoi konferentsii po gravitatsii i teorii otnositel'nosti, p.111. Izdatel'stvo Tbilisskogo universiteta. 1968.

316. Zakharov, V.N.— Trudy UDN 44 (4):118. 1969.

317. Weber, J. and D. Zipoy.— Nuov. Cim. 18:191. 1960.

318. Kerr, R.P. and N. Goldberg.— Journ. Math. Phys. 2:332. 1961.

319. Cahen, M. and J. Leroy.— Bulletin de la classe des sciences. Academie royale de Belgique, 51:966. 1965.

320. Cahen, M. and J. Leroy.— Bulletin de la classe des sciences. Academie royale de Belgique 51:1319. 1965.

321. Marder, L.— Proc. Roy. Soc. A313:83. 1969.

322. Bondi, H.— Nature 179:1072. 1957.

323. Bondi, H.— Nature 186:535. 1960.

324. Bondi, H. Atti del convegno sulla relatività generale: problemi dell'energia e ondra gravitazionali, p.143. Firenze. 1964 — 1965.

325. Bondi, H. Colloques internationaux du centre national de la recherche scientifique, Paris, 1967, p.195. Paris. 1969.

326. Couch, W.E., R.J. Torrence, A.J. Janis, and E.T. Newman.— Journ. Math. Phys. 9:484. 1968.

327. Bičák, J. GR-5.— Tezisy dokladov 5-i Mezhdunarodnoi konferentsii po gravitatsii i teorii otnositel'nosti, p.93. Izdatel'stvo Tbilisskogo universiteta. 1968.

328. Bičák, J.— Proc. Roy. Soc. A302:201. 1968.

329. Van der Burg, M.G.— Proc. Roy. Soc. A310:221. 1969.

330. Derry, L., R. Isaacson, and J. Winicour.— Phys. Rev. 185:1647. 1969.

331. Le Denmat, G.— Ann. Inst. Henri Poincaré 10:445. 1969.

332. Hallidy, W.H. and A.I. Janis.— Journ. Math. Phys. 11:578. 1970.

333. Newman, E.T. and L.A. Tamburino.— Journ. Math. Phys. 3:902. 1962.

334. Unti, T. amd R. Torrence.— Journ. Math. Phys. 7:535. 1966.

335. Collinson, C.D. and D.C. French.— Journ. Math. Phys. 8:701. 1967.

336. Collinson, C.D.— Journ. Phys. A (Gen. Phys.), Ser. 2, 2:621. 1969.

337. Rosen, N.— Bull. Res. Council Israel, 3:328. 1954.

338. Rosen, N.— Helv. Phys. Acta, Suppl. 4:171. 1956.

339. Takeno, H.— Tensor 7:97. 1957.

340. Takeno, H.— Tensor 9:76. 1959.

341. Takeno, H.— Tensor 9:162. 1959.

342. Takeno, H.— Tensor 10:34. 1960.

343. Takeno, H.— Tensor 11:99. 1961.

344. Takeno, H.— Progr. Theoret. Phys., Suppl., No.25:103. 1963.

345. Takeno, H.— Tensor 15:233. 1964.

346. Takeno, H.— Tensor 16:84. 1965.

347. Takeno, H.— Tensor (NS), 21:83. 1970.

348. Petrov, A.Z.— Izvestiya Vuzov, Seriya Matematiki, No.2:189. 1959.

349. Marder, L. On the Existence of Cylindrical Gravitational Waves.—King's College, preprint.
        London. 1957.

350. Geissler, D. and H.Treder.— Tensor, 8:165. 1958.

351. Treder, H.— Ann. d. Phys. 6:307. 1960.

352. Treder, H.— Schriftenreihe Inst. Math. Dtsch. Akad. Wiss. 11:143. 1962.

353. Kompaneets, A.S.— ZhETF 37:1722. 1959.

354. Kompaneets, A.S.— Tezisy i programma 1-i Sovetskoi gravitatsionnoi konferentsii, p.59.
        Izdatel'stvo MGU. 1961.

355. Vaidya, P.C. and J.M.Pandya.— Proc. Nat. Inst. Sci. India A26:459. 1960.

356. Vaidya, P.C. and J.M.Pandya.— Proc. Nat. Inst. Sci. India A27:620. 1961.

357. Vaidya, P.C. and J.M.Pandya.— Progr. Theoret. Phys. 35:129. 1966.

358. Sciama, D.W.— Proc. Cambridge Philos. Soc. (Math.) 57:436. 1961.

359. Bonnor, W.B.— Zs. Phys. 161:439. 1961.

360. Bonnor, W.B.— Communs. Math. Phys. 13:163. 1969.

361. Friedlander, F.G.— Proc. Roy. Soc. A269:53. 1962.

362. Friedlander, F.G.— Proc. Roy. Soc. A279:386. 1964.

363. Friedlander, F.G.— Proc. Roy. Soc. A299:264. 1967.

364. Pandey, S.N. and J.Krishna Rao.—Proc. Nat. Inst. Sci. India A28:425. 1962

365. Krishna Rao, J. and P.C.Vaidya.—Proc. Cambridge Philos. Soc. 61:763. 1965.

366. Harrison, B.K.— Phys. Rev. B138:488. 1965.

367. Leroy, J.— Compt. Rend. Acad. Sci. Colon. 270:1078. 1970.

368. Zakharov, V.D.— Tezisy dokladov III Meshvuzovskoi konferentsii po problemam
        geometrii, p.61. Izdatel'stvo Kazanskogo universiteta. 1967.

369. Johari, V.B.— Tensor, 18:330. 1967.

370. Misra, M.— Ann. Inst. Henri Poincaré 7:245. 1967.

371. Misra, M.— Journ. Math. Phys. 9:1052. 1968.

372. Lal, K.B. and H.Prasad,— Tensor, 20:45. 1969.

373. Dăngvu, H.— Compt. Rend. Acad. Sci. Colon. 271, A906. 1970.

374. Hoffman, R.B.—Journ. Math. Phys. 10:954. 1969.

375. Dozmorov, I.M.— Izvestiya Vuzov, Seriya Fiziki, No.9:43. 1969.

376. Dozmorov, I.M.— Izvestiya Vuzov, Seriya Fiziki, No.10:83. 1969.

377. Dozmorov, I.M.— Izvestiya Vuzov, Seriya Fiziki, No.11:121. 1969.

378. Szekeres, P.— Nature 228:1183. 1970.

379. Aichelburg, P.C.— Journ. Math. Phys. 11:2458. 1970.

380. Bonnor, W.B.— Nature 181, No.4617. 1958.

381. Bonnor, W.B.— Colloques internationaux du Centre national de la recherche scientifique.
        Les théories relativistes de la gravitation, Royaumont, 1959, p.141. Paris. 1962.

382. Bonnor, W.B.— British Journ. Appl. Phys. 14:555. 1963.

383. Pirani, F.A.E. — Proc. Roy. Soc. A252:96. 1959.

384. Peres, A.— Nuov. Cim. 11:13. 1959.

385. Lias, R.I.— Tezisy i programma 1-i Sovetskoi gravitatsionnoi konferentsii, p.63. Izdatel'-
        stvo MGU. 1961.

386. Mehra, A.L., P.C.Vaidya, and R.S.Kushwaha.— Acta Phys. Acad. Scient. Hungaricae
        26:339. 1969.

387. Murenbeeld, M. and J.R.Trollope.— Phys. Rev. D1:3220. 1970.

388. Choquet—Bruhat, Y. GR-5.—Tezisy dokladov 5-i Mezhdunarodnoi konferentsii po gravitatsii i teorii otnositel'nosti, p.169. Izdatel'stvo Tbilisskogo universiteta. 1968.

389. Choquet-Bruhat, Y.— Communs. Math. Phys. 12:16. 1969.

390. Dirac, P.— Naturwiss. Rundschau, 13:165. 1960.

391. Vavilov, B.T.— Izvestiya Vuzov, Seriya Fiziki, No.2:73. 1959.

392. Gertsenshtein, M.E. and V.I.Pustovoit.— Tezisy i programma 1-i Sovetskoi gravitatsionnoi konferentsii, p.64. Izdatel'stvo MGU. 1961.

393. Gertsenshtein, M.E. and V.I.Pustovoit.— ZhETF 42:163. 1962.

394. Carmeli, M.— Phys. Rev. 158:1243. 1967.

395. Cooperstock, F.I.— Phys. Rev. 163:1368. 1968.

396. Bonnor, W.B.— Zs. Phys. 177:240. 1964.

397. Fock, V.A. Colloques internationaux du Centre national de la recherche scientifique. Les théories relativistes de la gravitation, Royaumont, 1959, p.137. Paris. 1962.

398. Infeld, L. and R.Michalska-Trautman.— Ann. of Phys. 55:561. 1969.

399. Papapetrou, A.— Nucl. Phys. 57:319. 1964.

400. Papapetrou, A.— Ann. Inst. Henri Poincaré A1:117. 1964.

401. Papapetrou, A.— Colloques internationaux du Centre national de la recherche scientifique, Paris, 1967, p.201. Paris. 1969.

402. Tonnelat, M.A. —Compt. Rend. Acad. Sci. Colon. 261:2165. 1965.

403. Tonnelat, M.A. —Colloques internationaux du Centre nationale de la recherche scientifique. Paris, 1967, p.73. Paris. 1969.

404. Treder, H.J.— Colloques internationaux du Centre national de la recherche scientifique. Paris, 1967, p.191. Paris. 1969.

405. Cooperstock, F.I. and D.J.Booth.— Phys. Rev. 187:1796. 1969.

406. Unt, V.— Izvestiya AN Estonskoi SSR 18:170 (Fizika, Matematika.). 1969.

407. Unt, V. A Combined Bondi and Approximation Method is General Relativity. II. The General Case.— Acad. Sci. Estonian SSR, Inst. Phys. and Astron, preprint. 1969.

408. Zerilli, F.J.— Journ. Math. Phys. 11:2203. 1970 .

409. Rumer, Yu.B.— ZhETF 42:577. 1962.

410. Kroki, K.— Indian Journ. Phys. 38:190. 1964.

411. Mavrides, S.— Nuov. Cim. A45:859. 1966.

412. Mavrides, S. GR-5.— Tezisy dokladov 5-i Mezhdunarodnoi konferentsii po gravitatsii i teorii otnositel'nosti, p.133. Izdatel'stvo Tbilisskogo universiteta. 1968.

413. Synge, J.— Quart. Appl. Math. 26:153. 1968.

414. Berger, V.K. Problemy teorii gravitatsii i elementarnykh chastits (Problems of the Theory of Gravitation and Elementary Particles), No.4:74. Atomizdat. 1970.

415. Stanyukovich, K.P. Gravitatsionnoi pole i elementarnye chastitsy (The Gravitational Field and Elementary Particles). Nauka. 1965.

416. Stanyukovich, K.P. — Tezisy i programma 1-i Sovetskoi gravitatsionnoi konferentsii, p.103. Izdatel'stvo MGU. 1961.

417. Stanyukovich, K.P.— Vestnik MGU, Fizika, Astronomiya, No.5:71. 1961.

418. Stanyukovich, K.P.— Vestnik MGU, Fizika, Astronomiya, No.1:78. 1962.

419. Stanyukovich, K.P.— Vestnik MGU, Fizika, Astronomiya, No.2:17. 1968.

420. De Witt, B. Colloques internationaux du Centre national de la recherche scientifique. Les théories relativistes de la gravitation, Royaumont, 1959, p.335. Paris. 1962.

421. Halpern, L. and B.Laurent.— Nuov. Cim. 33:728. 1964.

422. Weber, J.— Phys. Rev. 117:306. 1960.

423. Weber, J. —Proc. of the Internat. School "Enrico Fermi", p.116. New York —London. Academic Press. 1962.

424. Weber, J.— Phys. Rev. Lett. 17:1228. 1966.

425. W e b e r, J.— Phys. Rev. Lett. 18:498. 1967.
426. W e b e r, J.— Phys. Today 21:34. 1968.
427. W e b e r, J.— Contemporary Physics, Trieste Symposium, 1968, 1:533. Vienna. 1969.
428. W e b e r, J.— Lett. Nuov. Cim. 4:653. 1970.
429. W e b e r, J.— Phys. Rev. Lett. 25:179. 1970.
430. B r a g i n s k i i, V.B. and G.I. R u k m a n .— Tezisy i programma 1-i Sovetskoi gravitatsionnoi
     konferentsii, p.133. Izdatel'stvo MGU. 1961.
431. B r a g i n s k i i, V.B. and G.I. R u k m a n .— Pis'ma ZhETF 41:304. 1961.
432. B r a g i n s k i i, V.B.— ZhETF 44:1562. 1963.
433. B r a g i n s k i i, V.B. GR-5.— Tezisy dokladov 5-i Mezhdunarodnoi konferentsii po gravi-
     tatsii i teorii otnositel'nosti, p.205. Izdatel'stvo Tbilisskogo universiteta. 1968.
434. B r a g i n s k i i, V.B.— Fizicheskie eksperimenty s probnymi telami (Physical Experiments
     with Test Bodies). Nauka. 1970.
435. G e r t s e n s h t e i n, M.E.— Tezisy i programma 1-i Sovetskoi gravitatsionnoi konferentsii,
     p.62. Izdatel'stvo MGU. 1961.
436. G e r t s e n s h t e i n, M.E. and V.I. P u s t o v o i t .— ZhETF 43:605. 1962.
437. B a s h k o v, V.I. Gravitatsiya i teoriya otnositel'nosti (Gravitation and the Theory of
     Relativity), No.2:107. Izdatel'stvo Kazanskogo universiteta. 1965.
438. B a s h k o v, V.I. Gravitatsiya i teoriya otnositel'nosti (Gravitation and the Theory of
     Relativity), No.6:72. Izdatel'stvo Kazanskogo universiteta. 1969.
439. M i r o n o v s k i i, V.N.— Astronomicheskii Zhurnal, 42:107. 1965.
440. S l a b k i i, L.I. GR-5.— Tezisy dokladov 5-i Mezhdunarodnoi konferentsii po gravitatsii
     i teorii otnositel'nosti, p.211. Izdatel'stvo Tbilisskogo universiteta. 1968.
441. D a u t c o u r t, G.— Astrophys. Lett. 3:15. 1969.
442. W i c k, G.— New Sci. 48:122. 1970.
443. P a p i n i, G.— Lett. Nuov. Cim. 4:1027. 1970.
444. B o c c a l e t t i, D., V. D e S a b b a t a, P. F o r t i n i, and C. G u a l d i .— Nuov. Cim B70:129.
     1970.
445. F o w l e r, W.A.— Rev. Mod. Phys. 36:545. 1964.
446. T h o r n e, K.S.— Colloques internationaux du Centre national de la recherche scientifique,
     Paris, 1967, p.73. Paris. 1969.
447. W e i n b e r g, S.— Contemporary Physics, Trieste Symposium, 1968, 1:559. Vienna. 1969.
448. K a f k a, P.— Phys. unserer Zeit 1:186. 1970.
449. S c i a m a, D.W.— Nature 224:1263. 1969.
450. K a u f m a n n, W.J.— Nature 227:157. 1970.
451. P e t e r s, P.C.— Phys. Rev. D1:1559. 1970.
452. S a s t r y, K.S. and S.M. A l l a d i n .— Astrophys. and Space Sci. 7:261. 1970.
453. C h a n d r a s e k h a r, S.— Phys. Rev. Lett. 24:611. 1970.
454. C h a n d r a s e k h a r, S.— Astrophys. Journ. 161:561. 1970.
455. C h a n d r a s e k h a r, S.— Astrophys. Journ. 161:571. 1970.
456. E z a w a, Z.F.— Journ. Phys. Soc. Japan 28:1576. 1970.
457. C h a u, W.Y.— Nature 228:655. 1970.
458. C h a u, W.Y. and R.N. H e n r i k s e n .— Astrophys. Journ. 161:L137. 1970.
459. A r i f o v, L.Ya.— Izvestiya Vuzov, Seriya Fiziki, No.3:32. 1967.
460. K r z y w o b l o c k i, M. — Acta Phys. Acad. Sci. Hungaria 23 :193. 1967.
461. M i t s k e v i c h, N.V.— Trudy UDN, 44(4):137. 1969.
462. P e t r o v, A.Z. Sovremennye problemy gravitatsii (Modern Problems of Gravitation).— Trudy
     2-i Sovetskoi gravitatsionnoi konferentsii, p.12. Izdatel'stvo Tbilisskogo universiteta. 1967.
463. B o n d i, H.— Phys. Bl. 26:352. 1970.
464. B o n d i, H.— Phys. Bl. 26:404. 1970.
465. V o d y a n i t s k i i, A.A. and F.A. D i m a n s h t e i n .— Ukrainskii Fizicheskii Zhurnal 13:1403.
     1968.

INDEX